Celebrating 90 years of giving

D0431626

Contents

Sponsored by

Tips & key to symbols

Key to symbols

NEW Gardens open for the first time, or after a long break.

Dogs on leads welcome

Full or partial wheelchair accessibility

Locally grown plants for sale

Children's activities, varying from quizzes, identification exercises to hands-on projects

Snowdrops & Winter Walks

Details of public transport access can be found either in the directions section or with a map navigation app

Champion Trees, from the UK Tree Register

NPC National Plant Collection®, from Plant Heritage

Gardens and Designed Landscapes by Historic Environment Scotland (links on our website)

Basic teas

Cream teas

Homemade teas

Refreshments

Top tips

Photography
Most of our gardens are privately owned, so please ask permission before taking photographs. Our Volunteer Photographers may take photos on the open day. Please notify them if you don't wish to appear in our promotional materials.

Gardening Advice
Our Garden Openers love to chat about their gardens. If there's a bit of advice you're after, do ask!

Children & Families
Children are welcome with an accompanying adult. Some openings offer children's activities – look for the children's activities symbol.

Group Visits
Many of our gardens are pleased to have groups visiting. Get in touch with the garden or contact the local District Organiser for more information.

Toilets
Private gardens do not normally have outside toilets. For security reasons, our Openers have been advised not to admit visitors into their homes.

Cancellations
All cancellations will be posted on our website, scotlandsgardens.org, under the garden listing.

Extra Assistance
Carers are offered free entry to our gardens and Assistance Dogs are always welcome.

By Arrangement
This is a great way to see a garden when it's quiet and Garden Owners will be delighted to hear from you to book a visit. Many gardens welcome visits from larger groups or clubs such as horticultural societies (regulations permitting), as well as individuals or couples. Do get in touch.

Always check our website before setting out, for any cancellations, last-minute changes to opening details or booking arrangements.

Our districts

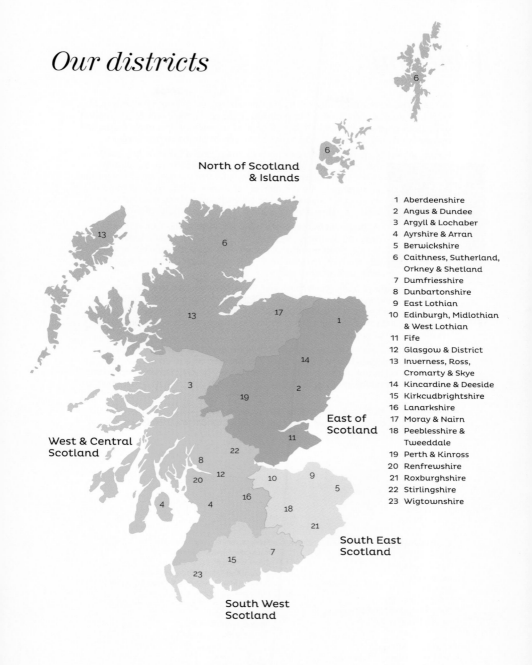

North of Scotland & Islands

East of Scotland

West & Central Scotland

South East Scotland

South West Scotland

1 Aberdeenshire
2 Angus & Dundee
3 Argyll & Lochaber
4 Ayrshire & Arran
5 Berwickshire
6 Caithness, Sutherland, Orkney & Shetland
7 Dumfriesshire
8 Dunbartonshire
9 East Lothian
10 Edinburgh, Midlothian & West Lothian
11 Fife
12 Glasgow & District
13 Inverness, Ross, Cromarty & Skye
14 Kincardine & Deeside
15 Kirkcudbrightshire
16 Lanarkshire
17 Moray & Nairn
18 Peeblesshire & Tweeddale
19 Perth & Kinross
20 Renfrewshire
21 Roxburghshire
22 Stirlingshire
23 Wigtownshire

Welcome

Wishing you a heartfelt welcome to our Guidebook and our 90th birthday! To celebrate that milestone, we're proud to share yet another amazing selection of glorious gardens with you. On behalf of all of us – volunteers, garden openers, trustees and staff – we can't wait to welcome you through the garden gate.

Liz Stewart, National Organiser

Having joined Scotland's Gardens Scheme in the midst of Covid in July 2020, I've yet to learn what a 'normal' year looks like for the charity. What I have learned, however, is how many dedicated volunteers contribute to the creation of our annual programme of garden openings; how welcoming and supportive they are, and how much joy they have in sharing their gardens with others.

Although at the time of writing this introduction, Covid is still very much making its presence felt, we have been touched by the sheer number of people who have, despite everything, been willing to open their gardens in 2021, showing their courage and generosity of spirit.

As an avid visitor of open gardens myself, I feel so privileged to have the opportunity to hop over the fence to work for this amazing charity. During the production of this book, I have earmarked so many amazing gardens, villages, groups, trails...that I don't think I'm going to be getting much work done in the office this side of September!

Please remember that this year is far from normal, so do bear with us as we continue to navigate this turbulent time. Please keep an eye on our website before setting out on a visit; things can change very quickly. Do keep up to date with the latest government guidance and remember your role as a responsible visitor.

But most importantly, do come and see us, enjoy your visits, be inspired by our gardens, support our charities – and tell all your friends! We look forward to seeing you in a garden soon.

Liz Stewart
National Organiser

Scotland's Gardens Scheme Head Office
2nd Floor
23 Castle Street
Edinburgh
EH2 3DN
T: 0131 226 3714
E: info@scotlandsgardens.org
W: scotlandsgardens.org

Charity no: SC011337
Scotland's Gardens Scheme
SCIO: SC049866

Front cover image Shepherd House, Inveresk
Back cover image 2 Durnamuck
Cover photographs © Ray Cox
Design: Ken Craig, Canongate Design
Artwork: Matt Armstrong, Serious Artworker
Maps by Alan Palfreyman Graphics
Contains OS Data © Crown Copyright and Database 2019
Printed by Belmont Press.
ISBN13: 9780901549365

MIX
Paper from responsible sources
FSC® C007785
www.fsc.org

Who's who

Scotland's Gardens Scheme is supported by our Head Office Staff and Trustees, all of whom bring a range of specialist skills and interests to our charity.

At our core are the hundreds of volunteers who bring the charity to life each year, by opening their gardens and facilitating these openings. We couldn't do it without them.

We are also proud to have HRH The Duchess of Rothesay as our President and, new this year, we are delighted that after many years as a Trustee, Charlotte Hunt has taken on the new role of Honorary Vice President.

HRH The Duchess of Rothesay

Head Office Staff

Liz Stewart
National Organiser

Hazel Reid
Office Manager

Julie Golding
Volunteer Manager

Daria Piskorz-Pronobis
Marketing Manager

Trustees

David Mitchell
Chairman

Sarah Landale
Deputy Chairman

Peter Yellowlees
Treasurer

David Buchanan-Cook
Trustee

Jonathan Cobb
Trustee

Stephen McCallum
Trustee

Emily Stair
Trustee

Charlotte Hunt
Honorary Vice President

Chairman's message

Looking across my snow-covered garden at the start of the year, reflecting on the past twelve unimaginable months, I am filled with gratitude towards everyone in our community for all their efforts to support the charity during this most difficult period.

Throughout this time, I have been energised by the resourcefulness shown as we adapted to new technology in order to support each other and our communities. This originality, along with our ability to continue to raise money for charity, was also deeply appreciated; the lessons learnt will definitely be used to ensure a more inclusive and sustainable future.

Looking ahead through our 90th birthday year whilst also considering our origins in 1931, (twenty years before the creation of our wonderful NHS) I remind myself that 'history should be the ship not the anchor' but it can also be a great teacher if we listen.

Going forward, the need to support professionals and activity which aid health and wellbeing within our communities, will undoubtedly be greater than at any other time in our history. Therefore, I am delighted that we will hopefully be able to open even more gardens this year.

The lessons learnt from the past are also clearly seen in the commitment, compassion and creativity of our garden openers and volunteers; these qualities being augmented by drive, resolve and an enthusiasm to share what they have with others by simply letting you into their gardens. Thank you to our community for wanting to open again and to you our visitors for wishing to visit and donate to charity. Enjoy the gardens, the teas, and plant sales as well as the company of the others you meet along the way.

Mario Testino ©

2021 marks the 90th anniversary of Scotland's Gardens Scheme. For 90 years, many generous people have opened their gardens to members of the public, sharing their skills and knowledge, and allowing others to enjoy the beautiful spaces they have created. As President of Scotland's Gardens Scheme, I am delighted to be able to celebrate this anniversary with you.

I am also glad to have the opportunity to say how proud I am of your innovation and determination, which have kept the charity running during the unprecedented challenges of 2020. As many gardens as possible were opened, raising valuable funds for the Scheme's core beneficiaries: The Queen's Nursing Institute Scotland, Maggie's and Perennial.

Last year taught us many things. Perhaps one of the most significant lessons was how precious and restorative are our outdoor spaces; and how vital they are for our physical and mental well-being. Some who found themselves with more time on their hands than usual may have discovered the joy of gardening and found out what huge pleasure it gives to so many of us. I very much hope, therefore, that in this anniversary year, we will see <u>all</u> gardening enthusiasts, both new and seasoned, joining the celebrations and being inspired by one another.

Happy 90th Birthday and happy gardening!

Camilla

⊕ Investec

To plant a garden is to invest in tomorrow

At Investec Wealth & Investment we understand that growth doesn't happen by chance. That is why we have been sponsoring Scotland's Gardens Scheme, a source of beauty and inspiration, since 2009.

Like SGS, our heritage dates back over a century, providing exceptional levels of service to our clients. With offices in Edinburgh, Glasgow and across the UK, our local wealth experts can provide financial planning and tailor-made solutions to help you achieve your goals and secure your family's financial future.

With Investment Your Capital is at Risk.

Know where life can take you.

investecwin.co.uk

Private Clients

Member firm of the London Stock Exchange. Authorised and regulated by the Financial Conduct Authority. Investec Wealth & Investment Limited is registered in England. Registered No. 2122340. Registered Office: 30 Gresham Street, London EC2V 7QN.

Offices at: Belfast Birmingham Bournemouth Bristol Cheltenham Edinburgh Exeter Glasgow Guildford Leeds Liverpool London Manchester Reigate Sheffield

Get involved & make a difference

Scotland's Gardens Scheme has had a rich and vibrant history of volunteer engagement since 1931 and we are thrilled to be celebrating our 90th birthday this year. We have only four staff and rely on our 200 volunteers and nearly 800 garden owners to make the charity the success that it is and there are many ways for you to get involved!

Open your garden

This is a wonderful way to raise funds for your favourite charity, while sharing your garden with others. We will help you to publicise your garden opening through our Guidebook, website, social media and press and you will be supported by a wonderful team of volunteers. 60% of the takings will go directly to your charity; many of our Garden Openers choose to support small, local charities that benefit hugely from the increased awareness and funds. The remaining 40% is split between the three core charities that Scotland's Gardens Scheme supports: Queen's Nursing Institute Scotland, Maggie's and Perennial, and the core costs of our charity.

Scotland's Gardens Scheme Volunteers

Become a volunteer

We have 23 District Volunteer teams across Scotland that support our gardens and there are many ways to get involved; being a District Organiser and leading a team, as a District Treasurer, as a District Volunteer who helps gardens to get ready to open, or perhaps by using your social media or photography skills. It is fun and rewarding, giving you the opportunity to see beautiful gardens, meet new friends and build your own gardening knowledge, whilst raising money for charity.

Become a trustee

We are seeking new trustees in 2021 and if you have skills that you think could support our Board of Trustees and our amazing charity, please do visit our website to find out more about the opportunity.

If you would like to explore being a volunteer or opening your garden in 2022, please visit our volunteering pages on the website or contact us at info@scotlandsgardens.org.

We would love to hear from you!

Julie Golding
Volunteer Manager

Julie Golding, Volunteer Manager

Our impact

Through the hard work of all our Garden Owners and Volunteers, Scotland's Gardens Scheme has raised over £1 million for charity over the last 5 years. Despite our ability to raise funds being heavily impacted in 2020 due to Covid, we honoured our charitable donations to our core beneficiaries and gave a total of £42,000 to QNIS, Maggie's and Perennial.

The gardens that did manage to open in 2020 were able to support other charities by giving 60% of the funds raised to their chosen causes, with the net remaining funds supporting Scotland's Gardens Scheme and our core beneficiaries.

While 2020 activities were curtailed, it's worth celebrating what the charity achieves in a 'typical' year with the following highlights from 2019:

Gardens open
500

71 *New gardens joined SGS*

Charities supported
238

Distributed to charities
£247,719

Most popular causes supported

- *Healthcare*
- *Supporting vulnerable people*
- *Community Centres, gardens, churches*

Volunteers
200
Approx numbers
Many more give their time on the day

District Volunteers hours worked
5500

Visitors
44,000

East Lothian: Tyninghame Garden © Sheila Sim

Our legacy programme

We have been incredibly fortunate over the years to have received a number of very generous legacies from supporters who kindly remembered our charity by leaving us a gift in their will.

These gifts have helped to support our charity in many ways. For example, legacies have enabled us to improve the technology that is the backbone of our Guidebook and garden openings; and vitally, over the past year when our garden gate income was seriously reduced due to Covid, those generous gifts helped us to survive the toughest times, whilst enabling us to plan ahead for future openings and to continue to support our network of volunteers and our beneficiary charities.

We know that gardens have been a lifeline to many people over the past year and we are looking forward to welcoming many more visitors this year. Leaving a gift in your will in the future will help us to continue to share that passion for gardens and gardening.

Every gift we receive, whether large or small, will make a huge difference to our charity, whether by helping us to invest in new materials and projects to support garden openings or enabling us to develop the ways in which we work © David Blatchford
with our charity partners and volunteers. Your support will help us to open ever more gardens to our valued visitors, new and old, helping us to share the unique joy of garden visits and most importantly, enable us to help even more charities in the future.

If you would like to find out more about leaving a charitable gift in your will, please get in touch for an informal chat by calling 0131 226 3714.

Alternatively, please email **info@scotlandsgardens.org** or visit **scotlandsgardens.org/donate/** for more information.

Underwood House © David Blatchford

The Queen's Nursing Institute Scotland beneficiary message

The Queen's Nursing Institute Scotland (QNIS) is a charity that promotes excellence in community nursing. We have been supported by Scotland's Gardens Scheme since its inception in 1931 and are proud of the relationship which has continued for 90 years.

In 2021, our incredibly successful Queen's Nurse Programme continues into its fifth year. The success of the programme has allowed us to explore the addition of specialist cohorts this year. Already there are 81 outstanding community nurses making a difference to their communities across Scotland. They can be found working in schools, general practices, offshore oil rigs, hospices and in people's homes, in diverse roles from community midwives to district nurses, advanced nurse practitioners to expert specialists.

2018 Queen's Nurse and Dementia Specialist, Lesley Wylie with one of her residents

You may recognise some of our Queen's Nurses from events near you, they are always keen to attend garden openings and express their thanks to owners and visitors for the support which has allowed them to flourish.

The latest round of our Catalysts for Change Programme, which also received funding from The National Lottery Community Fund, now moves into its second year. The programme provides grants to community nurses, alongside local partners, to explore short-term initiatives that prevent, reduce, or overcome health inequalities.

With the global health crisis illuminating health inequalities in our communities, there has been a specific call for projects which respond to those unique challenges and opportunities arising from the COVID-19 pandemic.

Last year was incredibly difficult for nurses, whether facing unprecedented challenges or being redeployed as part of the response to COVID-19. For many, peace and serenity were to be found within their gardens or allotments. Now, more than ever, gardens across Scotland have been of tremendous support to community nurses.

We hope that we will be able to see you at garden openings across 2021.

Clare Cable
Chief Executive and Nurse Director, QNIS

Queen's Nurses making a difference to communities all over Scotland, thanks to financial support from Scotland's Gardens Scheme for the last 90 years.

Qnis

THE QUEEN'S
NURSING
INSTITUTE
SCOTLAND

p: +44 (0)131 229 2333   w: www.qnis.org.uk   e: office@qnis.org.uk

How Perennial Helps

Perennial is the UK's only charity helping people in horticulture build and live better lives. If you work with flowers, plants, trees or grass, our friendly and experienced team are here to deliver completely free, confidential and personal support at any stage of life. We understand the devastating impact unexpected personal challenges and financial pressures has on lives. If you need help or know someone who does, please contact us on **0800 093 8543** or visit **perennial.org.uk**.

"Perennial's income has dropped dramatically due to Covid-19, yet the demand for their help continues to increase. Their partnership with Scotland's Gardens Scheme helps them to continue to deliver their frontline help and be confident to plan and launch new services."

Carole Baxter,
Perennial Trustee and Presenter of BBC Scotland Beechgrove TV programme.

Helping people
in horticulture
Perennial

Donate now
0800 093 8792
perennial.org.uk/donate

How we helped John*

In 2013 John was made redundant from his job as an estate gardener. His poor health left him unable to work and reliant on his partners income. At the end of 2018, she was also forced to stop working for health reasons. Now unable to pay bills, feed themselves, heat their home or get medical treatment their dog badly needed, they were becoming increasingly anxious.

They contacted Perennial and "haven't looked back".

"Perennial provided food and fuel for heating to help us over the colder months. Our caseworker, Vicki, and debt adviser, Ged, spoke to creditors on our behalf and gave us support with budgeting so that we could take control of our money.

Thanks to the brilliant team at Perennial we were successful with our application for benefits and our income recovered. Something we would never have been able to sort ourselves. They also helped us to successfully apply for a new boiler and central heating system after we had all but given up – it's just heaven to be warm again. We feel so grateful to Perennial."

*Name changed to preserve anonymity and photo is posed by models.

Find your way through cancer

Come to Maggie's

Maggie's provides free practical, emotional and social support for people with cancer and their family and friends.

Built in the grounds of NHS hospitals, our network of centres across the UK are warm and welcoming places, with professional staff on hand to offer the support you need to find your way through cancer.

Our centres are open Monday to Friday, 9am – 5pm, and no referral is required. We are also online at maggies.org.

Maggie's centres across Scotland receive vital funds from every garden opening. Our heartfelt thanks go to everyone who supports Scotland's Gardens Scheme by opening their garden, volunteering or visiting a garden.

Scotland's
GARDENS
Scheme
OPEN FOR CHARITY

maggies.org

Maggie Keswick Jencks Cancer Caring Centres Trust (Maggie's) is a registered charity, no. SC024414

MAGGIE'S
Everyone's home of cancer care

Maggie's beneficiary message

Many of our gardening friends tell us that something has shifted in the world of gardening since lockdown took hold in March 2020.

Restricted to our own homes and whatever gardens, window boxes or pots we were lucky to have, millions of people began to take an interest, and see growing and nurturing plants as an antidote to the stress and anxiety of the other aspects of our lives.

At Maggie's, we know that gardening and being in an outdoor space has therapeutic benefit, and the gardens that surround our centres provide a calming and positive effect on wellbeing, improving mindfulness and reducing stress levels. Run by experienced gardeners, our therapeutic gardening groups are open to anyone with cancer, their family and friends, and offer the chance to take part in a creative activity with other people who are going through a similar experience.

Hopefully this surge of new gardeners will herald a golden age of gardening and fresh appreciation of the beautiful and fascinating outdoor spaces that feature in Scotland's Gardens Scheme.

I would like to take this opportunity to thank you all for your most welcome support of Maggie's in Scotland again this year. All of our centres benefit from Scotland's Gardens Scheme donations and from every garden opening, for which we are enormously grateful.

We look forward to a wonderful year of gardening ahead, and enjoying the many green spaces and delightful gardens that Scotland's Gardens has made accessible to everyone.

Best wishes

Dame Laura Lee DBE
Chief Executive: Maggie's

© David Blatchford

VISIT SCOTLAND'S GARDENS

JUNE

Sat. 4th CULTER HOUSE, Milltimber
BUS STOP : POST OFFICE
Sun. 5th CLOVA, Lumsden
Sun 12th WHITEHOUSE, Alford
Sun. 19th KNOCKESPOCH, Clatt
Sun. 26th MANAR, Inverurie
Sun. 26th KINALDIE, Kinellar

JULY

Sun. 3rd HADDO HOUSE, Tarves
Sun. 10th FYVIE CASTLE, Fyvie
Sun. 17th AUCHRY, Cuminestown
Sun. 24th KIRKVILLE HOUSE, Skene
Sat. 30th EDGEHILL Milltimber
Sun. 31st LAITHERS, Turriff

AUGUST

Sat. 6th CASTLE FRASER, Kemnay
Sun. 7th 25 FOREST ROAD, Aberdeen
Sun. 7th PITMEDDEN, Udny
Sun. 7th SKENE HOUSE, Dunecht
Sun. 14th GLENTANAR, Aboyne

Sun. 14th FINZEAN HOUSE, Finzean
Sun. 21st DUNECHT HOUSE, Dunecht
Sun. 21st TEUCHAR LODGE, Cuminestown
Sun. 28th ARNAGE CASTLE, Ellon

June 1st to October 1st Williamston House, Insch

Organised by The Queen's Institute in aid of
THE SCOTTISH QUEEN'S NURSES' PENSION FUND

McLAGAN & CUMMING LTD., EDINBURGH

Poster c1938: Thank you to the QNIS Archive for sharing these images

90 Years of growing & giving

Scotland's Gardens Scheme was created in 1931 to help fund district nurses in Scotland; we take a look at how the Scheme has evolved, while retaining a consistent purpose; to raise funds for charity by opening gardens to the public, giving a precious glimpse behind the garden gate.

Following the success of the National Garden Scheme in England, a Scottish Scheme was created by the Countess of Mar and Kellie in 1931, to raise funds for the Scottish Queen's Institute of District Nursing (now the Queen's Nursing Institute Scotland or QNIS). A network of County Organisers around Scotland was tasked with persuading local owners to open their gardens, ensuring that all ran smoothly – much the same as our network of Districts and Volunteers today.

The Queen's Nurses were established in the second half of the 18th Century to support people living in poverty and deprivation, providing healthcare and practical support,

2021 will see Winton Castle opening for its 88th year

becoming an integral part of community life. These remarkable, intrepid Queen's Nurses could be found anywhere from city back streets and tenements, to the far flung reaches of rural Scotland and even the Outer Hebrides, a lifeline to countless families, yet in those days before the NHS, needed funding to thrive.

Scotland's Gardens Scheme gave vital financial support to the Queen's Nurses and in 1932, its second year, achieved an impressive £5,400 with 577 gardens opening. The Scheme even continued to flourish during the War Years when, although the number of participating gardens decreased, the funds raised increased as gardeners dug for victory, growing veggies for sale instead of the usual flowers!

Today, there are many constants as we look back to the early years; the Scheme is still led by a strong network of dedicated volunteers, all passionate about sharing gardens with others. In the early years, most of the open gardens were on large estates and we are proud to say that many still open for us today; 2021 will see Winton Castle opening for its 88th year! However, we now welcome gardens of all shapes, sizes, design and horticultural interest to delight the visitor, with group and village openings very popular.

In terms of charitable support, the Scheme's reach is much wider these days with 60% of funds raised from garden openings going directly to the Garden Owner's preferred cause, supporting around 250 charities each year, while the remaining 40% raised supports the running costs of the charity and our three core beneficiaries. We are proud that The Queen's Nursing Institute Scotland (QNIS) remains one of those core charities; without them, the Scheme would not exist and the roots of our histories are deeply entwined.

Queen's Nurse Catriona McKaskill – weighing baby in North Uist, Scotland, 'he's put on weight!' – 1950

Further reading:

"Caring and Sharing; Roots and reminiscences of Scotland's Gardens Scheme" by Juliet Edmonstone (2005) – **scotlandsgardens.org/our-history/**

Visit The Queen's Nursing Institute Scotland's website: **qnis.org.uk**

Argyll & Lochaber: Aberarder

Awards for longstanding service

In 2021 Scotland's Gardens Scheme is delighted to be celebrating a number of long service milestones, where gardens have opened with us for 50 years and 10 years.

Argyll and Lochaber
Aberarder

Mr Feilden of Aberarder recalls some wonderful open day memories:

'The garden opening day is always full of surprises, either the weather, or the individuals who come.
On several occasions we have had some of those who spent time at Aberarder as evacuees during the last war, returning to see it again. One time several years ago we were astonished to see a sea plane land on Loch Laggan below us and drive up on to the beach. The occupants then made their way on foot up to the garden to see it and have tea. It all helps to fill the money box.'

Aberarder will open on 31st May with Ardverikie, 2pm – 5.30pm.

A brilliant show of support and enthusiasm!

Argyll & Lochaber
Inveraray Castle and Gardens
Kildalloig
Knock Newhouse

Berwickshire
Lennel Bank

East Lothian
Broadwoodside

Edinburgh, Midlothian & West Lothian
101 Greenbank Crescent
Hunters Tryst

Inverness, Ross, Cromarty & Skye
Field House

Kincardine and Deeside
Kincardine Castle

Perth and Kinross
Fingask Castle
Parkhead House

Edinburgh: 101 Greenbank Crescent

Terrill Dobson

Terrill Dobson in her garden

Each year we recognise one of our volunteers who has shown outstanding service to Scotland's Gardens Scheme and, after a year that can only be described as extraordinary, it seems only fair to make this year's award to an exceptional person.

Diana Macnab Award
for outstanding service

Although Terrill Dobson has not solely been a volunteer, having been at the helm of the charity from 2016 to 2020 as Director, her career as a volunteer with Scotland's Garden Scheme long preceded her paid employment, continued during and then after her retirement last summer.

From her lovely Herbalist's Garden at her home at Logie in Angus, where she is a qualified herbalist, Terrill became involved in the Angus & Dundee District, opening her garden for Scotland's Gardens Scheme on numerous occasions. Having become an Area Organiser in 2007 and then a District Organiser in 2010, she increased her involvement to become a stalwart of the board as a Trustee. Terrill departed from the Board in 2016 to take on a very different role, this time leading the charity's Head Office team and undertaking some major projects, most notably the creation of and migration to a brand-new database, as well as evolving the charity's branding and website, using her background skills in technology and leadership.

All through her time as Director of Scotland's Gardens Scheme, Terrill remained in her voluntary role as District Organiser working with her local Committee to support a fantastic range of gardens which open regularly, as well as developing an impressive range of trails, group and village openings in the area, which are hugely popular with visitors.

Terrill's planned departure from the Scotland's Gardens Scheme office was somewhat delayed by the events of 2020 and she remained in post through the most tumultuous time of Covid, heroically navigating the heartbreaking cancellations of early Spring, supporting staff and volunteers, then organising a smooth transition to her replacement on her retirement in August.

It's not really a retirement, though, as Terrill remains a most active and dedicated volunteer. She continues to be a vibrant and inspired District Organiser, as you will see from the impressive array of gardens opening in Angus & Dundee this year, while continuing to provide valued advice and support to the Head Office team on a range of topics. Her dedication to Scotland's Gardens Scheme in many different roles has gone above and beyond, which makes her a natural choice for this special award.

WHAT'S HAPPENING OVER THE GARDEN FENCE?

JOIN US ON SOCIAL MEDIA FOR:
VIRTUAL TOURS & WORKSHOPS
GARDEN OPENINGS & EVENTS
VOLUNTEER NEWS
IMAGES & INSPIRATION

SIGN UP TO OUR E-NEWS - SCOTLANDSGARDENS.ORG/NEWSLETTER-SIGN-UP/

We'd love to hear from you

We'd like to learn a bit more about our garden visitors.

We want to know what you enjoy about garden visits, what you think of the Guidebook and our website – and what we can do to make your experience better.

Please scan the QR code with the camera of your smartphone then follow the links to our quick survey.

Or visit our website **scotlandsgardens.org/visitor-survey/**
We'll choose 10 randomly selected respondents and send a **FREE** copy of the **2022 Guidebook** as a small thank you for your feedback.

Thank you for your help!

Exceptional
Scottish
Gardens

Welcome to our gardens

We hope you enjoy browsing through our garden listings on the following pages.

Please remember a few things before you set out:

- **Plan ahead**

  check our website for any last-minute changes to opening details or booking arrangements

- **Be a responsible visitor**

  follow the latest Scottish Government guidance around travel, social distancing and outdoor visits

- **Arrange your visit**

  Did you know many of our gardens are open by arrangement?

  Just call or email the garden owners to organise a suitable time to visit – you will be very welcome.

  Check the 'By arrangement' listings for details.

Above all, enjoy your visits and we hope to see you in the garden.

Scotland's
GARDENS
Scheme

New gardens for 2021 NEW

Scotland's Gardens Scheme is delighted to welcome many new gardens opening across Scotland. We are so grateful to every Garden Opener for deciding to open their garden for charity and especially those opening for the first time this year. Please visit and help make their open day successful.

Our new gardens are joining a long tradition of charitable support at both a local and national level, whilst enabling the public to visit beautiful gardens that delight the eye and feed the soul.

If you would like to think about opening your garden with us, you will benefit from our 90 years of experience, including promotional support and insurance. We welcome all types, shapes and sizes of loved gardens.

Perthshire: Fehmarn © Camelia Hudema

Fife: Millfield Garden

Kirkcudbrightshire: Savat

Lanarkshire: Old Manse Wild Garden

Glasgow: The Hidden Gardens

Angus & Dundee: St Bride's Cottage

Edinburgh: Jupiter Artland & Bonnington House

Berwickshire: Harlaw Farmhouse © Christopher Jones

Fife: St Andrews Botanic Garden

Argyll & Lochaber: Berandhu

Angus & Dundee: Glenogilvy Schoolhouse

Wigtownshire: Rawson Garden

New gardens by district

Aberdeenshire

- Altries
- Chaplains' Court
- Heatherwick Farm

Angus & Dundee

- 10 Menzieshill Road
- Angus & Dundee Garden Trail
- Arbroath Collection of Gardens
- Brechin Gardens in Summer
- Gardyne Castle
- Glenogilvy Schoolhouse Garden
- Gray Cottage
- Kinblethmont House
- Primula Garden at Reswallie

Argyll & Lochaber

- Achabhraid
- Berandhu

Ayrshire & Arran

- 1 Burnton Road
- Dalrymple Community Garden
- Gardens of Fenwick
- Kilmaurs Gardens
- Kirkmuir Cottage (a re-entry that has not opened for six years)
- Underwood Lodge

Berwickshire

- Duns Open Gardens
- Harlaw Farmhouse
- Marlfield Gardens

Caithness, Sutherland, Orkney & Shetland

- Oape

Dumfriesshire

- Bonerick House

Dunbartonshire

- 4 Cairndhu Gardens
- 18 Duchess Park with High Glenan & Westburn

East Lothian

- Camptoun House
- Longwood
- Stenton Village

Edinburgh, Midlothian & West Lothian

- 2 Pentland Crescent
- Eskbank Village Gardens
- Greentree
- Jupiter Artland & Bonnington House
- Meadow Place
- The Gardens of Glenlockhart Valley

Fife

- Millfield Garden
- St Andrews Botanic Garden
- Whinhill

Glasgow & District

- The Hidden Gardens
  (a re-entry that has not opened for six years)

Inverness, Ross, Cromarty & Skye

- White Rose Cottage

Kincardine & Deeside

- Dallachy
- Lumphanan Gardens

Kirkcudbrightshire

- Arbigland House
  (a re-entry that has not opened for six years)
- Balmaclellan House
- Savat

Lanarkshire

- Auchlochan Walled Garden
- Biggar's Gardens
- Bothwell Village Gardens
- Gardens of the Highest Villages
- Meadowhead
- Old Manse Wild Garden

Moray & Nairn

- Cuthberts Brae
- Glebe House

Peeblesshire & Tweeddale

- Gattonside Village Gardens
- Lamancha Community Hub Plant Sale
- Prieston House
- West Linton Village Gardens

Perth & Kinross

- Fehmarn
- Lower Earn Small Gardens Trail
- Muckhart Open Gardens
- Princeland House
- The Croft
- The Old Farmhouse

Renfrewshire

- High Mathernock Farm
- Perch Corner

Roxburghshire

- Smailholm Village Gardens

Stirlingshire

- Ault Wharrie
- Bridge of Allan Gardens
- Gartmore Village

Wigtownshire

- Amulree
- Crinan
- Rawson Garden

Scotland's Gardens 🌷 Scheme plant sales

Plant Sale © David Blatchford

When you buy plants that have been grown locally, you can feel confident that they will thrive in your garden. Our plant sales are held across the country by our Volunteers and mainly consist of plants which have been lovingly propagated by local garden owners from their gardens. You'll find plenty of volunteers available to answer your gardening questions and you'll also help us to raise money for charity!

As well as the following large plant sales, many garden openings include plants for sale: keep an eye out for the Plants for Sale icon in the garden listings pages.

Angus Plant Sale

Saturday 24 April, 10am – noon
SGS Kilmacolm Plant Sale
Outside Kilmacolm Library
Kilmacolm PA13 4LE
⬤ Renfrewshire

Saturday 5 June, 10am – 3pm
Leith Hall Plant Sale
Huntly AB54 4NQ
⬤ Aberdeenshire

Saturday 6 June, 10am – noon
Lamancha Community Hub
Plant Sale (NEW)
3 miles south of the Leadburn Junction
on the A701
⬤ Peeblesshire & Tweeddale

Saturday 7 August, 2pm – 5pm
Angus Plant Sale
Logie Walled Garden
Kirriemuir DD8 5PN
⬤ Angus & Dundee

Sunday 5 September, 12-4pm
James Street Community Garden Plant Sale
Helensburgh G84 8EY
⬤ Dunbartonshire

Sunday 3 October, 10.30am - 2.30pm
Hill of Tarvit Plant Sale and Autumn Fair
Cupar KY15 5PB
⬤ Fife

Ayrshire: Gardens of Fenwick, 5 Fowld's View

Trails, groups & villages

Berwickshire: Marlfield Gardens © Kay Slater

We're delighted to announce a fabulous number of group openings this year, where gardens have joined forces to curate a collection of garden openings. We know these events are immensely popular with visitors and give the opportunity to enjoy gardens of many different shapes, sizes and designs.

Find out more about all of these in the District pages that follow.

Please do remember to check the listings on our website before setting out to make sure you are aware of the latest opening arrangements and any advance booking information.

East Lothian: Broadwoodside © Robert Dalrymple

Angus & Dundee

Angus & Dundee Garden Trail
A special collection of 15 beautiful gardens open Thursdays, Fridays and Saturdays in June.
Please visit the listing page later in this book and our website for booking details. Fantastic
value with the ticket price of £25 giving flexible access to gardens.

Thursdays, Fridays & Saturdays in June (dates and times vary per garden)

Angus & Dundee

Arbroath Collection of
Gardens
Saturday 3 July

Brechin Gardens in Summer
**Saturday & Sunday
24-25 July**

Argyll & Lochaber

Ardverikie with Aberarder
Monday 31 May

Ayrshire & Arran

Gardens of Fenwick
**Saturday & Sunday
24-25 July**

Kilmaurs Gardens
Sunday 15 August

Berwickshire

Coldstream Open Gardens
Sunday 11 July

Marlfield Gardens
Sunday 18 July
Also open by arrangement
1 March - 30 September

Duns Open Gardens
Sunday 22 August

Dunbartonshire

18 Duchess Park with
High Glenan and Westburn
Sunday 16 May

East Lothian

Tyninghame House and
The Walled Garden
**Sunday 9 May &
Sunday 4 July**

Stenton Village
Sunday 6 June

Longniddry Gardens
Sunday 27 June

Gifford Village and
Broadwoodside
Sunday 11 July

Edinburgh, Midlothian & West Lothian

The Gardens of Glenlockhart
Valley
Sunday 9 May

Moray Place and Bank
Gardens
Sunday 23 May

Dean Gardens
Sunday 6 June

Temple Village Gardens
Sunday 6 June

Eskbank Village Gardens
Sunday 13 June

Even More Gardens of the
Lower New Town
Sunday 20 June

Fife

Newburgh – Hidden Gardens
Sunday 27 June

Dalgety Bay Gardens
**Saturday & Sunday
24-25 July**

Crail: Gardens in the Burgh
**Saturday & Sunday
24-25 July**

Glasgow & District

Kew Terrace Gardens
Date to be confirmed
(please check the website)

Kilsyth Gardens
Sunday 30 May

Inverness, Ross, Cromarty & Skye

Kiltarlity Gardens
Sunday 15 August

Kincardine & Deeside

Lumphanan Gardens
Sunday 4 July

Lanarkshire

Biggar's Gardens
Sunday 25 July

Bothwell Village Gardens
Sunday 8 August

Gardens of the Highest
Villages
**Saturday & Sunday
21-22 August**

Peeblesshire & Tweeddale

West Linton Village Gardens
Sunday 18 July

Gattonside Village Gardens
Sunday 15 August

Perth & Kinross

Muckhart Open Gardens
**Saturday & Sunday
29-30 May**

Lower Earn Small
Gardens Trail
Sunday 13 June

Roxburghshire

Smailholm Village Gardens
Sunday 20 June

Yetholm Village Gardens
Sunday 4 July

Stirlingshire

Bridge of Allan Gardens
Sunday 6 June

Gartmore Village
Sunday 13 June

Champion Trees 🌳

East Lothian: Tyninghame House © Jannie Bos

Champion Trees are the widest, tallest, oldest or rarest examples of their species. Some examples in Scotland include trees that are 700 years old, have a girth of 11 yards or are over 66 yards tall. The Tree Register maintains

a database of these unique trees, which is updated by volunteers, and many of our gardens feature unique examples of both native and non-native species.

We've added the tree icon in our book to help you find them.

For further information visit: treeregister.org

Cruickshank Botanic Garden © Adam Price

● Aberdeenshire
Cruickshank Botanic Garden
Quercus ilex, Acer griseum and a tri-stemmed Nothofagus obliqua

● Argyll & Lochaber
Ardkinglas Woodland Garden
The mightiest conifer in Europe and others

Benmore Botanic Garden
Many rare trees and giant conifers

● Caithness & Sutherland
Amat
Abies Procera, Noble Fir

● East Lothian
Tyninghame House and The Walled Garden
Two British and seven Scottish

● Fife
St Andrews Botanic Garden
A number of rare species

Helensbank
The garden has a "notable" Cedar of Lebanon - 2nd largest in Fife

● Inverness, Ross, Cromarty & Skye
House of Aigas and Field Centre
Douglas fir, Atlas cedar and Sequoiadendron giganteum

Dundonnell House
Yew and holly

Old Allangrange
Yew and sweet chestnut

● Kirkcudbrightshire
Threave Garden
Acer platanoides 'Princeton Gold'; Carpinus caroliniana; X Cuprocyparis leylandii 'Picturesque' and a further 25 Scottish Champion Trees

● Peeblesshire & Tweeddale
Dawyck Botanic Garden
Numerous

● Perth & Kinross
Megginch Castle
Acer palmatum

Fingask Castle
Pinus wallichiana (Bhutan Pine) and the handsome remnants of what was the largest walnut in Scotland

Gleneagles House
Tallest Leylandii in Scotland

● Wigtownshire
Castle Kennedy and Garden
95 in total; including 12 British, 30 Scottish, 44 for Dumfries and Galloway and 9 trees described as 'otherwise remarkable'

Logan Botanic Garden
Polylepis and Eucalyptus

ARGYLE®
CONSULTING LIMITED

Expert financial solutions tailored to you.

argyleconsulting.co.uk

Financial
Planners

Chartered

National Plant Collections NPC

National Plant Collections ® (NPCs) are registered collections of plants – usually based on botanical groupings – which are cultivated with the aim of preserving them for future generations. As such, they play a critical role in the conservation work of the accrediting body, Plant Heritage.

Indigo – Portland Rose Helensbank

The process for becoming the holder of an NPC is quite challenging and the prospective holder must demonstrate detailed knowledge of the proposed collection. Other requirements include the maintenance of comprehensive plant records, accurate labelling of all plants, evidence of on-going research, and a plan for succession.

All collections must be accessible to the public.

For further information visit plantheritage.org.uk

'We were delighted to receive NPC accreditation in December 2020 for our collection of Portland roses which we have been collecting since 2005. Portlands are a small but important group of old roses which originated from crossing a Damask with a Gallica. They were the first group of reliable repeat flowering roses. In 1848 there were 84 varieties of Portlands growing at Kew; David Austin, in 'English Roses', believed that there were only about a dozen available today. Despite confusion over misclassifications, and the fact that some varieties have been known by more than one name over time, we have identified and collected 29 distinct varieties. And the search goes on! Portland roses are hardy, can tolerate light shade, have an elegant bushy form, and their repeating flowers are strongly scented. What's not to like?'

David Buchanan-Cook
Helensbank, Fife

Visit National Plant Collections

⬤ Argyll & Lochaber
Benmore Botanic Garden
Abies, South American temperate conifers, Picea

⬤ Fife
Backhouse at Rossie Estate
Narcissus (Backhouse cvs.)

Cambo
Galanthus

Helensbank
Portland Roses (New Collection)

⬤ Peeblesshire & Tweeddale
Dawyck Botanic Garden
Larix spp. and Tsuga spp

⬤ Perth & Kinross
Glendoick
Rhododendron sect. Pogonanthum, subsect. Uniflora, subsect. Campylogyna & subsect. Glauca and Cox hybrids

Megginch Castle
Scottish cider apples, Scottish Heritage apples and pears

Parkhead House
Lilium (Mylnefield lilies)

⬤ Stirlingshire
Milseybank
Meconopsis (New Collection)

⬤ Wigtownshire
Amulree
Nicotiana species

Logan Botanic Garden
Gunnera, Leptospermum, Griselinia, Clianthus and Sutherlandia

Visit four Botanic Gardens to see one of the richest plant collections on Earth.

Royal Botanic Garden Edinburgh

Arboretum Place and Inverleith Row,
Edinburgh EH3 5LR
Tel 0131 248 2909 | www.rbge.org.uk
Open every day from 10 am (except 1 January
and 25 December) | Garden is free | Entry
charges apply to Glasshouses

Royal Botanic Garden Edinburgh at **Logan**

Port Logan, Stranraer,
Dumfries and Galloway DG9 9ND
Tel 01776 860231 | www.rbge.org.uk/logan
Open daily 1 March to 15 November
Admission charge applies

Royal Botanic Garden Edinburgh at **Benmore**

Dunoon, Argyll PA23 8QU
Tel 01369 706261 | www.rbge.org.uk/benmore
Open daily 1 March to 31 October
Admission charge applies

Royal Botanic Garden Edinburgh at **Dawyck**

Stobo, Scottish Borders EH45 9JU
Tel 01721 760254 | www.rbge.org.uk/dawyck
Open daily 1 February to 30 November
Admission charge applies

The Royal Botanic Garden Edinburgh is a Charity registered in Scotland (number SC007983) and is a Non Departmental Public Body (NDPB) sponsored and supported through Grant-in-Aid by the Scottish Government's Environment and Forestry Directorate (ENFOR).

Aberdeenshire

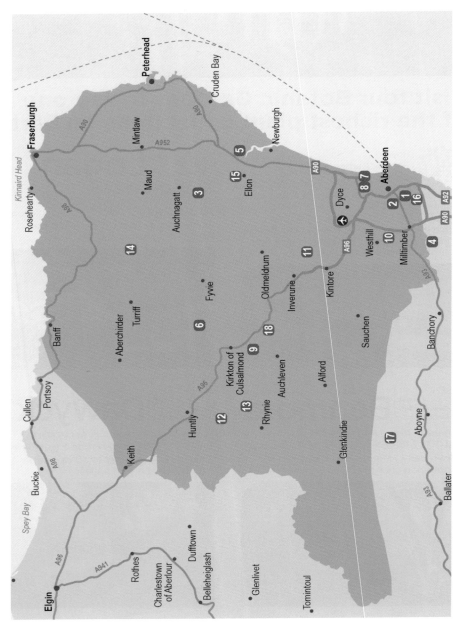

Aberdeenshire

OUR VOLUNTEER ORGANISERS

District Organisers:	Verity Walters	Tillychetly, Alford AB33 8HQ
		E: aberdeenshire@scotlandsgardens.org
Area Organisers:	Gill Cook	
	Anne Fettes	
	Jennie Gibson	6 The Chanonry, Old Aberdeen AB24 1RP
	Anne Lawson	Asloun, Alford AB33 8NR
	Helen Rushton	Bruckhills Croft, Rothienorman AB51 8YB
District Photographer:	Andy Leonard	Parkvilla, 47 Schoolhill, Ellon AB41 9AJ
Treasurers:	Ann Doyle	South Cottage , Fisherford, Inverurie AB51 8YS

GARDENS OPEN ON A SPECIFIC DATE

Auchmacoy, Ellon	Sunday, 11 April
Westhall Castle, Oyne, Inverurie	Sunday, 18 April
Cruickshank Botanic Garden, 23 St Machar Drive, Aberdeen	Saturday, 8 May
Airdlin Croft, Ythanbank, Ellon	Fri/Sat/Sun, 28/29/30 May
Leith Hall Plant Sale, Huntly	Saturday, 5 June
Heatherwick Farm, Kintore, Inverurie	Sunday, 20 June
Heatherwick Farm, Kintore, Inverurie	Sunday, 27 June
Bruckhills Croft, Rothienorman, Inverurie	Sunday, 4 July
Altries, Maryculter, Aberdeenshire	Saturday, 17 July
5 Woodlands Gardens, Cults, Aberdeen	Sunday, 18 July
Heatherwick Farm, Kintore, Inverurie	Sunday, 22 August
Tarland Community Garden, Aboyne	Sunday, 29 August
Parkvilla, 47 Schoolhill, Ellon	Saturday, 11 September

GARDENS OPEN BY ARRANGEMENT – BOOK A VISIT WITH THE GARDEN OWNER

Laundry Cottage, Culdrain, Gartly, Huntly	1 January - 31 December
Bruckhills Croft, Rothienorman, Inverurie	25 January - 11 March
Chaplains' Court, 20 The Chanonry, Old Aberdeen, Aberdeen	1 April - 30 September
105 Inchgarth Road, Pitfodels, Cults, Aberdeen	17 May - 13 June
Pinetrees Cottage, Banchory-Devenick	29 May - 4 July
Airdlin Croft, Ythanbank, Ellon	31 May - 31 July
Middle Cairncake, Cuminestown, Turriff	1 June - 31 August
Drumrossie Mansion House, Insch	1 June - 31 August
Easter Ord Farm, Easter Ord, Skene, Westhill	12 June - 22 August
Bruckhills Croft, Rothienorman, Inverurie	1 July - 31 August

Aberdeenshire

1 105 INCHGARTH ROAD
Pitfodels, Cults, Aberdeen AB15 9NX
Mr and Mrs W McGregor
T: 01224 861090 E: wahmcgregor@me.com

Informal cottage-style garden situated in one-third of an acre featuring azaleas, rhododendrons, orchids, peonies and a selection of alpines.

Open: By arrangement 17 May - 13 June, admission £5.00, children free.

Directions: From North Deeside Road, turn off along Station Road, Pitfodels. Access and parking along back lane.

Opening for: The Archie Foundation

105 Inchgarth Road

2 5 WOODLANDS GARDENS
Cults, Aberdeen AB15 9DU
Keith Thornton

A two-thirds of an acre plot planted out in 2008 and specialising in more unusual trees and shrubs. The collection of Magnolia trees has reached flowering size, and includes *sprengeri* 'Diva', *sargentiana* 'Star Wars' and *Michelia doltsopa*. The Rhododendron borders include early flowers, scented species and scented azaleas. Old roses feature with a collection of scented heritage French varieties, including *centifolia de peinte*, 'cabbage' roses and Pemberton musk roses. There is a small orchard of apple, pear and plum trees, and a large outdoor peach in the courtyard garden. Soft fruit and vegetable plots are laid out.

Open: Sunday 18 July, noon - 5pm, admission £5.00, children free.

Aberdeenshire

Directions: From the A90, take Milltimber junction A93 to Cults. At lights turn left up Kirk Brae, then right to Friarsfield Road. At top of hill, turn right into Woodlands housing estate, first left then first left again into Woodlands Gardens. From the A92 take the A93 to Braemar, after 200m turn right to Craigton Road, follow this for one mile, then Woodlands estate is on the left. The nearest bus stop is *Baird's Brae* on routes 19 or 201, then about 18 minutes' walk.

Opening for: Scottish SPCA: Drumoak branch & The New Arc

5 Woodland Gardens

3 AIRDLIN CROFT
Ythanbank, Ellon AB41 7TS
Richard and Ellen Firmin
T: 01358 761491 E: rsf@airdlin.com
W: www.airdlin.com

Since 1983 the garden has been developed to be both attractive to wildlife and horticulturally interesting, while also providing fruit and vegetables. One of two polytunnels produces figs, peaches and pumpkins while the other houses a collection of hostas, wrestling for space with seed-grown rhododendrons. Native trees form the backbone of the woodland garden, providing shelter for a range of shrubs and herbaceous plants from around the world. In the new, windswept garden, an embryonic shelterbelt is struggling to protect recent plantings. More details and photos can be found on the Airdlin website.

Open: Friday/Saturday/Sunday, 28/29/30 May, 1pm - 5pm. Also open by arrangement 31 May - 31 July. Admission £5.00, children free.

Directions: From the A948, three miles north of Ellon, take the left turn towards *Drumwhindle*. After another couple of miles take the second left towards *Cairnorrie*. Proceed for nearly a mile, ignoring the first Airdlin Croft at Coalmoss, and turn left at the first bend, go down our 300 yard track, parking is in the field at the bottom.

Opening for: Fauna & Flora International

Aberdeenshire

4 ALTRIES
Maryculter, Aberdeenshire AB12 5GD
Mr and Mrs Melfort Campbell

The Altries garden has been redesigned to give a feeling of space and to let in the light. The house itself is surrounded by a terraced area, borders and lawns. There is an exceptional view looking west up the River Dee, a woodland walk, a slate sphere sculpture using the original slates of the house following the refurbishment, a striking ten-foot wall making use of the down-takings of the house, a small new greenhouse with rose arbour path and further use of granite, and the original walled garden which has vegetables, fruit, and a picking garden. Each area of the garden has its own feeling of being a separate destination. Beautiful mature beech trees surround the area, giving a great sense of privacy.

Open: Saturday 17 July, 1pm - 5pm, admission £5.00, children free.

Directions: From Bridge of Dee, follow the South Deeside road, B9077. Half a mile after Maryculter House Hotel, turn left at yellow *SGS* sign, and follow signs to car park. For SatNav follow AB12 5GJ.

Opening for: River Dee Trust

5 AUCHMACOY
Ellon AB41 8RB
Mr and Mrs Charles Buchan

Auchmacoy House's attractive policies feature spectacular displays of thousands of daffodils.

Open: Sunday 11 April, 1pm - 4pm, admission £3.50, children free. Please, NO dogs

Directions: A90 from Aberdeen. Turn right to Auchmacoy/Collieston.

Opening for: The Royal British Legion: Ellon Branch

6 BRUCKHILLS CROFT
Rothienorman, Inverurie AB51 8YB
Paul and Helen Rushton
T: 01651 821596 E: helenrushton1@aol.com

An informal country-cottage garden extending to three-quarters of an acre with a further acre as wildflower meadow and pond. There are several distinct areas which include a white border, a butterfly alley, kitchen garden with polytunnel, greenhouse and fruit cage, an orchard and a blue and yellow border. Relax on one of the many seats in the garden and soak up the atmosphere.

Open: By arrangement 25 January - 11 March for Snowdrops and Winter Walks and 1 July - 31 August. Also open Sunday 4 July, noon - 5pm. Admission £5.00, children free.

Directions: From Rothienorman take the B9001 north for two-and-a-half miles. On the S bend turn left. Take the second left (*Bruckhills* sign). At the farmyard turn sharp right (opposite farmhouse), and the croft is at the end of the lane.

Opening for: Befriend A Child Ltd

Aberdeenshire

7 **CHAPLAINS' COURT**
20 The Chanonry, Old Aberdeen, Aberdeen AB24 1RQ
Irene Wischik
T: 01224 491675 E: irene@wischik.com

This historic walled garden has a long, well-stocked herbaceous border offering a succession of vivid colour from early spring to winter. It is divided by an ornamental pergola, a perfect place to sit and enjoy the garden. Large trees of ash, beech, horse chestnut, oak and sycamore give this garden a mature feel. A specimen Camperdown elm sits in the centre of the lawn, which in spring is covered in a carpet of crocuses, snowdrops and scilla. Vegetables and herbs produce plentiful crops, together with newly-planted espalier and fan-trained apple and pear trees.

Open: By arrangement 1 April - 30 September, admission £5.00, children free.

Directions: Bus 1 or 2 from Aberdeen city centre to St. Machar Drive, and head towards St. Machar Cathedral. Or drive down St Machar Drive, turn into The Chanonry and drive down until the junction with Don St.

Opening for: St Machar's Cathedral, Aberdeen, Church of Scotland: Restoration Fund

Chaplains' Court

Aberdeenshire

8 CRUICKSHANK BOTANIC GARDEN
23 St Machar Drive, Aberdeen AB24 3UU
Cruickshank Botanic Garden Trust, Aberdeen University
W: www.abdn.ac.uk/botanic-garden/

A tour is offered by the Curator, Mark Paterson, and Head Gardener, Richard Walker. The garden comprises a sunken garden with alpine lawn, a rock garden built in the 1960s complete with cascading water and pond system, a long double-sided herbaceous border, a formal rose garden with drystone walling and an arboretum. It has a large collection of flowering bulbs and rhododendrons, and many unusual shrubs and trees. It is sometimes known as 'Aberdeen's best kept secret'.
Champion Trees: *Quercus ilex, Acer griseum* and a tri-stemmed *Nothofagus obliqua.*

Open: Saturday 8 May, 2pm - 5pm, admission £5.00, children free.

Directions: Come down St Machar Drive over the four-way junction, just before the first set of traffic lights turn left into the Cruickshank Garden car park. The pedestrian garden entrance is off The Chanonry. Limited parking available for this day only in the Cruickshank car park – AB24 3UU.

Opening for: Friends Of The Cruickshank Botanic Garden

9 DRUMROSSIE MANSION HOUSE
Insch AB52 6LJ
Mr and Mrs Hugh Robertson
T: 01464 820249 E: drumrossie@yahoo.co.uk

The property, which can be traced back to the Crusades, is surrounded by three acres of landscaped lawns, formal walled garden, veg and greenhouse area and a newly planted orchard. There are 27 acres of wooded walks, paddocks and a large wildlife pond. Vegetables are grown in raised beds. The walled garden is laid out in lawns of a very high standard, with herbaceous borders and fruit trees on the south-facing wall. There is a large collection of hostas and alstroemerias, as well as herbaceous plants, heathers and azaleas, a productive vegetable garden, plant-raising area and polytunnel for early veg and flowers, a large glasshouse for tomatoes and a sunken greenhouse, which provides over-wintering heat for tender plants. A main feature is the well, which in days gone by provided the water supply to the house.

Open: By arrangement 1 June - 31 August, admission £5.00, children free. Teas available for larger groups.

Directions: Do not follow SatNav. Enter drive from Drumrossie Street off the crossroads in centre of village. The drive is through trees at the back of McColl's supermarket.

Opening for: Insch Parish Church

10 EASTER ORD FARM
Easter Ord, Skene, Westhill AB32 6SQ
Catherine Fowler
T: 01224 742278 E: catherine.a.fowler@gmail.com

A one-acre mature cottage garden with year-round interest. The garden has an open aspect with views towards Lochnagar. It is made up of 'rooms'. There is a fruit garden, large herbaceous borders, lawn areas, small wildlife pond, vegetable garden and mini-orchard with wildflowers.

Open: By arrangement 12 June - 22 August, admission £5.00, children free. Teas and home baking available at reasonable cost.

Aberdeenshire

Directions: Two miles from Westhill and can be reached using full postcode on SatNav. From Aberdeen take A944 towards Westhill. At the traffic lights before Westhill take the slip road on to the B9119 then immediately left towards Brotherfield. After one mile turn right at the T junction. After 350 yards turn left into the lane. Garden is first entrance on right.

Opening for: Aberdeen Royal Infirmary Roof Garden

---

11 HEATHERWICK FARM
Kintore, Inverurie AB51 0UQ
Lucy Narducci

This old farmhouse garden of 1½ acres has been regenerated over the past eight years and continues to evolve and develop. It has an open, spacious feel and new landscaping with additional planting has created distinct areas. The garden includes a formal square front lawn with perennial borders, a kitchen garden surrounded by orchard and a recently added native grass and wildflower meadow.

Open: Sunday 20 June, Sunday 27 June & Sunday 22 August, 1pm - 5pm, admission £5.00, children free.

Directions: From Inverurie centre, take the B9001 southwards. At the corner of St Mary's Place and St James's Place follow signs for *Keithhall*. Then follow signs for *Balbithan*. Heatherwick is signposted and on the left after Hogholm Stables. It is three miles from the centre of Inverurie.

Opening for: Myeloma UK

Heatherwick Farm

Aberdeenshire

12 LAUNDRY COTTAGE
Culdrain, Gartly, Huntly AB54 4PY
Judith McPhun
T: 01466 720768 E: judithmcphun@icloud.com

An informal cottage-style garden of about one-and-a-half acres by the river Bogie. Two contrasting steep slopes make up the wilder parts. The more intensively gardened area round the cottage includes a wide variety of herbaceous plants, shrubs and trees, an orchard area and fruit and vegetable plots, making a garden of year-round interest.

Open: By arrangement 1 January - 31 December, admission £5.00, children free. Snowdrops during February and March.

Directions: Four miles south of Huntly on the A97.

Opening for: Amnesty International UK Section Charitable Trust

13 LEITH HALL PLANT SALE
Huntly AB54 4NQ
The National Trust for Scotland
T: 01464 831148
W: www.nts.org.uk/visit/places/leith-hall/

The west garden was created by Charles and Henrietta Leith-Hay in the Arts and Crafts style during Edwardian times. In summer, the magnificent serpentine herbaceous and catmint borders provide a dazzling display and the kitchen garden produces heritage fruit and vegetables for sale. The carefully reconstructed rock garden is currently being replanted.

Open: Saturday 5 June, 10am - 3pm, admission £3.50, children free. The plant sale is a fantastic opportunity to buy a wide selection of potted perennials from the garden's herbaceous borders. Entrance to the plant sale is free.

Directions: On the B9002 one mile west of Kennethmont.

Opening for: The National Trust for Scotland: Leith Hall Garden

14 MIDDLE CAIRNCAKE
Cuminestown, Turriff AB53 5YS
Nick and Penny Orpwood
T: 01888 544432 E: orpwood@hotmail.com

A garden surrounded by farmland and attractive views. Visitors to the garden have described it as - 'beautiful... inspiring... full of good ideas ... fragrant roses... so much to see... superb vegetables.' Group visits welcome with afternoon tea served in our private winter garden. Also planned are a few special events which will be advertised nearer the time.

Open: By arrangement 1 June - 31 August, admission £5.00, children free. Homemade tea at additional charge.

Directions: Middle Cairncake is on the A9170 between New Deer and Cuminestown. It is clearly signposted.

Opening for: Scotland's Gardens Scheme & Parkinsons UK

Aberdeenshire

15 PARKVILLA
47 Schoolhill, Ellon AB41 9AJ
Andy and Kim Leonard
T: 07786 748296 E: andy.leonard@btinternet.com

A south-facing Victorian walled garden, lovingly developed from a design started in 1990 to give colour and interest all year. Enjoy densely planted herbaceous borders, pause under the pergola clothed in clematis, honeysuckle and rambling roses, continue on to the bottom of the garden where three ponds and wildflower beds reflect a strong focus on wildlife. This is a hidden gem of a garden that has won awards including *Ellon Best Garden* and with plants rarely seen in north east Scotland.

Open: Saturday 11 September, 2pm - 5pm, admission £5.00, children free.

Directions: From centre of Ellon head north towards Auchnagatt. Schoolhill is third left. From Auchnagatt head into Ellon along Golf Road, Schoolhill is first right after the golf course. Limited on-street parking, car parks in Ellon (five minutes walk) and Caroline's Well Wood. Public toilets in Ellon town centre.

Opening for: *St Mary On The Rock Episcopal Church Ellon, Alzheimer Scotland & Ellon Men's Shed*

Parkvilla © Andy Leonard

Aberdeenshire

Tarland Community Garden

16 PINETREES COTTAGE
Banchory-Devenick AB12 5XR
Angela and Derek Townsley
T: 01224 869141 E: angela.townsley@me.com

A mature garden set in three-quarters of an acre, filled with a wide range of hardy plants including rhododendrons, azaleas, acers, topiary and roses, with two ponds. An alpine house is fronted by stone troughs filled with rock plants. Set in a backdrop of mature pine trees to the north and open fields to the south.

Open: By arrangement 29 May - 4 July, admission £5.00, children free. Teas by arrangement.

Directions: Banchory-Devenick is four miles from Bridge of Dee. Turn off B9077 at Banchory-Devenick church. Follow to T junction, turn right. Next right is Butterywells Steading. Turn into opening and follow track, go around the back of farmhouse (Lochend) and continue on track to Pinetrees.

Opening for: Fighting For Sight Aberdeen

17 TARLAND COMMUNITY GARDEN
Aboyne AB34 4ZQ
The Gardeners of Tarland

Tarland Community Garden opened in 2013 and is a Tarland Development Group project. It provides an inclusive and accessible community growing space for local residents. It has indoor (polytunnel) and outdoor raised beds for rent, plus communal planting areas including a soft fruit cage, fruit trees and a herb garden. It is a place for members to grow produce, learn, share and have fun.

Open: Sunday 29 August, noon - 4pm, admission £3.00, children free.

Aberdeenshire

Directions: Take the B9094 from Aboyne or the A96 and B9119 from Aberdeen. Arriving at the village square the gardens will be clearly signposted.

Opening for: Tarland Development Group

18	**WESTHALL CASTLE**

Oyne, Inverurie AB52 6RW
Mr Gavin Farquhar
T: 01224 214301 E: enquiries@ecclesgreig.com

Set in an ancient landscape in the foothills of the impressive and foreboding hill of Bennachie, is a circular walk through glorious daffodils with outstanding views. This interesting garden is in the early stages of restoration, with large groupings of rhododendrons and specimen trees. Westhall Castle is a 16th-century tower house, incorporating a 13th-century building of the bishops of Aberdeen. There were additions in the 17th, 18th and 19th centuries. The castle is semi-derelict, but stabilised from total dereliction. A fascinating house encompassing 600 years of alteration and additions.

Open: Sunday 18 April, 1pm - 4pm, admission £5.00, children free.

Directions: Marked from the A96 at Old Rayne and from Oyne Village.

Opening for: Bennachie Guides

Westhall Castle

Angus & Dundee

Sponsored by
⊕ Investec

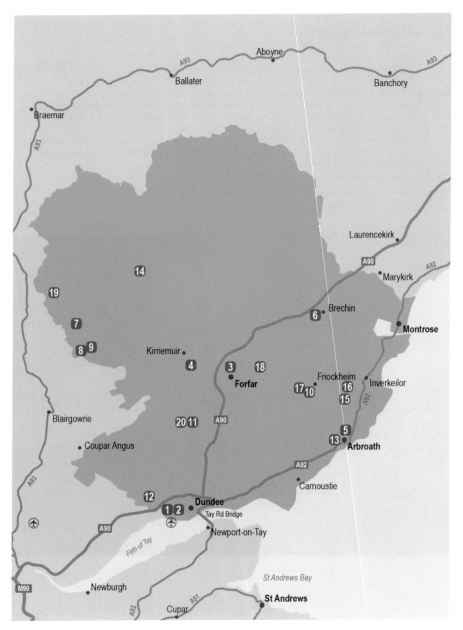

Angus & Dundee

OUR VOLUNTEER ORGANISERS

District Organisers:	Pippa Clegg	Easter Derry, Kilry, Blairgowrie PH11 8JA
	Terrill Dobson	Logie House, Kirriemuir DD8 5PN
		E: angusdundee@scotlandsgardens.org
Area Organisers:	Debbie Butler	Top Croft, Arniefoul, Angus DD8 1UD
	Moira Coleman	Templeton House, Arbroath DD11 4QP
	Jan Crow	Lower Duncraig, 2 Castle Street, Brechin DD9 6JN
	Frances Dent	12 Glamis Drive, Dundee DD2 1QL
	John Dent	12 Glamis Drive, Dundee DD2 1QL
	Jeanette Ogilvie	House of Pitmuies, Guthrie DD8 2SN
	Mary Stansfeld	Dunninald Castle, By Montrose DD10 9TD
	Claire Tinsley	Ethie Mains, Ethie DD11 5SN
Treasurer:	James Welsh	Dalfruin, Kirtonhill Road, Kirriemuir DD8 4HU

GARDENS OPEN ON A SPECIFIC DATE

Lawton House, Inverkeilor, by Arbroath	Sunday, 7 March
Lawton House, Inverkeilor, by Arbroath	Sunday, 14 March
10 Menzieshill Road, Dundee	Saturday/Sunday, 17/18 April
Gray Cottage, 23 Church Road, Liff, Dundee	Saturday/Sunday, 8/9 May
10 Menzieshill Road, Dundee	Saturday/Sunday, 15/16 May
Gardyne Castle, by Forfar	Saturday/Sunday, 15/16 May
Glenogilvy Schoolhouse Garden, Milton of Ogilvie, Forfar	Saturday/Sunday, 22/23 May
The Mill, Glen Isla, Blairgowrie	Sunday, 30 May
Easter Derry, Kilry	Sunday, 30 May
Angus & Dundee Garden Trail, Various locations	Thur/Fri/Sat, 3/4/5 June
Angus & Dundee Garden Trail, Various locations	Thur/Fri/Sat, 10/11/12 June
Angus & Dundee Garden Trail, Various locations	Thur/Fri/Sat, 17/18/19 June
Easter Cammock, Glenisla, Blairgowrie	Sunday, 20 June
The Mill, Glen Isla, Blairgowrie	Sunday, 20 June
Angus & Dundee Garden Trail, Various locations	Thur/Fri/Sat, 24/25/26 June
Easter Derry, Kilry	Sunday, 27 June
Arbroath Collection of Gardens, Locations across Arbroath	Saturday, 3 July
Brechin Gardens in Summer, Locations across Brechin	Saturday/Sunday, 24/25 July
Estir Bogside, Alyth	Saturday, 31 July
Easter Derry, Kilry	Saturday, 31 July
Angus Plant Sale, Logie Walled Garden, Kirriemuir	Saturday, 7 August
12 Glamis Drive, Dundee	Saturday/Sunday, 21/22 August
Hospitalfield Gardens, Hospitalfield House, Westway, Arbroath	Saturday, 25 September
12 Glamis Drive, Dundee	Saturday/Sunday, 16/17 October

Angus & Dundee

GARDENS OPEN REGULARLY

Kinblethmont House, by Arbroath, Angus	20 February - 28 February
Pitmuies Gardens, House of Pitmuies, Guthrie, by Forfar	1 April - 30 September
Primula Garden at Reswallie, Reswallie, Forfar	1 April - 31 May (Tuesdays & Thursdays)

GARDENS OPEN BY ARRANGEMENT – BOOK A VISIT WITH THE GARDEN OWNER

Torwood, Milton of Ogilvie, Glenogilvy, Glamis, by Forfar	1 January - 31 December
Inchmill Cottage, Glenprosen, near Kirriemuir	1 April - 31 October
Primula Garden at Reswallie, Reswallie, Forfar	1 April - 31 May
10 Menzieshill Road, Dundee	19 April - 14 May
Easter Cammock, Glenisla, Blairgowrie	17 July - 31 July

Angus & Dundee

1 10 MENZIESHILL ROAD
Dundee DD2 1PW
Frances Tait
T: 01382 665719

NEW

On a sloping site facing the river, No 10 is home to one of the nine wells in this part of the west end of Dundee. At one time, the well provided drinking water for a nearby farmhouse and two cottages. It was also the first and last water available to carriers' horses on their way to and from Dundee. Now it feeds rhododendrons and camellias, many of which came from the Rothschilds' garden at Exbury, Hampshire. Of particular interest are magnolia 'Manchu Fan' and rhododendrons 'Loderic King George' and 'Lady Chamberlain'. More recently, an area near the well has been given over to bulbs and small herbaceous plants, various irises and primulas.

Open: Saturday/Sunday, 17/18 April, 1pm - 5pm. Also open Saturday/Sunday, 15/16 May, 1pm - 5pm. And open by arrangement 19 April - 14 May. Admission £3.00, children free.

Directions: Turn off A85/Riverside Avenue at the roundabout towards the Dundee Botanic Garden. Pass the Botanics and the road bears left and becomes Perth Road. Take a right on to Invergowrie Drive and then first left on Menzieshill Road. Buses 5 and 9 to the foot of Glamis Road and walk west to Invergowrie Drive.

Opening for: *Plant Heritage*

10 Menzieshill Road

Angus & Dundee

12 GLAMIS DRIVE
Dundee DD2 1QL
John and Frances Dent

This established garden with mature trees occupies a half-acre south-facing site overlooking the River Tay and Fife hills. The tennis court lawn has herbaceous borders. The woodland area includes hidden features, garden ornaments and a miniature topiary garden and bower. A small rose garden, a fountain and two oriental-themed water gardens complete the tour.

Open: Saturday/Sunday, 21/22 August, 2pm - 5pm. Also open Saturday/Sunday, 16/17 October, 4pm - 8pm. Admission £5.00, children free. Homemade teas, live music and plant stall at the August opening, and refreshments and a variety of floodlighting effects at the October opening.

Directions: Buses 5, 22 or 73 from Dundee city centre. Please note there is no roadside parking on Glamis Drive. Limited disabled parking available at the house.

Opening for: Maggie Keswick Jencks Cancer Caring Centres Trust (Dundee) (Saturday/Sunday, 21/22 August) & UK Committee Dr Graham's Homes, Kalimpong, India (Saturday/Sunday, 16/17 October)

Reswallie House, Angus & Dundee Garden Trail

Angus & Dundee

3 **ANGUS & DUNDEE GARDEN TRAIL**
Various locations across Angus & Dundee
Gardeners of Angus & Dundee
E: angusdundee@scotlandsgardens.org

The Angus & Dundee Garden Trail offers a flexible way to keep up your weekly dose of beautiful gardens and is excellent value for money. Many of these gardens are new to SGS and run from Dundee city centre to the coast around Arbroath, through Forfar to Edzell and down to Meigle. Visit a community garden, a productive walled garden, as well as 12 other private gardens of varying sizes and styles. Dundee Botanic Garden will promote the trail with entry for trail ticket holders over the first weekend and Maggie's Dundee garden will also be available to visit throughout the trail.

5 Glamis Place (NEW) Il Gardino de Giovanni, Dundee DD2 1NB (John Egan)
Open Saturdays in June 11am - 4pm
8 Leemount Lane (NEW) Broughty Ferry DD5 1LA (Hannah Anthony)
Open Thursday in June 10am - 4pm
Balhary Walled Garden (NEW) Balhary, Alyth PH11 8LT (Teri and Paul Hodge-Neale)
Open Fridays and Saturdays in June 2pm - 6pm
Dundee Botanic Garden (NEW) Riverside Drive, Dundee DD2 1QH (University of Dundee)
Open for the trail Thursday 3, Friday 4, Saturday 5 June only, 10am - 5pm
Forfar Open Garden 36 Lochside Road, Forfar DD8 3JD (Forfar Open Gardeners)
Open Saturdays in June 10am - 2:30pm
Greengaites (NEW) 3, Glamis Drive, Dundee DD2 1QG (Elaine and Graham Lowe)
Open Saturdays in June 1pm - 5pm
Lawton House Inverkeilor, by Arbroath DD11 4RU (Katie and Simon Dessain)
Open Thursdays in June 10am - 2pm
Maggie's Dundee (NEW) Ninewells Hospital, Tom McDonald Ave, Dundee DD2 1NH (Maggie's)
Available to visit at any time
Newtonmill House by Brechin DD9 7PZ (Stephen and Rose Rickman)
Open Fridays in June 10am - 2pm
North Lodge (NEW) 36 Church Street, Edzell DD9 7TQ (Robin and Paul McIntosh)
Open Fridays in June noon - 4pm
Primula Garden at Reswallie (NEW) Reswallie, Forfar DD8 2SA (Colin Gair)
Open Thursdays in June 2pm - 5pm
Reswallie House (NEW) Forfar DD8 2SA (Caroline and Hugh Graham Watson)
Open Thursdays in June 2pm - 5pm
St Bride's Cottage (NEW) South Kingennie, Broughty Ferry DD5 3PA (Alison and Donald Gordon)
Open Fridays and Saturdays in June 1pm - 5pm
The Doocot (NEW) Kinloch, Meigle, Blairgowrie PH12 8QX (Liz and George McLaren)
Open Fridays in June 2pm - 5pm
Torwood (NEW) Milton of Ogilvie, Glenogilvy, Glamis by Forfar DD8 1UN (John Gordon)
Open Saturdays in June 2pm - 5pm

Open: The Angus & Dundee Garden Trail offers various gardens and times over the Thursdays, Fridays and Saturdays of June. Admission £25.00 (early bird £20.00 before 1 May) children free. Tickets available on the event listing on the Scotland's Gardens Scheme website or at the gardens on the day. Gardens can be visited individually, and tickets purchased at each garden for £5.00. Full details, including map and local tearoom and garden centres to visit, will also be available online.

Directions: Directions to each garden will be provided with the tickets.

Opening for: Maggie Keswick Jencks Cancer Caring Centres Trust (Dundee)

Angus & Dundee

4 ANGUS PLANT SALE
Logie Walled Garden, Kirriemuir DD8 5PN
SGS Angus & Dundee Organisers
E: angusdundee@scotlandsgardens.org

Our annual plant sale is now becoming an Angus 'regular' event, so please join us. We will offer a good, interesting selection, sourced from private gardens and with some donations from our local nurseries. It's advisable to come promptly and bring boxes and trays. Donations of plants either before or during sales will always be welcome.

Open: Saturday 7 August, 2pm - 5pm, admission £3.00, children free. Light refreshments will be available.

Directions: From the A90, take A926 towards Kirriemuir. Just after Maryton, take a left into Logie Business Park and then take second left onto the single track road. Then take the first left on to a beech tree lined drive and follow signs to *The Walled Garden*.

Opening for: All proceeds to SGS Beneficiaries

5 ARBROATH COLLECTION OF GARDENS
Locations across Arbroath DD11 4AH
The Gardeners of Arbroath
W: www.ashbrook.co.uk

37 Duncan Avenue (NEW) Arbroath DD11 2DA (Alison Connelly): The front garden has a small terrace with wonderful evergreen grasses planted into gravel with a group of trees, an unusual weeping malus, liquidambar and unusual beech. The rear garden is a feast of interesting planting, including acers, hostas, hellebores, ferns and many more. There are many secret gardens to discover with all their nooks and crannies.
Ashbrook Nursery and Garden Centre Forfar Road, Arbroath DD11 3RB (Anne Webster): This family-run garden centre grows the majority of its plants, including over 2,000 varieties of bedding and patio plants, alpines, herbaceous perennials, ferns and grasses. There are also comprehensive A-Z displays of trees, conifers, shrubs, alpines and perennials.
Brechin Road Allotments 85a Brechin Road, Arbroath DD11 1TA (Arbroath Allotments Association): The Brechin Road site is open this year and as always has loads of interest including plants, vegetables, fruit and creative sheds and shelters. A team of helpers will be on hand to answer any questions.
HOPE Organic Garden The Plot next to Hospitalfield House, The Westway, Arbroath DD11 2NH (The HOPE Trustees): An organic fruit and vegetable garden, which provides training and work experience for adults with learning and/or physical disabilities. Note, this garden closes at 4pm.
Inverbrothock School Sensory Garden and Forest Garden (NEW) East Kirkton Road, Arbroath DD11 4GR (Inverbrothock Pupils and Staff): These two gardens have been designed and created by the pupils, staff and parents. The Sensory Garden is a great asset to all children and staff, especially children who need additional support. There are areas of raised beds for growing vegetables, a dry river bed with interesting grasses and plants, large stone features to climb on, and different shelters and corners to play in. A polytunnel is used for outdoor classes and seed sowing. The Forest Garden includes interesting mounds and trees, an area to build dens and play amongst trees. Gardens created by and for young minds.
Springfield Rose Garden Springfield Park, Arbroath DD11 1AH (Friends of the Rose Garden): Springfield Rose Garden is a small, traditional, walled garden set in Springfield Park, close to the centre of Arbroath. The day to day upkeep and maintenance is managed by the volunteers, 'Friends of the Rose Garden', who work in co-operation with, and under the direction of the local authority, to improve and regenerate the rose garden. It is a work in progress.

Open: Saturday 3 July, 1pm - 5pm, admission £5.00, children free. Ashbrook Nursery will run tours of the nursery at 2pm, 3pm and 4pm. Teas will be available at the Brechin Road Allotments.

Angus & Dundee

Directions: Tickets and maps will be available from the various gardens and Ashbrook Nursery on the day. Look for the SGS yellow arrows around town to help you locate the gardens.

Opening for: The Arbroath Garden Allotment Association SCIO

6 BRECHIN GARDENS IN SUMMER
Locations across Brechin DD9 6LE
The Gardeners of Brechin

24 North Latch Road Brechin DD9 6LE (Alistair and Mary Gray): Learn how the owners grow and show vegetables and how these can be a spectacular display of colourful bedding-full greenhouses.

9 Pearse Street Brechin DD9 6JR (Irene and James Mackie): A recently redesigned garden with ten newly planted trees, a wide interestingly planted colourful herbaceous border and a lovely lawn. There's a secluded and rural feel to this town garden. A huge collection of ferns is a unique feature of this garden, unusually planted to mingle with other herbaceous plants.

Andover Primary School Garden (NEW) 50A Drumachlie Park, Brechin DD9 7BU (Andover School Staff and Pupils): An area of barren ground in a forgotten corner of the school has been transformed into a colourful and abundant space where classes have been growing and harvesting their own produce. It makes a magical hiding space for games and is also popular with butterflies and other insects!

Bishops Walk 11A Argyll St, Brechin DD9 6JL (Steff and Mike Eyres): Winding paths lead through an eclectic mix of perennials, shrubs, conifers (including a young wollemi pine in a pot) and roses within this walled garden, accessed through the potting shed.

Brechin Cathedral Allotments Chanory Wynd, Brechin DD9 6EU (Brechin Cathedral Allotments Gardeners): Eleven varied plots reflect the interests and personalities of each plot-holder and include fruit, vegetables and herbs. A unique feature is the historical 'College Well' used by medieval monks.

Brechin in Bloom Community Garden Montrose Street DD9 7EF (Brechin Community Garden Volunteers): Started in 2015 on an abandoned allotment site, this community scheme shares experience and learning skills involved in gardening for their own use and for local people. Additions since last year include a log cabin and mud kitchen.

Latchlea (NEW) 17A North Latch Road, Brechin DD9 6LE (Pamela Stevens): A new garden begun as a way of coping with bereavement. Inspired by the Queen saying that 'everyone should plant as many trees as possible', 100 trees are newly planted along The Old Lady Walk. Features include some fine stonework, shrubs, herbaceous plants and bulbs and also a courtyard garden.

Liscara Castle Street, Brechin DD9 6JW (June and Mike Hudson): A 'secret' south-facing small garden with raised beds, circular lawn and fountain, espaliered pear tree and pretty summerhouse.

Lower Duncraig 2, Castle Street, Brechin DD9 6JN (Jan and Andrew Crow): A small town garden recently redesigned to include less grass and more plants. Plants are selected mainly for their value to wildlife and a small pond supports this. Space has been found for a few trees and 20 different roses.

Rosehill West (NEW) 15C North Latch Road, Brechin DD9 6LF (Dr Robert and Mrs Jenny Martin): An acre of newly planted garden, formerly a field, featuring mature original trees, herbaceous areas, fruit trees (quince and crab apple), and a path through recently planted trees. A work in progress!

Open: Saturday/Sunday, 24/25 July, noon - 5pm, admission £5.00, children free. Teas and tickets will be available at the cathedral hall, with tickets also available at the gardens.

Directions: Gardens are located around the town of Brechin. Look for the SGS yellow arrows.

Opening for: Brechin Cathedral & Brechin Healthcare Group

Angus & Dundee

7 EASTER CAMMOCK

Glenisla, Blairgowrie PH11 8PF
June and John Browning
T: 01575 582222

Panoramic views of Glen Isla and a large variety of wildflowers in July are a highlight of Easter Cammock. Large pond surrounded by water plants, perennial and annual wild flowers and many relatively young plants. Established woodland area, rockery, herbaceous borders. Access by farm track.

Open: Sunday 20 June, 2pm - 5pm. Also open by arrangement 17 July - 31 July. Admission £3.00, children free. The Mill is also open 20 June and both gardens can be visited for £5.00. The 'by arrangement' openings in July will be for wildflowers.

Directions: From Perth take A94 through Coupar Angus to just before Meigle. Take B954 and follow signs to Glenisla. From Dundee take A923 to Muirhead, then B954, turn right just after Meigle and follow signs to Glenisla as above. Continue on B954 Glenisla road until it meets the B951 from Kirriemuir at Backwater crossroads. Turn left towards Glenisla on B951. Approx two miles on, turn left at *Easter Cammock* sign opposite red postbox. Up farm track, bend left at T junction, drive through farm and follow road for half mile to Easter Cammock.

Opening for: Barnardo's Scotland: Dundee Group & Scotland's Charity Air Ambulance

8 EASTER DERRY

Kilry PH11 8JA
Pippa and Roger Clegg

This two-acre garden has glorious heather-clad hills as a backdrop, along with lily pond, herbaceous borders, scree bed, vegetable garden, greenhouse and polytunnel.

Open: Sunday 30 May, Sunday 27 June & Saturday 31 July, 2pm - 5pm, admission £3.00, children free.

Directions: From Perth take A94 to Coupar Angus and just before Meigle take the B954 and follow signs to Glen Isla and then to Kilry, signed to the left. Follow road round right-hand-bend at church and take first left. Easter Derry is first house on left. From Dundee take A923 to Muirhead and then B954 to Meigle and Kilry, then follow signs as above.

Opening for: Barnardo's Scotland: Dundee Group & Scotland's Charity Air Ambulance

9 ESTIR BOGSIDE

Alyth PH11 8HU
Morag and Andrew Buist

Garden started in 1995. Herbaceous borders, cottage garden and potager. In 2010 the garden was extended to adjacent land to allow planting of native trees, wildflowers, mown paths, two ponds and a glasshouse.

Open: Saturday 31 July, 2pm - 5pm, admission £3.00, children free. Easter Derry is also open 31 July and both gardens can be visited for £5.00. Visitors are welcome to bring a picnic to enjoy in the garden.

Directions: From Perth Take A94 to Coupar Angus and just before Meigle take the B954 and follow signs to Glen Isla for approximately three miles until you see *Garden Open* signs on the left, by the road. From Dundee take the A923 to Muirhead and then B954 to Meigle, then turn right up B954 towards Glen Isla and follow signs as above.

Opening for: Barnardo's Scotland: Dundee Group & Scotland's Charity Air Ambulance

Angus & Dundee

10 **GARDYNE CASTLE**
by Forfar DD8 2SQ
William and Camilla Gray Muir

Gardyne Castle, dating from the 16th century, is one of the most attractive small castles in Angus. After a turbulent history of battles with the neighbouring Guthries, the fortified house now sits in the centre of an enchanting garden created by its current owners over the past 18 years. To the east, the walled garden runs down to the Denton Burn. The castle's extraordinary stone-capped turrets overlook a long romantic double border, bursting with tulips and alliums in May. The castle's southern front was extended in the 17th, 18th and early 20th centuries and is complemented by a large enclosed knot garden of box and yew mixed with white roses and lavender. Beyond is an immaculate formal lawn surrounded by yew topiaries and specimen trees, leading to a wildflower meadow with a gentle path leading down through an orchard. To the north, a new upper garden, centred on an extraordinary pepper pot doocot, provides an area for quiet contemplation with white planting, a fishpond and the family's collection of chickens. Beyond the formal gardens the grounds merge into mature woods and parkland with a spectacular display of bluebells and romantic walks along the Denton Burn.

Open: Saturday/Sunday, 15/16 May, 2pm - 5pm, admission £5.00, children free. The garden is only available to visit on these dates.

Directions: Turn off A932 at signpost to *Pitmuies Garden*. Go over two stone bridges and follow road uphill past small hamlet. Take first road on left. At sharp right-hand bend take private drive straight ahead (beside cream lodge).

Opening for: *Guthrie and Rescobie Parish Church*

Gardyne Castle

Angus & Dundee

11 GLENOGILVY SCHOOLHOUSE GARDEN
Milton of Ogilvie, Forfar DD8 1UN
Rosemary and Fred Stephen

This spacious country garden of approximately one acre faces south to the Sidlaws over the Glen Ogilvie Burn. In early summer the cherry trees, rhododendrons and azaleas are especially colourful and the emerging herbaceous planting, roses and summer bedding are reflected in the large tranquil landscaped pond. Many wandering paths lead you on different levels through 'rooms' and dells with hidden surprise characters, past a young birch meadow, fruit espalier walk and vegetable area with its model compost bays, then under a shady scented wisteria-draped pergola leading back to the main lawn. There is a variety of seating areas at select points along the way.

Open: Saturday/Sunday, 22/23 May, 10am - 5pm, admission £5.00, children free.

Directions: From the A90, take the A94 towards Glamis and turning left up the hill on the A928. Turn off the A928 into Glen Ogilvy and the Schoolhouse is the first stone-built house on left.

Opening for: North Angus District Scout Council: Glamis Scout Hall Redevelopment Fund

12 GRAY COTTAGE
23 Church Road, Liff, Dundee DD2 5NN
Graham Haddow

With wonderful views over Dundee, open farmland and the Tay across to Fife, Gray Cottage sits on the edge of Liff village. Built in 1886 for the Land Steward of Gray Estate, its half-acre mature garden has a wide variety of shrubs and trees and is particularly colourful in May/June when rhododendrons, azaleas, and pieris are at their best. The peaceful garden is one to explore with a number of corners and hidden areas which are linked and connected by hedge tunnels and natural 'windows'. One fascinating feature is a very large rhododendron with its interior branches fully exposed to give an almost mystical quality. Red squirrels, pheasants, woodpeckers, jays and the occasional fox are all regular visitors to Gray Cottage garden, and James McIntosh Patrick painted 'The Elm Tree, Perthshire' from the garden.

Open: Saturday/Sunday, 8/9 May, 10am - 5pm, admission £4.00, children free.

Directions: Liff village is two miles northwest of Dundee. Gray cottage is next to the only church in Liff. The church steeple is the landmark and the cottage is down the track to the left.

Opening for: All proceeds to SGS Beneficiaries

13 HOSPITALFIELD GARDENS
Hospitalfield House, Westway, Arbroath DD11 2NH
Hospitalfield Trust
E: info@hospitalfield.org.uk
W: www.hospitalfield.org.uk

Visit the gardens at Hospitalfield in Arbroath to be among the first to experience the new garden designed by Nigel Dunnett. The artist Patrick Allan-Fraser (1813-1890) remodelled a 13th-century hospital to create his 19th-century home in the Arts and Crafts style. The walled gardens have been cultivated since the early medieval period, from the medicinal garden and the orchard, to the Victorian passion for collecting ferns. This beautiful space, set against the red sandstone neo-Gothic architecture, has been comprehensively developed to a design by celebrated designer Nigel Dunnett, to tell the 800-year horticultural story of this extraordinary site. Enjoy the café and discover the fascinating restored Fernery at Hospitalfield.

Angus & Dundee

Open: Saturday 25 September, 11am - 4pm, admission £6.00, children free.

Directions: See website for directions and more details about Hospitalfield and its international cultural programme rooted in contemporary visual arts.

Opening for: Donation to SGS Beneficiaries

 INCHMILL COTTAGE
Glenprosen, near Kirriemuir DD8 4SA
Iain Nelson
T: 01575 540452

This is a long, sloping and terraced garden at over 800 feet in the Braes of Angus, developed to be a garden for all seasons. Half is dominated by bulbs, rhododendrons, azaleas, primulas, meconopsis and clematis. The other half is mainly later summer bulbs, herbaceous plants and roses. There is also a rockery/scree and fernery.

Open: By arrangement 1 April - 31 October, admission £3.00, children free. Book ahead please, maximum of 10 people.

Directions: Please DO NOT use SatNav. From Kirriemuir take the B955 (signposted *The Glens*) to Dykehead (about five miles). From there follow the *Prosen* sign for about five miles. Inchmill is the white-fronted cottage beside the phone box.

Opening for: The Archie Foundation

Gray Cottage

Angus & Dundee

15 KINBLETHMONT HOUSE

by Arbroath, Angus DD11 4RW
The Ramsay family
E: info@kinblethmont.com
W: www.kinblethmont.com

Kinblethmont is an historic estate which, with its advantageous elevated position, has been settled since Pictish times. In the centre is the Victorian mansion house surrounded by beautiful policy woodlands where specimen trees and snowdrops abound. Paths take you through the woods past the old pet cemetery, the remains of 16th century Kinblethmont and the walled garden with children's play area. A longer walk will take you up around the solar park with spectacular views over to the Angus hills and the North Sea.

Open: 20 February - 28 February, 10am - 4pm for Snowdrops and Winter Walks, admission £4.00, children free. The estate has some lovely holiday cottages for anyone wanting to make a weekend of it.

Directions: From Forfar/Brechin, take the A933 towards Arbroath, turn left to Friockheim. Drive through Friockheim and continue along the road, past the crematorium, until you reach a T junction. Turn right and continue along this road, past a crossroads, until you enter Kinblethmont estate on your left.

Opening for: *All proceeds to SGS Beneficiaries*

Pitmuies Gardens

Angus & Dundee

16 **LAWTON HOUSE**

Inverkeilor, by Arbroath DD11 4RU
Katie and Simon Dessain

Woodland garden of beech trees, carpeted with snowdrops, aconites and crocuses in spring, set around a 1755 house. There is also a walled garden planted with fruit trees and vegetables. The property was owned for many years by Elizabeth and Patrick Allan Fraser who built Hospitalfield House in Arbroath.

Open: 7 March - 14 March, 10am - 4pm for Snowdrops and Winter Walks, admission £3.00, children free.

Directions: Take B965 between Inverkeilor and Friockheim, turn right at sign for *Angus Chain Saws.* Drive approximately 200 yards, then take first right.

Opening for: Siobhan's Trust

17 **PITMUIES GARDENS**
House of Pitmuies, Guthrie, by Forfar DD8 2SN
Jeanette and Ruaraidh Ogilvie
T: 01241 828245 E: ogilvie@pitmuies.com
W: www.pitmuies.com

Two renowned semi-formal walled gardens adjoin an 18th-century house and steading, sheltering long borders of herbaceous perennials, superb old-fashioned delphiniums and roses, together with pavings rich with violas and dianthus. An extensive and diverse collection of plants, interesting kitchen garden, spacious lawns, and river, lochside and woodland walks beneath fine trees. A wide variety of shrubs with good autumn colour and a picturesque turreted doocot and a 'Gothick' wash house. Myriad spring bulbs include carpets of crocus following massed snowdrops and daffodils.

Open: 1 April - 30 September, 10am - 5pm, admission £5.00, children free.

Directions: From Forfar take A932 east for seven miles and gardens are signposted on the right. From Brechin take A933 south to Friockheim and turn right onto A932; then gardens are signposted on the left after one-and-a-half miles.

Opening for: Donation to SGS Beneficiaries

Angus & Dundee

18 PRIMULA GARDEN AT RESWALLIE
Reswallie, Forfar DD8 2SA
Colin Gair
T: 07747 688402 E: colingair161@btinternet.com

The Primula Garden started as a wedding gift of primula to gardener Colin Gair and his wife Iris in 1971. Colin moved to Reswallie in 2011 after Iris died, and he maintains and expands her collection as a tribute. Space was created to expand the original garden by the collapse of trees, the removal of *Rhododenron ponticum*, excavations in search of a family dog and the destruction of a rabbit warren. Today there are 45 species of primula, including rare ones, each with a sign including name, country of origin, flower colour and flowering season. These are planted among meconopsis, miniature rhododendron, hostas, various bulbs and many other plants. The garden is also in memory of David Lloyd-Jones and Helen Lloyd-Jones who died after the garden had started.

Open: 1 April - 31 May (Tuesdays and Thursdays), 2pm - 5pm. Also open by arrangement 1 April -31 May. Admission £4.00, children free.

Directions: Take the A932 from Forfar and signposted to *Arbroath*. Continue about three miles and turn left signposted to *Reswallie*. Take the second right down the hill.

Opening for: Marie Curie & Macmillan Cancer Support

19 THE MILL
Glen Isla, Blairgowrie PH11 8QL
Valerie and Charles Summers

Wonderful location in Glen Isla includes small wood, stream and natural pond. Haven for wildlife. Island beds, formal herbaceous borders and rockery around the house, blending with wilder areas.

Open: Sunday 30 May and Sunday 20 June, 2pm - 5pm. Admission £3.00, children free. Open 30 May with Easter Derry and on 20 June with Easter Cammock. Two gardens can be visited for £5.00.

Directions: From Dundee and Perth see directions for Easter Cammock. From their sign, continue on through Kirkton of Glenisla for approximately two miles, turn right signposted Auchavan. One mile on, The Mill is the second of two houses on left of road.

Opening for: Barnardo's Scotland: Dundee Group & Scotland's Charity Air Ambulance

Angus & Dundee

20	**TORWOOD**

TORWOOD
Milton of Ogilvie, Glenogilvy, Glamis by Forfar DD8 1UN
John Gordon
T: 07988 010418 E: j.gordon.82@btinternet.com
W: www.gardendisplays.co.uk

A small, attractively laid-out country garden striving towards year-round interest, enjoyment and relaxation through association and succession planting of trees, shrubs, herbaceous, perennials and bulbs. John's aim for his gardening is to focus on ecologically-based, wildlife-friendly planting schemes, guided by natural and semi-natural habitats. This approach is demonstrated beautifully in his garden, separated into rooms focusing on different colour schemes and styles, including a small woodland area, mixed borders and prairie-style planting.

Open: By arrangement 1 January - 31 December, admission £4.00, children free. Torwood is also open in June with the Angus & Dundee Garden Trail 2021.

Directions: Take A928 between Kirriemuir turnoff on A90 or Glamis turnoff on A94. Follow road signposted *Glenogilvie, Handwick, Dryburn*. Torwood is second house from the end on the left.

Opening for: *Alzheimer Scotland*

Primula Garden at Reswallie

Argyll & Lochaber

Sponsored by

✧ Investec

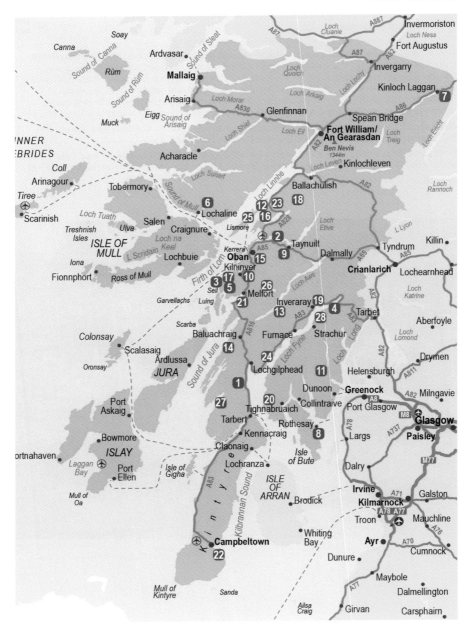

Argyll & Lochaber

OUR VOLUNTEER ORGANISERS

District Organiser:	Minette Struthers	Camasmaddy, Ardmaddy Castle, by Oban PA34 4QY E: argyll@scotlandsgardens.org
Area Organisers:	Yvonne Anderson	Craigiebank, 122 Main Street, Lower Largo KY8 6BP
	Grace Bergius	Craignish House, Ardfern, by Lochgilphead PA31 8QN
	Shian Carlow	Balliemore, Loch Striven, Dunoon PA23 8RH
	Mary Lindsay	Dal an Eas, Kilmore, Oban PA34 4XU
District Photographer:	Maurice Wilkins	Dunrobian, Laurel Road, Oban PA34 5EA
Treasurer:	Minette Struthers	Camasmaddy, Ardmaddy Castle, by Oban PA34 4QY

GARDENS OPEN ON A SPECIFIC DATE

Benmore Botanic Garden, Benmore, Dunoon	Sunday, 28 March
Kames Bay, Kilmelford	Saturday/Sunday, 1/2 May
Knock Newhouse, Lochgair	Saturday/Sunday, 8/9 May
Fasnacloich, Appin	Sunday, 16 May
Strachur House Flower & Woodland Gardens, Strachur	Saturday/Sunday, 22/23 May
Inveryne Woodland Garden, Kilfinan, Tighnabruaich	Saturday/Sunday, 29/30 May
Achabhraid, Ormsary Road, Lochgilphead, Argyll	Saturday/Sunday, 29/30 May
Ardverikie with Aberarder, Kinloch Laggan, Newtonmore	Monday, 31 May

GARDENS OPEN REGULARLY

Ardmaddy Castle, by Oban	1 January - 31 December
Ardkinglas Woodland Garden, Cairndow	1 January - 31 December
Barguillean's 'Angus Garden', Taynuilt	1 January - 31 December
Achnacloich, Connel, Oban	1 January - 31 December (Sats only)
Ardtornish, by Lochaline, Morvern	1 January - 31 December
Kinlochlaich Walled Garden, Appin	3 March - 31 October
Druimneil House, Port Appin	1 April - 31 October
An Cala, Ellenabeich, Isle of Seil	1 April - 31 October
Ascog Hall Garden and Fernery, Ascog, Isle of Bute	1 April - 31 October
Inveraray Castle Gardens, Inveraray	1 April - 31 October
Crinan Hotel Garden, Crinan	1 May - 31 August

Argyll & Lochaber

GARDENS OPEN BY ARRANGEMENT – BOOK A VISIT WITH THE GARDEN OWNER

Braevallich Farm, by Dalmally	1 January - 31 December
Maolachy's Garden, Lochavich, by Kilmelford	1 March - 31 October
Dal an Eas, Kilmore, Oban	1 April - 30 September
Ormsary House, Ormsary, Lochgilphead	1 April - 31 October
Berandhu, Appin, Argyll.	1 April - 31 October
Knock Newhouse, Lochgair	12 April - 12 October
Lismore Secret Garden, Isle of Lismore, Oban	1 May - 1 October
Barochreal, Kilninver, Oban	1 May - 30 September
Eas Mhor, Cnoc-a-Challtuinn, Clachan Seil, Oban	1 May - 30 September
Kildalloig, Campbeltown	1 May - 31 October

Argyll & Lochaber

1 ACHABHRAID

Ormsary Road, Lochgilphead, Argyll PA31 8NY
Mrs K Haig
T: 01546 600226

With an open view over Loch Fyne, our small garden is a work in progress. May is the time for rhododendrons, azaleas, camellias, primroses, bluebells, daffodils, hostas and potted geraniums. The columbines spill out of the flower bed into the gravel back yard and the copper beech, birch and maple trees are wearing their spring colours. We are already harvesting from the kitchen garden. This year we hope the wildflower area will come into its own. You can get a taste of the garden at *achabhraid.squarespace.com.* Access is across the gravel back yard which may limit wheelchair access.

Open: Saturday/Sunday, 29/30 May, 1pm - 5pm, admission by donation.

Directions: Two miles south of Ardrishaig turn right on the B8024 to Kilberry. Achabhraid is on the right-hand side approximately one mile up the road.

Opening for: *Children 1st*

Achabhraid

Argyll & Lochaber

2 ACHNACLOICH
Connel, Oban PA37 1PR
Mr T E Nelson
T: 01631 710223 E: charlie_milne@msn.com

The 20-acre woodland garden, overlooking Loch Etive, has been planted over the last century with a wide range of trees and shrubs from Asia, China, Japan, North America, Chile and New Zealand. Many have grown to considerable size. The light woodland canopy consists of native oaks and a number of magnificent 150-year-old Scots pines and European larch. Amongst these are open glades, carpeted with bluebells and numerous other bulbs. Two ponds and streams are planted with primulas, iris species, lysichitum, and astilbes. The woodland contains innumerable species of rhododendron and azalea, of which the triflorums and yunnanense are outstanding. Amongst these are species of acer, betula, camellia, cercidiphyllum, cornus, crinodendron, drimys, embothrium, enkianthus, eucryphia, hoheria, magnolia, malus, nothofagus, pieris, sorbus, stewartia, telopea and viburnum. Beside the house is a giant Douglas fir from Douglas' original introduction. One of the first Dawyck beeches stands beside the drive. The autumn colour is very fine.

Open: 1 January - 31 December (Saturdays only), 10am - 4pm, admission £5.00, children free.

Directions: On the A85 two miles east of Connel. The car park is at the bottom of the drive.

Opening for: Macmillan Cancer Support

3 AN CALA
Ellenabeich, Isle of Seil PA34 4RF
Mrs Sheila Downie
W: www.gardens-of-argyll.co.uk/view-details.php?id=447

A wonderful example of a 1930s designed garden, An Cala sits snugly in its horseshoe shelter of surrounding cliffs. A spectacular and very pretty garden with streams, waterfall, ponds, many herbaceous plants as well as azaleas, rhododendrons and cherry trees in spring. Archive material of Thomas Mawson's design was found recently and is available to visitors.

Open: 1 April - 31 October, 10am - 6pm, admission £5.00, children free.

Directions: Proceed south from Oban on Campbeltown Road for eight miles, turn right at the *Easdale* sign, a further eight miles on the B844; the garden is between the school and the village. Bus Oban – Easdale.

Opening for: Cancer Research UK

4 ARDKINGLAS WOODLAND GARDEN
Cairndow PA26 8BG
Ardkinglas Estate
T: 01499 600261
W: www.ardkinglas.com

In a peaceful setting overlooking Loch Fyne, the garden contains one of the finest collections of rhododendrons and conifers in Britain. This includes the mightiest conifer in Europe — a silver fir, as well as many other Champion Trees. There is a gazebo with a unique scriptorium based around a collection of literary quotes. The garden has a Fairy Trail and a Gruffalo Trail; come and find him! It is a *VisitScotland* 3-star garden.
Champion Trees: The mightiest conifer in Europe and others.

Open: 1 January - 31 December, dawn - dusk, admission £5.00, children free.

Directions: Entrance through Cairndow village off the A83 Loch Lomond/Inveraray road.

Opening for: Donation to SGS Beneficiaries

Argyll & Lochaber

5 | ARDMADDY CASTLE

by Oban PA34 4QY
Mr and Mrs Archie Struthers
T: 01852 300353 E: minette@ardmaddy.com
W: ardmaddy.com/places-visit/

The gardens lie in a most spectacular setting in the centre of a horseshoe valley sheltered by mixed mature woodlands and the elevated castle standing on a volcanic mound to seaward. The walled garden is full of magnificent rhododendrons, a collection of rare and unusual shrubs and plants, the Clock Garden with its cutting flowers, the Crevice Garden, fruit and vegetables grown with labour saving formality, all within dwarf box hedging. Beyond, a woodland walk, with its 60-foot *Hydrangea petiolaris*, leads to the Water Garden which in spring has a mantle of bluebells and daffodils and in early summer a riot of *Primula candelabra*, irises, rodgersias and other damp-loving plants and grasses. There is also lovely autumn colour. This is a plantsman's garden for all seasons.

Open: 1 January - 31 December, 9am - dusk, admission £5.00, children free. Seasonal vegetables, summer fruits and plant stall. Toilet suitable for the disabled.

Directions: Take the A816 south of Oban for eight miles. Turn right onto the B844 to Seil Island/Easdale. Four miles on, turn left on to Ardmaddy Road (signposted) for a further two miles.

Opening for: Donation to SGS Beneficiaries

6 | ARDTORNISH

by Lochaline, Morvern PA80 5UZ
Mrs John Raven
W: www.ardtornishgardens.co.uk

Ardtornish Estate spreads out around Loch Aline, a huge, wooded, U-shaped bay, a natural haven. Wonderful gardens of interesting mature conifers, rhododendrons, deciduous trees, shrubs and herbaceous, set amid magnificent scenery. Much of the garden is covered by native birch, alongside extensive planting of exotic species, under mature groups of larch, firs and pine, whose strong form and colour complement the pink sandstone towers and gables of Ardtornish House.

Open: 1 January - 31 December, 10am - 6pm, admission £5.00, children free.

Directions: Three miles from Lochaline along the A884.

Opening for: Donation to SGS Beneficiaries

Argyll & Lochaber

7   ARDVERIKIE WITH ABERARDER
Kinloch Laggan, Newtonmore PH20 1BX
The Feilden family, Mrs P Laing and Mrs E T Smyth-Osbourne
T: 01528 544300

Aberarder Kinloch Laggan, Newtonmore PH20 1BX (The Feilden family): The garden has been laid out over the last 20-years to create a mixture of spring and autumn plants and trees, including rhododendrons, azaleas and acers. The elevated view down Loch Laggan from the garden is exceptional.
Ardverikie Kinloch Laggan, Newtonmore PH20 1BX (Mrs P Laing and Mrs E T Smyth-Osbourne): Lovely setting on Loch Laggan with magnificent trees. Walled garden with large collection of acers, shrubs and herbaceous plants. Architecturally interesting house (not open) featured in *Monarch of the Glen* and *The Crown*.

Open: Monday 31 May, 2pm - 5:30pm, admission £5.50, children (aged 16 and under) free.

Directions: Aberader On the A86 between Newtonmore and Spean Bridge. The entrance to the lodge is about 200 metres west of the Ardverikie entrance next to the small cottage.
Ardverikie On the A86 between Newtonmore and Spean Bridge. The entrance is at the east end of Loch Laggan via the bridge by Gatelodge.

Opening for: Laggan Parish Church & Highland Hospice

8   ASCOG HALL GARDEN AND FERNERY
Ascog, Isle of Bute PA20 9EU
Karin Burke
T: 01700 503461 E: info@ascogfernery.com
W: www.ascogfernery.com

The outstanding feature of this three-acre garden is the Victorian Fernery, a magnificent gilded structure fed by natural spring waters and housing many fern species, including Britain's oldest exotic fern, a 1,000-year-old *Todea babara* or king fern. Rare and unusual species await the visitor wandering through the original garden 'rooms' while the stables and coach house ruins feed the imagination with memories of long-lost times. The garden is generally well-labelled and contains a plant-hunters' trail. A climate change BioTape was introduced in 2018.

Open: 1 April - 31 October, 10am - 5pm, admission £5.00, children free. Restricted mobility parking at the top of the drive (close to the house). Personal assistance available for disabled access to the Fernery.

Directions: Three miles south of Rothesay on the A844. Close to the picturesque Ascog Bay. There is a bus every half hour Rothesay - Kilchattan.

Opening for: Donation to SGS Beneficiaries

9   BARGUILLEAN'S 'ANGUS GARDEN'
Taynuilt PA35 1HY
The Josephine Marshall Trust
T: 01866 822333 E: info@barguillean.co.uk
W: www.barguillean.co.uk

Nine-acre woodland garden around an 11-acre loch set in the Glen Lonan Hills. Spring-flowering shrubs and bulbs, extensive collection of rhododendron hybrids, deciduous azaleas, conifers and unusual trees. The garden contains a large collection of North American rhododendron hybrids from famous contemporary plant breeders. Some paths can be steep. Three marked walks from 30 minutes to one-and-a-half hours.

Argyll & Lochaber

Open: 1 January - 31 December, 9am - dusk, admission £5.00, children free. Coach Tours by appointment

Directions: Three miles south off the A85 Glasgow/Oban road at Taynuilt, road marked *Glen Lonan*, three miles up a single track road, turn right at the sign.

Opening for: Donation to SGS Beneficiaries

10 BAROCHREAL

Kilninver, Oban, Argyll PA34 4UT
Nigel and Antoinette Mitchell
T: 01852 316151 E: antoinettemitchell1946@gmail.com
W: www.barochreal.co.uk

The garden was started in 2006. Fencing and stone walling define it from the rest of Barochreal land. Every year an area has been added, resulting in the gardens you will see today. There are rhododendron banks, a water feature, waterfalls and burns, a pond, a walled rose garden, active beehives, tiered areas, a greenhouse and wild garden across the burn. Maintained walking tracks in the fields lead to viewpoints. Biodiversity studies revealed that rare butterflies inhabit the small glen by the waterfall, there are forty different species of moths including rare micro moths and over seventy species of wildflowers in the fields, including three types of wild orchids. There is an abundance of wildlife including red squirrels, pine martens and a wide range of birds can be seen. This garden is a haven of tranquillity.

Open: By arrangement 1 May - 30 September, admission £5.00, children free. A small selection of plants for sale.

Directions: Fifteen minutes south of Oban. Please disregard SatNav. On the main A816 Oban to Lochgilphead road just to the south of the village of Kilninver on the left-hand side of the road. Bus Oban - Lochgilpead stops at Kilninver School, short walk after.

Opening for: Argyll Animal Aid

11 BENMORE BOTANIC GARDEN

Benmore, Dunoon PA23 8QU
A Regional Garden of the Royal Botanic Garden Edinburgh
T: 01369 706261 E: benmore@rbge.org.uk
W: www.rbge.org.uk

Benmore's magnificent mountainside setting is a joy to behold. Its 120 acres boast a world-famous collection of plants from the Orient and Himalayas to North and South America, as well as an impressive avenue of giant redwoods, one of the finest entrances to any botanic garden. Established in 1863, these majestic giants stand over 150 foot high. Seven miles of trails throughout lead to a restored Victorian Fernery and a dramatic viewpoint at 420 feet looking out to surrounding mountains and Holy Loch. There are also traditional Bhutanese and Chilean pavilions and the magnificent Golden Gates. Keep an eye out for red squirrels and other wildlife as you explore the garden.
National Plant Collection: Abies, South American Temperate Conifers, Picea.

Open: Sunday 28 March, 10am - 6pm, admission details can be found on the garden's website. Also see website for details of regular opening times – www.rbge.org.uk

Directions: Seven miles north of Dunoon or 22 miles south from Glen Kinglass below Rest and Be Thankful pass. On the A815. Bus service is limited.

Opening for: Donation to SGS Beneficiaries

Argyll & Lochaber

12 BERANDHU
Appin, Argyll PA38 4DD
John and Fiona Landale
T: 01631 730585. M: 07900 377 414 E: johnllandale@gmail.com

A sheltered one-and-a-half acre coastal garden in a scenic setting offering fabulous views over Loch Laich to Loch Linnhe, Castle Stalker and the Morvern hills beyond. Craggy limestone abounds on the undulating site, some of which forms natural rockeries. Native trees mix with introduced firs and conifers. A variety of rhododendrons and azaleas provide spring and early summer colour. A mix of limestone overlaid with peat gives an unusual mix of wild flowers. This well-tended garden also has lovely wild areas of bog garden and woodland.

Open: By arrangement 1 April - 31 October, admission £5.00, children free.

Directions: In Appin turn off the A828 Connel to Ballachulish road at *Gunn's Garage* signposted for *Port Appin*. After one mile when the road turns uphill, first entrance on the right, half way up the hill.

Opening for: The Appin Village Hall & Alzheimer Scotland

13 BRAEVALLICH FARM
by Dalmally PA33 1BU
Mr Philip Bowden-Smith
T: 01866 844246 E: philip@brae.co.uk

Discover two gardens, one at the farm and the upper garden 120 feet above the house. The former is approximately one-and-a-half acres and developed over the last 40 years. Its principal features include dwarf rhododendron, azaleas (evergreen and deciduous), large drifts of various primula, meconopsis and bluebells, and mixed herbaceous perennials/shrubs; there is also quite a serious kitchen garden. The second garden has been developed over the last 30 years out of a birch and sessile oak wood and is a traditional West Coast glen garden intersected by two pretty burns with waterfalls. The garden has been extended over the last few years and now covers nearly ten acres with extensive new paths and a suspension bridge over the ravine. Whilst the plants are important, many say that it is the topography with its differing vistas which make this garden such a peaceful and special place.

Open: By arrangement 1 January - 31 December, admission £5.00, children free.

Directions: South east of Loch Awe on the B840, 15 miles from Cladich, seven miles from Ford.

Opening for: Mary's Meals

14 CRINAN HOTEL GARDEN
Crinan PA31 8SR
Mrs N Ryan
T: 01546 830261 E: nryan@crinanhotel.com
W: www.crinanhotel.com

Small rock garden with azaleas and rhododendrons created in a steep hillside over a century ago, with steps leading to a sheltered, secluded garden with sloping lawns, herbaceous beds and spectacular views of the canal and Crinan Loch.

Open: 1 May - 31 August, dawn - dusk, admission by donation. Raffle of signed, limited edition fine art print by Frances Macdonald. Tickets available at the coffee shop, art gallery and hotel.

Directions: Take the A83 to Lochgilphead, then the A816 to Oban, then the A841 Cairnbaan to Crinan. Daily bus.

Opening for: Feedback Madagascar

Argyll & Lochaber

Berandhu

Argyll & Lochaber

15 DAL AN EAS
Kilmore, Oban PA34 4XU
Mary Lindsay
T: 01631 770246 E: dalaneas@live.com

An informal country garden with the aim of increasing the biodiversity of native plants and insects while adding interest and colour with introduced trees, shrubs and naturalised perennials. There is a structured garden round the house and beyond there are extensive flower-filled 'meadows' with five different species of native orchid. Grass paths lead to waterfalls, vegetable plot, woodland garden, views and ancient archaeological sites.

Open: By arrangement 1 April - 30 September, admission by donation. Teas on request.

Directions: From Oban take the A816 to Kilmore three-and-a-half miles south of Oban. Turn left on road to Barran and Musdale. Keep left at junction for Connel. Dal an Eas is approximately one mile on the left before the big hedges.

Opening for: Hope: Oban

16 DRUIMNEIL HOUSE
Port Appin PA38 4DQ
Mrs J Glaisher (Gardener: Mr Andrew Ritchie)
T: 01631 730228 E: druimneilhouse@btinternet.com

Large garden overlooking Loch Linnhe with many fine varieties of mature trees and rhododendrons and other woodland shrubs. Nearer the house, an impressive bank of deciduous azaleas is underplanted with a block of camassia and a range of other bulbs. A small Victorian walled garden is currently being restored. Owner, Janet Glaisher, is the winner of the Diana Macnab Award 2020. She has opened Druimneil House for Scotland's Garden Scheme for a remarkable 37 years.

Open: 1 April - 31 October, dawn - dusk, admission by donation. Teas normally available. Lunch by prior arrangement.

Directions: Turn in for Appin off the A828 (Connel/Fort William Road). After two miles take a sharp left at Airds Hotel and it's the second house on the right.

Opening for: All proceeds to SGS Beneficiaries

17 EAS MHOR
Cnoc-a-Challtuinn, Clachan Seil, Oban PA34 4TR
Mrs Kimbra Lesley Barrett
T: 01852 300469 E: kimbra1745@gmail.com

All the usual joys of a west coast garden plus some delightful surprises! A small contemporary garden on a sloping site – the emphasis being on scent and exotic plant material. Unusual and rare blue Borinda bamboos (only recently discovered in China) and bananas. The garden is at its best in mid to late summer when shrub roses and sweet peas fill the air with scent. The delightful sunny deck overlooks stylish white walled ponds with cascading water blades. Recent additions include a 20-foot citrus house, Chinese pergola walk and peony border.

Open: By arrangement 1 May - 30 September, admission £5.00, children free.

Directions: Turn off the A816 from Oban onto the B844 signposted *Easdale*. Over the bridge onto Seil Island, pass *Tigh an Truish* pub and turn right after a quarter-of-a-mile up Cnoc-a-Challtuin road. The public car park is on the left at the bottom; please park there and walk up the road. Eas Mhor is on the right after the second speed bump. Please do not block the driveway. Bus Oban - Clachan Seil, two/three per day.

Opening for: Small Paws Rescue: Oban

Argyll & Lochaber

18 FASNACLOICH

Appin PA38 4BJ
Mr and Mrs David Stewart

South-facing 15-acre woodland garden sloping down to Loch Baile Mhic Cailein in Glen Creran. Partly laid out in the mid-19th century with extensive structural water features added in the early 20th century. The garden mainly consists of hybrid and species rhododendrons, azaleas and magnolias with, over the last 25 years, a more recent addition of trees from Eastern Europe, Central Asia and the Northern United States (including a small pinetum).

Open: Sunday 16 May, noon - 5pm, admission £5.00, children free.

Directions: On the A828 at the roundabout on the north side of Creagan Bridge take the road for Invercreran. At the head of the loch go straight ahead for about one-and-a-half miles. The house is on the right side.

Opening for: Mary's Meals

19 INVERARAY CASTLE GARDENS

Inveraray PA32 8XF
The Duke and Duchess of Argyll
T: 01499 302203 E: enquiries@inveraray-castle.com
W: www.inveraray-castle.com

Rhododendrons and azaleas abound and flower from April to June. Very fine specimens of *Cedrus deodars*, *Sequoiadendron giganteum* (wellingtonia), *Cryptomeria japonica*, *Taxus baccata* and others thrive in the damp climate. The Flag-Borders on each side of the main drive with paths in the shape of Scotland's national flag, the St Andrew's Cross, are outstanding in spring with *Prunus* 'Ukon' and *P. subhirtella* and are underplanted with rhododendrons, eucryphias, shrubs and herbaceous plants giving interest all year. Bluebell Festival during flowering period in May.

Open: 1 April - 31 October, 10am - 5pm, admission £5.00, children under five free. Please also check on-line for current opening times. We recommend that you book on-line at www.inveraray-castle.com. Only assistance dogs within the garden.

Directions: Inveraray is 60 miles north of Glasgow on the banks of Loch Fyne on the A83 and 15 miles from Dalmally on the A819. Regular bus service from Glasgow - Lochgilphead.

Opening for: Donation to SGS Beneficiaries

Argyll & Lochaber

 20

INVERYNE WOODLAND GARDEN
Kilfinan, Tighnabruaich PA21 2ER
Mrs Jane Ferguson

In ten acres of a 100-year-old amenity wood at Inveryne Farm, on a sloping site, somewhat sheltered from Loch Fyne, the garden was begun in 1994. Scrub birches were gradually cleared, bridges installed and amongst rocky outcrops were planted rhododendrons, azaleas, dogwoods, Japanese maples, sorbuses, eucryphias, hydrangeas and more. Gunnera, primulas and rodgersias cling to the banks of the burn and ferns provide the backdrop for our growing shrubs. Storms have varied its character and created features, and it is still a work in progress. Spring and autumn colour and an interest in varied vistas and textures of bark and leaf inspire us.

Open: Saturday/Sunday, 29/30 May, 1pm - 5pm, admission £5.00, children free. Please park at the red-roofed barn.

Directions: Approximately six miles north of Tighnabruaich towards Kilfinan on the B8000. After turning right at the crossroads at Millhouse, follow the road past the turning to Ardmarnock, over the little bridge at the bottom of the hill. The next track on the left is unpaved and leads to Inveryne.

Opening for: Cowal Elderly Befrienders SCIO

21

KAMES BAY
Kilmelford PA34 4XA
Stuart Cannon
T: 01852 200205 E: stuartcannon@kames.co.uk

Kames Bay garden has evolved from two acres of scrub and bracken on an exposed lochside hill into a natural, almost wild garden spread over 13 acres, which blends into the contours of the coastal landscape. A garden where visitors can wander at peace on the woodland walk, or the hillside walk edged with wild primroses and violets, or around the pond edged with hydrangeas. Relax on hidden benches to enjoy the magnificent views over Loch Melfort and the islands to the west. An enchanting garden full of vibrant colours, especially in the spring, with more than 100 varieties of azaleas and rhododendrons.

Open: Saturday/Sunday, 1/2 May, 2pm - 6pm, admission £5.00, children free.

Directions: On the A816 Oban to Lochgilphead road. Opposite Kames Bay and the fish farm. Two-and-a-half miles south of Kilmelford and two-and-a-half miles north of Arduaine.

Opening for: St Columba's – Poltalloch

22

KILDALLOIG
Campbeltown PA28 6RE
Mr and Mrs Joe Turner
T: 07979 855930 E: kildalloig@gmail.com

Coastal garden with some interesting and unusual shrubs including Australasian shrubs and trees, climbing roses, and herbaceous perennials. There is a woodland walk and a pond garden with aquatic and bog plants.

Open: By arrangement 1 May - 31 October, admission £5.00, children free.

Directions: Take the A83 to Campbeltown, then three miles south east of town past Davaar Island.

Opening for: Marie Curie & Macmillan Cancer Support

Argyll & Lochaber

23 **KINLOCHLAICH WALLED GARDEN**
Appin PA38 4BD
Miss F M M Hutchison
T: 07881 525754 E: fiona@kinlochlaich.plus.com
W: www.kinlochlaichgardencentre.co.uk

Octagonal walled garden incorporating a large Nursery Garden Centre with a huge variety of plants growing and for sale. Bluebell woodland walk and spring garden. Many rhododendrons, azaleas, trees, shrubs and herbaceous plants, including many unusual ones such as embothrium, davidia, stewartia, magnolia, eucryphia and tropaeolum. A quarter of the interior of the walled garden is borders packed with many unusual and interesting plants, espaliered fruit trees, and with an ancient yew in the centre, and another quarter is vegetable growing.

Open: 3 March - 31 October, 10am - 4pm, admission £3.00, children free. Winter by appointment – we are generally about.

Directions: On the A828 in Appin between Oban, 18 miles to the south, and Fort William, 27 miles to the north. The entrance is next to the police station. Bus Oban to Fort William.

Opening for: The Appin Village Hall & Feis na h'apainne

Kildalloig

Argyll & Lochaber

Lismore Secret Garden. ©Mairi Fleck

Argyll & Lochaber

24 **KNOCK NEWHOUSE**
Lochgair PA31 8RZ
Mr and Mrs Hew Service
T: 01546 886628 E: corranmorhouse@aol.com

Like all good gardens, our woodland garden has evolved over time. It is centered on a 250 foot lochan, a small waterfall and lily pond. The first trees and rhododendrons were planted in the 60s, with major additions in the 90s. A variety of cut leaf and flowering trees were added after the storms of 2011/12. As a result the garden now has a wide range of specimen trees, camellias, hoheria, eucryphia, stewartia to name a few in addition to the azaleas and rhododendrons. The flowering starts in January and continues with spring flowers then bluebells and into the autumn when the colours are spectacular. We are delighted to welcome visitors at any time so please let us know when you would like to visit.

Open: Saturday/Sunday, 8/9 May, noon - 4:30pm. Also open by arrangement 12 April - 12 October. Admission £5.00, children free.

Directions: On the A83. The house is not visible from the road. From Lochgilphead, half-a-mile south of Lochgair Hotel and on the left-hand side of the road, and from Inveraray on the right-hand side of the road half-a-mile after the Lochgair Hotel; the drive opening is marked and enters the woods.

Opening for: Christ Church Scottish Episcopal Church & Marie Curie

25 **LISMORE SECRET GARDEN**
Isle of Lismore, Oban, Argyll PA34 5UL
Eva Tombs
T: 01631 760128 E: eva.tombs@gmail.com

This unique garden forms part of a biodynamic farm on the Island of Lismore in the Inner Hebrides. Created quite recently from a field, the garden has a strong geometric layout that reflects the ecclesiastical history of the island. It has a vegetable garden, a tree nursery, a physic garden and an orchard. Wildflowers, birds, bees and butterflies abound. Standing stones, meadows, new woodlands, mountains and the sea encompass the whole. Some weeds and long grass benefit the Lismore herd of rare breed Shetland horned cattle that roam the fields round about.

Open: By arrangement 1 May - 1 October, admission £5.00, children free. Plants, seeds, vegetables, flowers and meat for sale. No dogs please, there are lots of animals around. Refreshments by arrangement.

Directions: Please telephone for directions.

Opening for: Lismore Parish Church (Church of Scotland)

Argyll & Lochaber

26 MAOLACHY'S GARDEN
Lochavich, by Kilmelford PA35 1HJ
Georgina Dalton
T: 01866 844212

Three acres of woodland garden with a tumbling burn, created in a small glen over 40 years. At an altitude of 450 feet and two weeks behind the coastal changes, the growing season is shorter. By not struggling to grow tender or late species, the owner can enjoy those that are happy to grow well here and give everyone much pleasure. Snowdrops, followed by early rhododendrons, masses of daffodils in many varieties, bluebells, wildflowers and azaleas, primulas and irises. A productive vegetable patch and tunnel feed the gardener and family.

Open: By arrangement 1 March - 31 October, admission £5.00, children free.

Directions: Ignore SatNav. A816 to Kilmelford. Turn uphill between the shop and the church, signposted *Lochavich 6*, steep and twisty road with hairpin bend shortly after leaving the village, check for passing places. Maolachy Drive is four miles from the village. Cross three county cattle grids; after the third ignore the forestry tracks to left and right. Continue downhill towards Loch Avich, and Maolachy is up on the left, first house after Kilmelford.

Opening for: Kilninver & Kilmelford Parish Church Of Scotland & Hope: Oban

27 ORMSARY HOUSE
Ormsary, Lochgilphead, Argyll PA31 8PE
Lady Lithgow
T: 01880 770738 E: mclithgow@ormsary.co.uk

Ormsary is on the shore of Loch Caolisport looking across to Islay and Jura. The house policies are resplendent in spring with bluebells and daffodils under fine oak trees. There are woodland gardens with azaleas, rhododendrons and a collection of trees and shrubs. The walled garden, which has evolved over a couple of centuries, is on two levels. The top half is a kitchen garden producing plants, fruit and vegetables for the house; a winter garden and 'Muscat of Alexandria' vinery have been heated by hydroelectric power for 100 years. A magnificent *Polylepis australis* beckons to the lower Secret Garden with its lawn, roses, magnolias and long mixed border. It opens onto the banks of Ormsary Water. There are also woodland walks accessed via the upper woodland garden.

Open: By arrangement 1 April - 31 October, admission £5.00, children free.

Directions: Take the A83 road from Lochgilphead towards Campbeltown for four miles, then take the B8024 signposted to *Kilberry*, travel ten miles and follow signs to the *Estate office* for directions to the garden.

Opening for: All proceeds to SGS Beneficiaries

Argyll & Lochaber

28   **STRACHUR HOUSE FLOWER & WOODLAND GARDENS**
Strachur PA27 8BX
Sir Charles and Lady Maclean

The flower garden is sheltered by magnificent beeches, limes, ancient yews and Japanese maples. There are herbaceous borders, a burnside rhododendron and azalea walk, rockery, tulips and spring bulbs. Enjoy the old woodland of Strachur Park, laid out in 1782, and the wildlife rich lochan.

Open: Saturday/Sunday, 22/23 May, 1pm - 5pm, admission £5.00, children free.

Directions: Turn off the A815 at Strachur House Farm entrance. Park in farm square. Bus Dunoon - Inveraray. From Edinburgh/Glasgow take the ferry from Gourock to Dunoon.

Opening for: British Red Cross

Strachur House Flower & Woodland Gardens

Ayrshire & Arran

Sponsored by

Investec

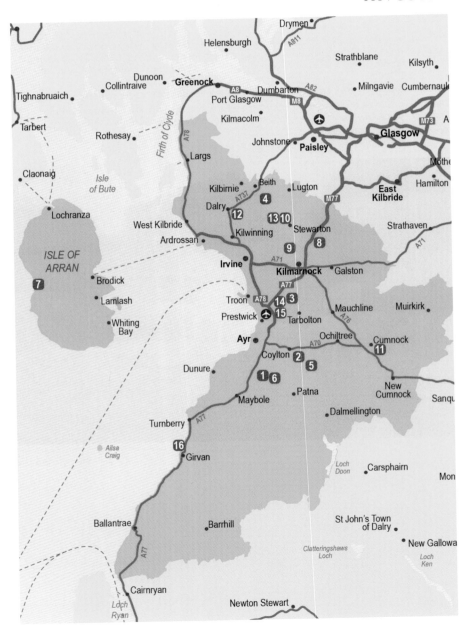

Ayrshire & Arran

OUR VOLUNTEER ORGANISERS

District Organisers:	Rose-Ann Cuninghame	45 Towerhill Avenue, Kilmaurs KA3 2TS E: ayrshire@scotlandsgardens.org
	Lavinia Gibbs	Dougarie, Isle of Arran KA27 8EB
Area Organisers:	Kim Donald MBE	19 Waterslap, Fenwick, Kilmarnock KA3 6AJ
	Pattie Kewney	Failford House, Mauchline, Ayrshire KA5 5TA
	Fiona McLean	100 Main Road, Fenwick KA3 6DY
	Rosie Pensom	Rose House, 3E Templetonburn, Crookedholm, KA3 6HR
	Wendy Sandiford	Harrowhill Cottage, Kilmarnock KA3 6HX
	Sue Veitch	Auldbyres Farm Garden, Coylton KA6 6LE
	Linda Vosseler	39 Langmuir Quadrant, Kilmaurs KA3 2UA
District Photographers:	David Blatchford	1 Burnton Rd, Dalrymple, Ayr KA6 6DY
	Rob Davis	24 Bellevue Crescent, Ayr KA7 2DR
Treasurers:	Lizzie Adam	Bayview, Pirnmill, Isle of Arran KA27 8HP
	Carol Freireich	1 Burnside Cottages, Colyton, Ayr KA6 5JX

GARDENS OPEN ON A SPECIFIC DATE

Underwood House, Craigie, Ayrshire	Saturday/Sunday, 8/9 May
Kirkmuir Cottage, Stewarton	Saturday/Sunday, 22/23 May
Netherthird Community Garden, Craigens Road, Netherthird	Saturday, 29 May
The Carriage House, Blair Estate, Dalry	Saturday/Sunday, 12/13 June
Barnweil Garden, Craigie, near Kilmarnock	Sunday, 20 June
Barrmill Community Garden, Barrmill Park and Gardens	Sunday, 27 June
Dougarie, Isle of Arran	Tuesday, 29 June
Gardens of Fenwick, Fenwick	Saturday/Sunday, 24/25 July
Whitewin House, Golf Course Road, Girvan	17 July - 1 August (Sats & Suns only) & 7-14 August (Sats only)
Kilmaurs Gardens, 39 Langmuir Quadrant, Kilmaurs	Sunday, 15 August
Underwood House, Craigie, Ayrshire	Saturday/Sunday, 21/22 August
Underwood Lodge, Craigie, Kilmarnock, South Ayrshire	Saturday/Sunday, 21/22 August

GARDENS OPEN REGULARLY

Dalrymple Community Garden, Barbieston Road, Dalrymple	1 January - 31 December

Ayrshire & Arran

GARDENS OPEN BY ARRANGEMENT – BOOK A VISIT WITH THE GARDEN OWNER

Burnside, Littlemill Road, Drongan	1 April - 31 August
Auldbyres Farm Garden, Coylton	10 April - 30 September
Townend of Kirkwood, Stewarton	1 May – 5 May, 10 May - 30 June & 1 September - 31 October
Barnweil Garden, Craigie, near Kilmarnock	15 May - 15 July
1 Burnton Road, Dalrymple	1 June - 31 August
Whitewin House, Golf Course Road, Girvan	1 July - 31 August
Barnweil Garden, Craigie, near Kilmarnock	5 October - 20 October

Ayrshire & Arran

1 BURNTON ROAD

1

Dalrymple KA6 6DY
David and Margaret Blatchford
T: 01292 561988 E: d.blatchford273@btinternet.com

A tiny slice of jungle nestled within a small triangular plot. To the front of the house are two beds planted with nectar-secreting plants and in a larger bed, a sea of *Stipa tenuissima* studded with perennials. To the rear, a small patio is home to some bonsai and a collection of potted terrestrial ferns including rare blechnum species and succulents. A serpentine path meanders through dense planting of palms, bamboos and tree ferns. Of particular note are hardy and tender bromeliads and aroids such as arisaema and colocasia. Flower highlights are provided by lilies (species and cultivars), cannas and gingers.

Open: By arrangement 1 June - 31 August, admission £5.00, children free.

Directions: From the north take the A77 Ayr to Stranraer. At the junction with the A713 take the left and follow the road past the hospital to junction with B742, turn right into the village and park in the White Horse car park at the T junction. The garden is on the corner of Burnton and Barbieston Roads. From the south off the A77 take the B7034, turn right. Follow into village, at Kirkton Inn junction turn left. Follow Barbieston Road. Bus 52 from Ayr.

Opening for: Dalrymple, Skeldon and Hollybush Project

1 Burnton Road ©David Blatchford

Ayrshire & Arran

2 AULDBYRES FARM GARDEN
Coylton KA6 6HG
Marshall and Sue Veitch
E: su.pavet@btinternet.com

Surrounded by a working farm, this compact garden has mature shrubs, wildlife pond, bog garden and stream. The exposed location has been challenging, but compensated for by stunning views towards Ayr and Arran. Shelter is provided by an unobtrusive boundary fence, 'borrowing' the panoramic landscape. The crisp freshness of the well-behaved spring borders, with woodland gems, gives way to a riot of summer perennial favourites. In addition, an extensive 'pot theatre' of containers brightens the farmyard with seasonal displays. There are small vegetable beds and a five-bay polytunnel (grapevine, tomatoes, basil, cucumber and oleanders). Dogs on leads, for family farm walks through bluebell woods.

Open: By arrangement 10 April - 30 September, admission £5.00, children free.

Directions: In Coylton take road signposted B742, past Coylton Arms Pub in Low Coylton, *Auldbyres* signposted on left after half-a-mile.

Opening for: Beatson West of Scotland Cancer Centre

3 BARNWEIL GARDEN
Craigie, near Kilmarnock KA1 5NE
Mr and Mrs Ronald W Alexander
E: ronaldwalexander@btinternet.com

The garden, now approaching 50 years in its development, surrounds an 18th century farmhouse with a large lawn on the south side, flanked by herbaceous borders with a soft colour palette of blue, pink, purple and white. The whole is surrounded by woodland walks featuring Oscar's ditch and lined with foliage plants including rodgersias, regal and ostrich ferns, red and white candelabra primulas, black iris and the rarely seen *Pettiphyllum pettatum and Smilacena*. Elsewhere in the woodland there is a fine gunnera stand and the Golden Glade with golden acer, philadelphus and other golden leaved shrubs and underplantings. On the north side of the house are rectangular borders flanking the view from the big arched window to Ben Lomond 60 miles away. On each side of these borders are long rose borders, backed by beech hedges. The roses, mostly David Austin, should be well into their first flush.

Open: Sunday 20 June, 2pm - 5pm. Also open by arrangement 15 May - 15 July and 5 October - 20 October. Admission £6.00, children free.

Directions: Two miles from Craigie. Right off the B730, two miles south of the A77 heading to Tarbolton.

Opening for: Tarbolton Parish Church of Scotland & The Ridley Foundation

4 BARRMILL COMMUNITY GARDEN
Barrmill Park and Gardens KA15 1HW
The Barrmill Conservation Group
T: 07920 098171

This large woodland garden is carved from a 19th-century whinstone quarry and situated within an 1890s parkland, once known for the quoiting green provided for the village thread mill and ironstone pit workers of that time. Enhancement of the gardens began in 2010 by volunteers with assistance from *The Beechgrove Garden*. Features include enchanted woodland walks, the Vale Burn, views of the Dusk Water, a restored 19th-century cholera pit aka 'the Deid Man's Plantin', wish trees, wishing wells, doors to the Elfhame, guided walks, nature trail and traditional Ayrshire quoits game. The woodland backdrop is complemented by an understorey of natural planting throughout.

Ayrshire & Arran

Open: Sunday 27 June, 2pm - 5pm, admission £4.00, children free.

Directions: From Stewarton take the A735 to Dunlop, go left down Main Street B706 to Burnhouse, over at crossroads to Barrmill B706. From Lugton south on the A736, right at Burnhouse, B706 to Barrmill. From Glasgow on the M8 take J28a signposted *Irvine*, on Beith bypass take left B706 to Barrmill.

Opening for: Barrmill and District Community Association

---

5 BURNSIDE

Littlemill Road, Drongan KA6 7EN
Sue Simpson and George Watt
T: 01292 592445 E: suesimpson33@btinternet.com

This maturing and constantly changing six-and-a-half acre garden began in 2006. There is a wide range of plants from trees to alpines, giving colour and variability all year. Next to the road flows the Drumbowie Burn parallel to which is a woodland border with snowdrops, erythroniums, hellebores, trilliums, rhododendrons and acers. Near the house are a raised bed and large collection of troughs with an interesting range of alpines. The garden boasts herbaceous beds, ericaceous garden, screes, three alpine glasshouses with award-winning plants, polytunnel, pond and arboretum – underplanted with daffodils, camassia, fritillaries and crocus. With a view towards matrimonial harmony there are two sheds which may be of interest.

Open: By arrangement 1 April - 31 August, admission £6.00, children free. Hot drinks and baking available on request £2.50.

Directions: From A77 Ayr bypass take A70 Cumnock for five-and-a-quarter miles, at Coalhall, turn onto B730 Drongan (south) for two-and-a-half miles. Burnside entrance is immediately adjacent to a black/white parapeted bridge. Ordnance survey grid ref: NS455162.

Opening for: Beatson Cancer Charity

6 DALRYMPLE COMMUNITY GARDEN

Barbieston Road, Dalrymple KA6 6DY
Dalrymple Community Landscape Project

Opened in September 2019, the garden, situated opposite the shops in Barbieston Road, is run by a dedicated team of volunteers; part of the Dalrymple, Skeldon and Hollybush Project. A large central lawn is surrounded by extensive areas of original meadow turf and already we have seen the appearance of wildflowers, with a concomitant increase in insect diversity, and the appearance of butterflies associated with wild grasses. Damselflies and amphibians have begun to visit the two ponds. We have planted several thousand spring bulbs including snake's head fritillaries and camassias and as the new year progresses we will be adding willows and other native shrubs to provide a richer habitat.

Open: 1 January - 31 December, dawn - dusk.

Directions: From the north take the A77 Ayr to Stranraer. At the A713 junction take the left and follow the road past the hospital to the B742 junction, turn right into the village and park behind the shops in the centre of the village. From south off the A77 take the B7034 and turn right. Bus 52 from Ayr.

Opening for: Dalrymple, Skeldon and Hollybush Project

Ayrshire & Arran

7 DOUGARIE
Isle of Arran KA27 8EB
Mrs S C Gibbs
E: office@dougarie.com

Most interesting terraced garden in castellated folly built in 1905 to celebrate the marriage of the 12th Duke of Hamilton's only child to the Duke of Montrose. Good selection of tender and rare shrubs and herbaceous border. Small woodland area with trees including azara, abutilon, eucryphia, hoheria and nothofagus.

Open: Tuesday 29 June, 2pm - 5pm, admission £4.00, children free.

Directions: Five miles from Blackwaterfoot. Regular ferry sailing from Ardrossan and Claonaig (Argyll). Information from Caledonian MacBrayne, Gourock, T: 01475 650100. Parking is free.

Opening for: *Pirnmill Village Association*

8 GARDENS OF FENWICK
Fenwick KA3 6AJ
Mrs Kim Donald T: 01560 600239 M: 07836 583546
E: fenwickvillage@scotlandsgardens.org

10 Raith Road
Fenwick KA3 6DQ (Mrs Sandra Macpherson): Front garden landscaped with gravel and shrubs and east-facing back garden with terraces, grass and beds with perennials and shrubs; masses of pots and containers. Terrace at the top provides tranquil seating and quirky ornaments lurk in the shrubbery. A new wildlife pond, lined with marginal planting.

2 Fulton's Crescent (NEW)
Fenwick KA3 6GJ (Janek Sawczyn & Marko Surakka): A cottage garden with peonies, delphiniums, foxgloves, and lavender. Walled courtyard for entertaining with paved dining area, summerhouse and terraced seating. Clematis, wisteria, Virginia creeper, hawthorn, bamboo, box and acer offer privacy and structure. Foliage planting includes grasses, hostas, teasels and rodgersia.

20 Raith Road (NEW)
Fenwick KA3 6DB (Mr and Mrs Paul Fox): Developed over 25 years, copper beech hedge frames garden with hanging baskets and annuals at front, small lawns and lavender hedge leads to an orchard and raised vegetable beds. Gate to rear with lawn bordered by variety of shrubs and roses. Conservatory with patio enclosed by rhododendrons, azalea, clematis and honeysuckle, and summer plantings.

25 Kirkton Road (NEW)
Fenwick, Ayrshire KA3 6DJ (Mr and Mrs Paul Whitton): Hilly garden with mature hedges, trees, fruit, vegetables and compost area. Side borders are filled with heathers, perennials, succulents, shrubs, climbers and roses. Masses of pots, greenhouse and a path lined with dahlias and summer bedding leads to sloping lawn with well-planted borders.

5 Fowld's View (NEW)
Fenwick KA3 6GF (Linda Creanor): This garden, established in 2016, complements a modern house. Based on a circular design with lawn and patio, it has mixed planting in surrounding borders with small trees, shrubs and varied herbaceous perennials. A north east aspect presents challenges with shady areas, where hebes, hostas and acers provide colour and interest.

9a Maunsheugh Road (NEW)
Fenwick KA3 6AN (John Logan): Immaculate south-facing lawn edged with flamboyant begonias and a mass of containers. To the rear are patio areas, raised beds with begonias, dahlias, annuals, heathers and shrubs, summer house, vegetable beds and greenhouse. A lawn runs to a seating area set off by roses.

Ayrshire & Arran

Open: Saturday 24 July 11am - 5pm & Sunday 25 July noon - 5pm, admission £8.00, children free. Refreshments and plant stall on George V playing fields, disabled parking at Church Hall car park. Entrance strictly by ticket available from phone numbers or email address above. Check SGS website for updates.

Directions: From N: Take J7 off M77 Fenwick, turn left into village, right at roundabout and Kirkton Road is on left. From S: Take slip road off A77 Kilmarnock/Fenwick turn right for Fenwick (B7038) after two roundabouts enter village on to Main Road. Signs will lead to gardens.

Opening for: Ayrshire Hospice & Ayrshire Cancer Support

---

9 KILMAURS GARDENS
39 Langmuir Quadrant, Kilmaurs KA3 2UA
Mrs L Vosseler
E: kilmaursgardens@scotlandsgardens.org

10 Shaw Road, Kilmaurs, KA3 2UD (Karen & John Woods): A contemporary rear garden planted in 2018, which is south-facing with an open aspect to adjoining fields. A water rill with underwater lighting spans the garden creating some changes in level, including a raised seating area under a pergola. A sundial provides a sculptural element. Planting is informal, with bamboo on both sides. Early interest comes from bergenia, primulas and euphorbias, followed by bulbs and perennials, including iris, grasses, persicaria, ferns, astilbe and rodgersia. Raised sleeper beds sit in a small area set aside for herbs and vegetables.

17 Shaw Road, Kilmaurs KA3 2UD (Marianne Partyka): Contemporary south-facing garden established in 2018 with views out to farmland and Arran. This exposed garden has been designed over two levels to negotiate the sloped site. The raised patio is surrounded by a number of raised beds and borders filled with hardy evergreen shrubs and perennials for year-round interest. The largest of the raised beds is filled with herbaceous perennials and grasses contrasted with pops of colour from a variety of cottage plants, seasonal bulbs and bedding.

39 Langmuir Quadrant Kilmaurs KA3 2UA (Rainer & Linda Vosseler): A small west-facing garden in a new estate was created in spring 2017. The garden is mainly herbaceous perennial plants, with roses, climbers, annuals and evergreen shrubs. A slate path with slate edging meanders through the garden. Excellent countryside views. The front garden displays larger perennial plants. The main objective of the garden is to produce cut flowers and foliage from April to October.

Open: Sunday 15 August, 1pm - 5:30pm, admission £5.00, children free. Entrance by ticket available from email above. Check SGS website for updates. On arrival go to the car park in Langmuir Quadrant for garden directions.

Directions: Kilmaurs village is to the northwest of Kilmarnock and south of Stewarton. From Glasgow or Ayr on the M77 follow signs to Kilmaurs. B751 from Fenwick to Kilmaurs and B769 from Irvine to Kilmaurs. From Kilmaurs Railway Station (KA3 2TU), turn left onto Crofthead Road, turn left at signs for Langmuir Quadrant, where there is a car park.

Opening for: Ayrshire Hospice & Pancreatic Cancer Scotland

Ayrshire & Arran

10 KIRKMUIR COTTAGE

Stewarton KA3 3DZ
Mr and Mrs Brian Macpherson
T: 01560 483816 E: dhmmacp@gmail.com

A one-and-a-half-acre mature garden with paths weaving through many different areas including woodland, formal borders, laburnum arch, herbaceous borders, rhododendrons and azaleas. Large lawn area and wildlife pond. Garden also features many interesting and unusual artefacts and sculptures.

Open: Saturday/Sunday, 22/23 May, 11am - 5pm, admission £6.00, children free.

Directions: From M77 take B778 to Stewarton. At traffic lights turn left, and continue to mini-roundabout. Turn right at mini-roundabout signposted *B778 Kilwinning*. Continue for 100 yards under the railway bridge, take immediate left at war memorial. Parking for Kirkmuir Cottage will be well signposted.

Opening for: Capability Scotland

Netherthird Community Garden © Rob Davis

11 NETHERTHIRD COMMUNITY GARDEN

Craigens Road, Netherthird, Cumnock KA18 3AR
Netherthird Community Development Group
E: jamielor@aol.com
W: Facebook (Netherthird Community Development Group)

Netherthird Community Garden will be opening with a 'Wildlife for Families Theme' to suit all ages. Follow our nature trail, wild orchids, new bog garden, beehives to aid pollination, and meet our hens. See our long cottage border bursting with shrubs, perennials and annuals, vegetable beds and polytunnels where we grow tomatoes and plants. The striking wooden gazebos were funded by the Prince's Trust for outdoor lessons. Visit the swing park, the vast sandpit, bouncy castle, a treasure hunt and fancy dress class for young dog owners. All run by, and for, volunteers and the local community.

Ayrshire & Arran

Open: Saturday 29 May, noon - 3pm, admission £3.00, children free. Teas at the vintage beach hut café.

Directions: Driving south on the A76 Cumnock bypass, look for the roundabout signposted *B7083*. Take this exit which heads to Cumnock. After a few hundred yards, take a right turn into Craigens Road. Netherthird Primary School is on the right and parking is available there. The Community Garden is nearby. There is disabled parking at the garden.

Opening for: Netherthird Community Development Group

12 THE CARRIAGE HOUSE
Blair Estate, Dalry KA24 4ER
Mr and Mrs Luke Borwick
T: 01294 832816 E: lina@blairtrust.co.uk

The Stables were built (c1800) on a rocky outcrop with little soil depth. In 2001, The Carriage House was created from old stables, cowshed and dairy. The Garden has evolved over the past fifteen years, and has been designed by the owners to provide colour and interest all year round, many plants provided by friends and family. Divided into many different 'rooms', some contain sculptures by artists including Lucy Poett, Lucy Fisher and Mary Stormonth Darling. Ironwork by Kev Paxton. Small copses have been formed in the adjoining ten-acre field, containing many interesting trees and shrubs. Paths are designed to take you round the field to discover items of interest, such as the mermaids rescuing a girl, some unusual trees such as a variegated tulip tree, a golden dawn redwood, and a wellingtonia grown from seed here at Blair.

Open: Saturday/Sunday, 12/13 June, 2:30pm - 5pm, admission £5.00, children free.

Directions: A737 from Beith. At roundabout before Dalry take first left signposted *Stewarton*. Then go straight on, signposted *Bike Route Irvine*. Keep going for approximately two miles and keep the estate wall on right till you come to South Lodge (white building) Turn right down drive for Blair Estate Carriage House is on the right. Public transport to Dalry.

Opening for: Dalry Trinity Church of Scotland, Dalry St Margaret's Parish Church of Scotland & Friends of Hilary Storm School Uganda

13 TOWNEND OF KIRKWOOD
Stewarton KA3 3EW
Mrs Katrina Clow
T: 01560 483926 M: 07914 316119 E: katrina.clow@btinternet.com

Townend of Kirkwood is a young garden, started eight years ago on three acres of boggy field. There was little shelter and it has taken some time to plant up the shelter and mixed hedging surrounding the site, but where the ground had been cultivated, plants have flourished. On the left as you drive in, there is a large wildlife pond, dug when work began – in the hope of containing some of the abundant water. Take the right fork as you approach the house and you will drive through the most mature, more formal planting – a lawn surrounded by borders of mixed shrubs. Drive into the yard, where the old rubble walls have all been rebuilt. On the other side of the drive is new planting around and above the pond, all reflecting the owner's love of trees and shrubs, particularly ericaceous-rhododendrons, azaleas, acers and interesting trees, but there are herbaceous plants too.

Open: By arrangement 1 May - 5 May, 10 May - 30 June & 1 September - 31 October, admission £5.00, children free. Groups of four or more would be appreciated.

Directions: Two miles north of Stewarton on the B778. There is plenty of parking space.

Opening for: The Younger (Benmore) Trust

Ayrshire & Arran

14 UNDERWOOD HOUSE

Craigie, Ayrshire KA1 5NG
Baroness Ford of Cunninghame OBE
T: 01563 830719 E: margaretford@hotmail.co.uk

The garden was laid out in 1780 in the landscape style, fashionable at the time. The original features of the garden remain unchanged, with sweeping lawns, large specimen trees, and a natural pond and burn which runs through the whole garden. The woodland is being restored and replanted with specimen rhododendrons, hydrangeas and woodland carpeters. A formal pleasure garden is being created in sympathetic style. Underwood House provides activity, training and employment for young people with neurological conditions. In 2019, a beautiful, sensory area was created by partner schools working with young volunteers from the Prince's Trust.

Open: Saturday/Sunday, 8/9 May, 10am - 4pm. Also open Saturday/Sunday, 21/22 August, 10am - 4pm. Admission £5.00, children free. Visitors should make contact in advance, and will be given a timed slot during the open days.

Directions: South bound on A77 pass Hansel Village, take next left signposted *Underwood/ Ladykirk*. At the stone bridge turn left, continue to Underwood Lodge. Pass the Lodge, go for 150 yards. Take left to Underwood House. From Ayr on A77 take exit to Symington, take first right, signposted *Underwood/Ladykirk*. Cross over A77 on to south carriageway.

Opening for: *Underwood House SCIO*

Underwood House © David Blatchford

Ayrshire & Arran

15 UNDERWOOD LODGE
Craigie, Kilmarnock, South Ayrshire KA1 5NG
Marilyn Badman
T: 01563 830439 E: mbadman1@sky.com

Underwood Lodge has a secluded garden surrounded by farmland and woodland which give some protection and adds to the ambience. The main structure of the garden has been in place for 18 years, however significant remodelling has taken place in the last two years. The one-acre garden comprises a variety of mature trees, shrubs, herbaceous and wall-grown plants. A woodland garden is at an embryonic stage with the construction of a woodland path, the planting of some semi-mature rhododendrons and some underplanting of woodland plants. The planting within all areas of the garden demonstrates an understanding of form and texture of plants, which adds to its enjoyment.

Open: Saturday/Sunday, 21/22 August, noon - 5pm, admission £4.00, children free.

Directions: Southbound on the A77, pass Hansel Village and take the next left signposted *Underwood/Ladykirk*. Northbound on the A77 take the exit to Symington then first right, to join Southbound Carriageway. Take the Underwood/Ladykirk turning. At the stone bridge, turn left and Underwood Lodge is the first house on the left.

Opening for: Annbank Parish Church Of Scotland

16 WHITEWIN HOUSE
Golf Course Road, Girvan KA26 9HW
Linda Finnie and Graeme Finnie
T: 01465 712358 M: 07855 269247 E: lafinnie@hotmail.com

Historic Whitewin House was built for Baronet Henry Tate of Tate and Lyle. The house stands in one acre of formal Victorian gardens, rockeries and beautiful scalloped lawns, with a plethora of statuary which complements the use of authentic Victorian bedding plants, trees and shrubs, ideally mirroring the ambience and grandeur of the house interior. Whitewin House and gardens majestically stand overlooking the magnificent vista of the Firth of Clyde, Ailsa Craig, Arran and the Kintyre peninsula. Amongst proposed enhancements will be the completion of a water feature. Linda and Graeme Finnie look forward to welcoming new and past visitors in 2021.

Open: Saturday/Sunday, 17/18 July, Saturday/Sunday, 24/25 July, Saturday 31 July & Sunday 1 August, Saturday 7 August & Saturday 14 August, 2pm - 5pm. Also open by arrangement 1 July - 31 August. Admission £5.00, children free.

Directions: Approaching Girvan from the north on the A77 the turning to Golf Course Road is on the right hand side of the road before the town centre (follow signs for the *Golf Course*). From the south on the A77 come through Girvan, turn left at the lights, then first left and follow signs for the *Golf Course*. Entrance to the property will be signposted.

Opening for: All proceeds to SGS Beneficiaries

Berwickshire

6 MARLFIELD GARDENS
Coldstream TD12 4JT
Christine and Forbes McLennan
T: 01890 840700 E: forbes.mclennan@gmail.com

Marlfield, previously a traditional 80 acre farm, now a quiet hamlet with three lovely gardens:
Marlfield Farmhouse (Christine and Forbes McLennan) – this two acre garden has been open for the past three years with extensive lawns, specimen trees, herbaceous borders and a large raised bed allotment style vegetable garden.
West Cottage (Max and Kate Lowe) – a beautiful cottage garden, intensively planted with herbaceous borders, mixed shrubberies, vegetable and fruit plot.
The Lodge (NEW) (Ron Whittaker 07766 296453) – open for the first time, newly re-designed, this half-acre garden, with fine views of the surrounding countryside, is a lovely mix of lawns, herbaceous borders, wild flower meadow, vegetables and fruit.

Open: Sunday 18 July, 1pm - 5pm. Also open by arrangement 1 March - 30 September. Admission £5.00, children free.

Directions: Four miles north of Coldstream on the old Duns road. Half-a-mile off the main road.

Opening for: Macmillan Cancer Support

Marlfield Farmhouse © Malcolm Ross

Berwickshire

7	**NETHERBYRES**

Eyemouth TD14 5SE
Col S J Furness
T: 01890 750337

An unusual elliptical walled garden, dating from 1740, with a mixture of flowers, fruit and vegetables. A very old pear tree, possibly dating from the 18th century, and the largest rose in Berwickshire, *Rosa filipes* 'Kiftsgate'. A wide variety of roses and herbaceous borders.

Open: Sunday 4 July, 2pm - 5pm. Also open by arrangement 1 May - 31 August. Admission £5.00, children free.

Directions: Half-a-mile south of Eyemouth on the A1107 to Berwick.

Opening for: St Ebba Episcopal Church Eyemouth

8	**RUTHVEN HOUSE**

Coldstream TD12 4JU
Keith and Karen Fountain
T: 01890 840680 E: ruthvenhouse@btconnect.com

The three acres of Ruthven's garden have lovely views towards the Cheviots. The garden's central feature is two ponds joined by a winding stream. The garden is composed of various differing areas – herbaceous borders, woodland areas, a gravel garden, a knot garden, rockeries, an orchard laid to meadow, a kitchen garden, a nuttery, a small lavender field and, adjacent to the house, a formal rose garden. Much of the work to create the garden from the original few small beds around the house has only been undertaken in the last few years, so the garden has not yet reached complete maturity and there's always something on the go. The small fold of Highland cattle in the adjacent field complete the scene.

Open: Sunday 27 June, 1pm - 5pm. Also open by arrangement 1 January 30 September. Admission £5.00, children free.

Directions: Four miles north of Coldstream on the old Duns road.

Opening for: Macmillan Cancer Support

Ruthven House © Malcolm Ross

Caithness & Sutherland

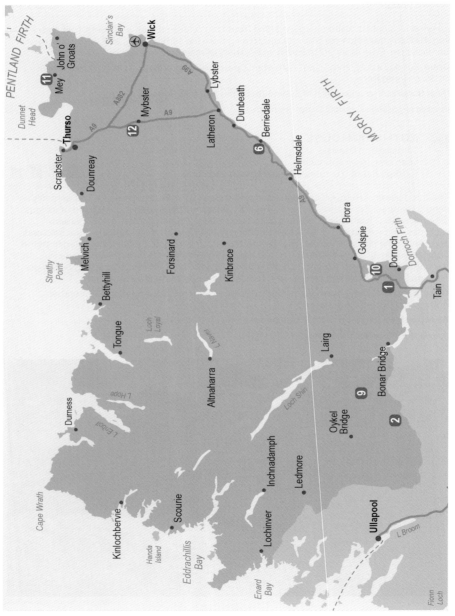

PENTLAND FIRTH

Dunnet Head

Sinclair's Bay

Wick

Mey · John o' Groats

11

A882

Mybster

12

A9

Lybster

Dunbeath

Latheron

Berriedale

6

Helmsdale

MORAY FIRTH

Thurso

A9

Scrabster

Dounreay

Brora

Golspie

Dornoch Firth

Dornoch

10

Strathy Point

Melvich

Forsinard

Kinbrace

Bettyhill

Loch Loyal

L Naver

Tongue

1

Tain

Durness

L Hope

Altnaharra

Lairg

Loch Shin

Bonar Bridge

9

L Eriboll

Oykel Bridge

2

Cape Wrath

Kinlochbervie

Scourie

Inchnadamph

Ledmore

Handa Island

Eddrachillis Bay

Lochinver

Enard Bay

Ullapool

L Broom

Fionn Loch

Shetland

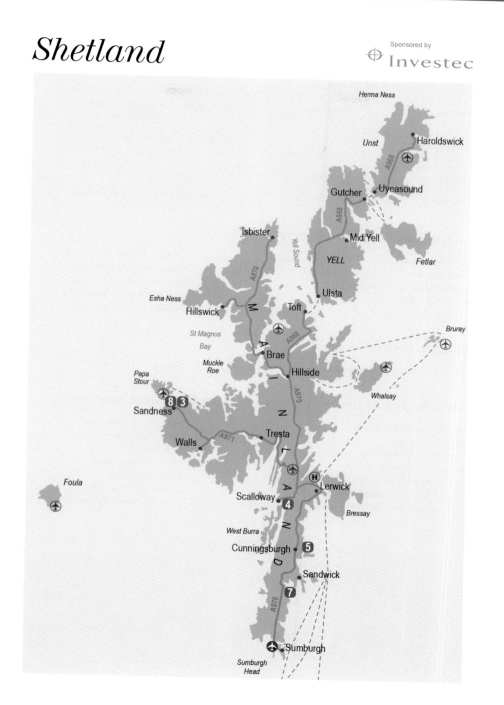

Caithness, Sutherland, Orkney & Shetland

OUR VOLUNTEER ORGANISERS

District Organiser:	Sara Shaw	Amat, Ardgay, Sutherland IV24 3BS E: caithness@scotlandsgardens.org
Area Organisers:	Mary Leask Steve Mathieson	VisitScotland, Market Cross, Lerwick ZE1 0LU VisitScotland, Market Cross, Lerwick ZE1 0LU
District Photographer:	Colin Gregory	Iona, Reay, Caithness, KW14 7RG
Treasurer:	Nicola Vestey	Tarlogie House, Tarlogie, Tain IV19 1QA

GARDENS OPEN ON A SPECIFIC DATE

Amat, Amat Lodge	Saturday/Sunday, 29/30 May
The Castle and Gardens of Mey, Mey	Friday 2 July & Friday 16 July
Skelbo House, Skelbo, Dornoch	Saturday/Sunday, 17/18 July
42 Astle, Dornoch	Saturday/Sunday, 17/18 July
Langwell, Berriedale	Sunday, 1 August

GARDENS OPEN REGULARLY

Norby, Burnside, Sandness, Shetland	1 January - 31 December

GARDENS OPEN BY ARRANGEMENT – BOOK A VISIT WITH THE GARDEN OWNER

Cruisdale, Sandness, Shetland	1 January - 31 December
Amat, Amat Lodge	1 May - 29 August
Oape, Strath Oykel, Ardgay , Sutherland	1 May - 31 July
Nonavaar, Levenwick, Shetland	1 May - 30 September
Highlands Garden, East Voe, Scalloway, Shetland	1 May - 31 October
Keldaberg, Cunningsburgh, Shetland	1 June - 30 September
The Garden at the Auld Post Office B&B, Spittal-by-Mybster	4 July - 29 August (Sundays only)

Caithness, Sutherland, Orkney & Shetland

1 42 ASTLE
Dornoch IV25 3NH
Fay Wilkinson

Organic wildlife garden at the edge of boggy moorland. Mixed planting of trees, shrubs, also herbaceous perennials and fruit and vegetables, many on raised beds for improved drainage. There is a natural pond.

Open: Saturday/Sunday, 17/18 July, 10am - 4pm, admission £4.00, children free.

Directions: A9 from the south: Pass turn off to Dornoch, take first left after Tall Pines Restaurant, signposted *Astle*. After one and a half miles take left fork, cross river and no 42 is the second house on left. A9 from north: Turn right 100 yards before the Tall Pines Restaurant.

Opening for: Bumblebee Conservation Trust

2 AMAT
Amat Lodge IV24 3BS
Jonny and Sara Shaw
T: 01863755320 E: sara.amat@aol.co.uk

With more time in 2020, there have been some big changes to various borders in the garden, enlarging some of them and introducing more unusual plants. The river Carron flows around the edge of the garden and the old Amat Caledonian Forest is close by. Large specimen trees surround the house, plus many new ones planted in the policies in the last few years. There are herbaceous borders, many rhododendrons and a rockery, all set in a large lawn. It is possible to go on a short woodland and river walk and you may see red squirrels which were reintroduced some years ago and are often in and around the garden. To help insect life we are no longer mowing the lawn but it does have paths through it.
Champion Trees: Abies Procera, Noble Fir.

Open: Saturday/Sunday, 29/30 May, 2pm - 5pm. Also open by arrangement 1 May - 29 August. Admission £5.00, children free.

Directions: Take the road from Ardgay to Croick, nine miles. Turn left at the red phone box and the garden is 500 yards on the left.

Opening for: Creich Croick & Kincardine District Day Care Association & Guide Dogs

3 CRUISDALE
Sandness, Shetland ZE2 9PL
Alfred Kern
T: 01595 870739

The garden is in a natural state with many willows, several ponds and a variety of colourful hardy plants that grow well in the Shetland climate. Work started in 2003 and the garden has continued to expand over the years, with more work planned.

Open: By arrangement 1 January - 31 December, admission £3.00, children free. Delighted to receive visitors, please don't hesitate to call.

Directions: From Lerwick head north on the A970, then at Tingwall take the A971 to Sandness, on the west side of Shetland. Cruisdale is opposite the school, on the right-hand side with a wind generator in the field.

Opening for: Royal Voluntary Service

Caithness, Sutherland, Orkney & Shetland

4 HIGHLANDS GARDEN

East Voe, Scalloway, Shetland ZE1 0UR
Sarah Kay
T: 01595 880526 M: 07818 845385 E: info@easterhoull.co.uk
W: www.selfcatering-shetland.co.uk/the-garden/ and www.sarahkayarts.com

The garden is in two parts. The upper garden is mostly a rockery, with a large selection of plants, shallow pond, seating area and newly built polycrub and greenhouse with fruit and vegetables. The lower garden is on a steep slope with a spectacular sea view over the village of Scalloway. There is a path to lead visitors around and the garden features a large collection of plants, vegetable patch, deep pond and pergola. It was awarded a *Shetland Environmental Award* in 2014 for its strong theme of recycling. The owner also has an art studio which you are most welcome to visit when you view the garden.

Open: By arrangement 1 May - 31 October, admission £3.50, children free.

Directions: Follow the A970 main road towards the village of Scalloway. Near the top of the hill heading towards Scalloway take a sharp turn to the left, signposted *Easterhoull Chalets*. Follow the road to chalets (painted blue with red roofs) and you will see the yellow *SGS* sign for the garden. Bus 4 from Lerwick/Scalloway.

Opening for: Macmillan Cancer Support

Highlands Garden

5 KELDABERG

Cunningsburgh, Shetland ZE2 9HG
Mrs L Johnston
T: 01950 477331 E: linda.keldaberg@btinternet.com

A 'secret garden' divided into four areas. A beach garden of grasses, flowers and driftwood. The main area is a sloping perennial border leading down to a greenhouse, vegetable plot, up to a decked area with containers and exotic plants including agaves, pineapple lilies, cannas and gunneras. The new area has trees, raised vegetable beds, a rockery, retaining walls and an arbour in which to rest. There is a pond with goldfish and aquatic plants and now a polycrub to grow vegetables, fruit trees and a grapevine.

Caithness, Sutherland, Orkney & Shetland

Open: By arrangement 1 June - 30 September, admission £3.50, children free.

Directions: On the A970 south of Lerwick is Cunningsburgh, take the Gord junction on the left after passing the village hall. Continue along the road to the second house past the *Kenwood* sign.

Opening for: Chest Heart & Stroke Scotland

---

6 LANGWELL

Berriedale KW7 6HD
Welbeck Estates
T: 01593 751278 / 751237 E: alexa.macauslan@gmail.com

A beautiful and spectacular old walled garden with outstanding borders situated in the secluded Langwell Strath. Charming wooded access drive with a chance to see deer.

Open: Sunday 1 August, noon - 4pm, admission £4.00, children free.

Directions: Turn off the A9 at Berriedale Braes, up the private (tarred) drive signposted *Private – Langwell House*. It is about one-and-a-quarter miles from the A9.

Opening for: RNLI

---

7 NONAVAAR

Levenwick, Shetland ZE2 9HX
James B Thomason
T: 01950 422447

This is a delightful country garden, sloping within drystone walls and overlooking magnificent coastal views. It contains ponds, terraces, trees, bushes, varied perennials, annuals, vegetable garden and greenhouse.

Open: By arrangement 1 May - 30 September, noon - 6pm, admission £4.00, children free.

Directions: Head south from Lerwick. Turn left at the *Levenwick* sign soon after Bigton turnoff. Follow the road to the third house on the left after the Midway stores. Park where there is a *Garden Open* sign. Bus 6 from Lerwick - Sumburgh.

Opening for: Cancer Research UK

---

8 NORBY

Burnside, Sandness, Shetland ZE2 9PL
Mrs Gundel Grolimund
T: 01595 870246 E: gundel.g5@btinternet.com

A small but perfectly formed garden and a prime example of what can be achieved in a very exposed situation. Blue painted wooden pallets provide internal wind breaks and form a background for shrubs, climbers and herbaceous plants, while willows provide a perfect wildlife habitat. There are treasured plants such as *Chionochloa rubra*, pieris, Chinese tree peonies, a selection of old-fashioned shrub roses, lilies, hellebores and grasses from New Zealand. There is also a lovely selection of interesting art and textiles in the house.

Open: 1 January - 31 December, dawn - dusk, admission £3.00, children free.

Directions: Head north on the A970 from Lerwick then west on the A971 at Tingwall. At Sandness, follow the road to Norby, turn right at the Methodist Church, Burnside is at the end of the road. Bus 10 Sandness - Walls.

Opening for: Survival International

Caithness, Sutherland, Orkney & Shetland

9 **OAPE**
Strath Oykel, Ardgay, Sutherland IV24 3DP
Michele Buss and John Raworth
T: 07999 817715 E: scrumpyjack9@yahoo.co.uk

A perfect example of what can be achieved in a small garden. It is packed full of different plants in various situations and is situated in a lovely rural setting.

Open: By arrangement 1 May - 31 July, admission £4.00. Sadly no children are allowed in the garden.

Directions: Take A837 to Invercassley and turn left shortly after leaving village. Go up hill and take first right and Oape is first house on left.

Opening for: Maggie's: Inverness

Oape

10 **SKELBO HOUSE**
Skelbo, Dornoch IV25 3QG
Alison Bartlett
E: SkelboHouseGarden@gmail.com

Extensive woodland garden with spectacular views over Loch Fleet. Mixed herbaceous borders, rose garden and shrubberies surround the house. Lawns slope down to a small lochan and river walkway. Mature trees throughout. Large kitchen garden.

Open: Saturday/Sunday, 17/18 July, 10am - 4pm, admission £5.00, children free.

Directions: From the south: On A9 take the small turning opposite Trentham Hotel (just past the Dornoch turn offs). At the side of Loch Fleet turn left, at the ruined castle take the second farm road which is fairly rough, and follow round to your right. If coming from the north take the Loch Fleet road signposted to *Embo* from the A9.

Opening for: Mary's Meals International or MMI

Caithness, Sutherland, Orkney & Shetland

11 ## THE CASTLE AND GARDENS OF MEY
Mey KW14 8XH
The Queen Elizabeth Castle of Mey Trust
T: 01847 851473 E: enquiries@castleofmey.org.uk
W: www.castleofmey.org.uk

Her Majesty Queen Elizabeth the Queen Mother, bought what was then Barrogill Castle in 1952 before renovating and restoring the z-plan castle and creating the beautiful gardens you see today; renaming it The Castle and Gardens of Mey. This romantic and unique garden is a reminder that, however daunting the weather, it is often possible with a little vision and energy to create and maintain a garden in the most unlikely of locations. The castle now includes an animal centre, gift shop and tearoom serving delicious locally sourced food and drinks, often using produce from the castle's very own gardens.

Open: Friday 2 July & Friday 16 July, 10am - 5pm, admission details can be found on the garden's website.

Directions: On the A836 between Thurso and John O'Groats.

Opening for: All proceeds to SGS Beneficiaries

12 ## THE GARDEN AT THE AULD POST OFFICE B&B
Spittal-by-Mybster, Caithness KW1 5XR
Lynne and Weyland Read
T: 01847 841391 E: auldpostoffice@btinternet.com
W: www.auldpostoffice.com

Surrounded by eight acres of Alaskan Lodgepole pine trees, this secluded garden has a variety of beds and borders containing evergreen plants, shrubs, grasses and perennials. The one-third acre garden provides a meandering walk under the pergola to beds set in the lawn. The fish share their pond with grasses and lilies, and the garden walk continues beneath 20-year-old pine trees, under-planted with shade-loving perennials. Heather, junipers and conifers provide an all-year-round centrepiece. There are many seating areas to rest awhile and, for the hardy, a stout footwear walk can be taken through the surrounding woodland. Planting has been chosen to encourage bees, birds and butterflies, and the hens potter in their woodland enclosure.

Open: By arrangement 4 July - 29 August, Sundays only (except Sunday 15 August). Admission £4.00, children free.

Directions: On the A9 at Spittal.

Opening for: Cancer Research UK

Dumfriesshire

Sponsored by
Investec

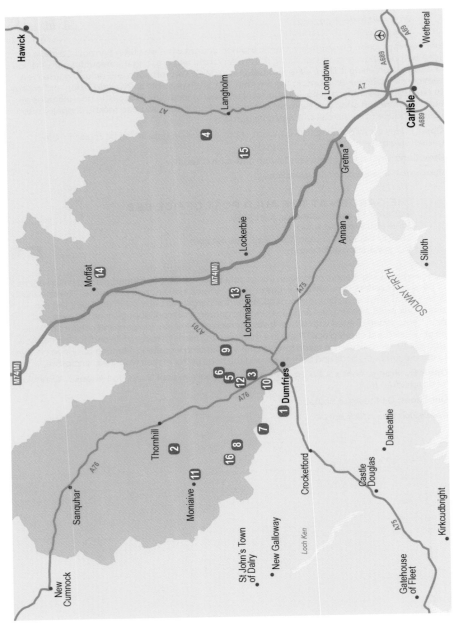

Dumfriesshire

OUR VOLUNTEER ORGANISERS

District Organiser:	Sarah Landale	Dalswinton House, Dalswinton, Auldgirth DG2 0XZ E: dumfriesshire@scotlandsgardens.org
Area Organisers:	Fiona Bell-Irving Guy Galbraith Liz Mitchell	Bankside, Kettleholm, Lockerbie DG11 1BY Stanemuir, Parkgate, Dumfries DG1 3NE Drumpark, Irongray DG2 9TX
District Volunteer:	Margot Macintyre	18 Edinburgh Road, Dumfries DG1 1JQ
District Photographer:	Stuart Littlewood	E: stu@f8.eclipse.co.uk
Treasurer:	Leslie Jack	Gledenholm House, Ae, Dumfries DG1 1RF

GARDENS OPEN ON A SPECIFIC DATE

Craig, Langholm	Sunday, 21 February
Dalswinton House, Dalswinton	Sunday, 16 May
Portrack, The Garden of Cosmic Speculation, Holywood	Sunday, 30 May
Leap Cottage, West Cluden, Dumfries	Sunday, 6 June
Bonerick House, Irongray , Dumfries	Sunday, 6 June
Glenae, Amisfield	Sunday, 13 June
Cowhill Tower, Holywood	Sunday, 20 June
Dunesslin, Dunscore	Sunday, 27 June
Capenoch, Penpont, Thornhill	Sunday, 4 July
Whiteside, Dunscore	Sunday, 11 July
Westwater Farm, Langholm	Sunday, 18 July
Dalswinton Mill, Dalswinton, Dumfries	Sunday, 1 August
Shawhead, 7 Vendace Drive, Lochmaben	Saturday/Sunday, 7/8 August
Shawhead, 7 Vendace Drive, Lochmaben	Sunday, 19 September

GARDENS OPEN REGULARLY

Craig, Langholm	22 February - 1 March

GARDENS OPEN BY ARRANGEMENT – BOOK A VISIT WITH THE GARDEN OWNER

Peilton, Moniaive	1 April - 31 May
Waterside Garden, Waterside, Moffat, Dumfriesshire	15 April - 18 October
Drumpark, Irongray	1 May - 30 September
Whiteside, Dunscore	1 May - 31 May

Dumfriesshire

1 BONERICK HOUSE
Irongray , Dumfries DG2 9SE
Isobel Strathmore
T: 01387 730415 E: isostrathmore@hotmail.com

Stunning views of gorse covered White Hill, with ruins of a Roman fort at the top. The garden is one acre with a wooded stepped climb to a "Hobbit House". Close to the road is a border of peonies and fleur-de-lys, with plenty of thistles and roses. Alastair Clark, the retired gardener from Portrack, has been working on developing the garden over the last year.

Open: Sunday 6 June, 2pm - 5pm, admission £5.00, children free. An ice-cream van will be offering hot and cold refreshments. Leap Cottage is also open the same day and it is easily possible to visit both gardens as they are very close to one another.

Directions: Take the Terregles Road from Dumfries for approximately 4 miles, past Terregles and on towards Shawhead. The house is on the right opposite a white farm steading. Bus route 373 (Dumfries-Shawhead) passes directly by the house. Timetables available online.

Opening for: Maggie's

2 CAPENOCH
Penpont, Thornhill DG3 4LZ
Mr and Mrs Robert Gladstone
E: maggie.gladstone@gmail.com

There are rare trees throughout the grounds and the main garden is the remnant of that laid out in Victorian times. There is a pretty little raised knot garden called the Italian Garden and a lovely old Victorian conservatory. Parking is available in a field half way up the drive, but you may prefer to park in Penpont Village and walk the whole way to Capenoch. There are lovely wildflowers in the oak woods on either side of the drive.

Open: Sunday 4 July, 2pm - 5pm, admission £5.00, children free. Please note there is disabled parking at the House and picnics are allowed, as there will be no teas available.

Directions: Take the A702 west from Thornhill, drive through Penpont and the entrance to the house is at the lodge on the left-hand side, just at the speed restriction sign.

Opening for: The Jo Walters Trust

3 COWHILL TOWER
Holywood DG2 0RL
Mr and Mrs P Weatherall
T: 01387 720304 E: cmw@cowhill.co.uk

This is an interesting walled garden. There are topiary animals, birds and figures and a beautiful woodland walk. Splendid views can be seen from the lawn right down the Nith Valley. There are also a variety of statues from the Far East.

Open: Sunday 20 June, 2pm - 5pm, admission £5.00, children free.

Directions: Holywood is one-and-a-half miles off the A76, five miles north of Dumfries.

Opening for: Maggie's

Dumfriesshire

4 CRAIG
Langholm DG13 0NZ
Mr and Mrs Neil Ewart
T: 013873 70230 E: nmlewart@googlemail.com

Craig snowdrops have evolved over the last 30 or so years. Round the house and policies, a large variety has been planted with a varied flowering season stretching from the start of January until April and peaking mid-February. Large drifts of *Leucojum vernum* (winter snowflake) have started to naturalise here, and along the riverbank a variety of snowdrops swept down by the river have naturalised in the adjacent woodland, known as the Snowdrop Walk.

Open: Sunday 21 February, noon - 4pm and 22 February - 1 March, 1pm - 4pm for Snowdrops and Winter Walks. Admission £5.00, children free.

Directions: Craig is three miles from Langholm on the B709 towards Eskdalemuir.

Opening for: Kirkandrews Kirk Trust

5 DALSWINTON HOUSE
Dalswinton DG2 0XZ
Mr and Mrs Peter Landale
T: 01387 740220 E: sarahlandale@gmail.com

Late 18th-century house sits on top of a hill surrounded by herbaceous beds and well-established shrubs, including rhododendrons and azaleas, overlooking the loch. Attractive walks through woods and around the loch. It was here that the first steamboat in Britain made its maiden voyage in 1788 and there is a life-size model beside the water to commemorate this. Over the past years, there has been much clearing and development work around the loch, which has opened up the views considerably.

Open: Sunday 16 May, 2pm - 5pm, admission £5.00, children free.

Directions: Take the A76 north from Dumfries to Thornhill. After seven miles, turn right to Dalswinton. Drive through Dalswinton village, past the orange church on the right and follow estate wall on the right. Entrance is by either the single lodge or double lodge entrance set in the wall.

Opening for: Kirkmahoe Parish Church of Scotland

Dalswinton House © Stuart Littlewood

Dumfriesshire

6 DALSWINTON MILL
Dalswinton, Dumfries DG2 0XY
Colin and Pamela Crosbie
T: 01387 740070 E: colincrosbiehort@btinternet.com

A newly-created plantsman's garden set around an 18th-century watermill with the Pennyland Burn running through it. The garden contains a wide range of perennials, trees and shrubs that favour the local climate and have been planted during the last few years. A variety of statuary can be found throughout the garden which sits in a hollow and can be only accessed by steps and there are slopes throughout the garden. Unfortunately, this makes the garden unsuitable for anyone with mobility requirements.

Open: Sunday 1 August, 2pm - 6pm, admission £4.00, children free.

Directions: Garden lies in Dalswinton, halfway between the A76 and the A701 on the Auldgirth to Kirkton Road. From Auldgirth take the first left after the Dalswinton Village Hall. The Mill is on the corner before the bridge. We are unable to offer disabled parking.

Opening for: *Dumfries & Galloway Health Board Endowment Fund: Diabetes*

Dalswinton Mill © Stuart Littlewood

7 DRUMPARK
Irongray DG2 9TX
Mr and Mrs Iain Mitchell
T: 01387 820323 E: iain.liz.mitchell@gmail.com

Well-contoured woodland garden and extensive policies nurture mature azaleas, rhododendrons and rare shrubs among impressive specimen trees. Water garden with primulas and meconopsis. Victorian walled garden with fruit trees and garden produce. There is also a beautiful herbaceous border. All planting is set in a natural bowl providing attractive vistas.

Dumfriesshire

Open: By arrangement 1 May - 30 September, admission £5.00, children free.

Directions: Dumfries bypass, head north on the A76 for a half mile, turn left at the signpost to *Lochside Industrial Estates* and immediately right onto Irongray Road; continue for five miles; gates in sandstone wall on left (half mile after Routin' Brig).

Opening for: Loch Arthur

Drumpark © Stuart Littlewood

 8 **DUNESSLIN**
Dunscore DG2 0UR
Iain and Zara Milligan
E: zaramilligan@gmail.com

Set in the hills with wonderful views and borrowed landscapes, the principal garden consists of a series of connecting rooms filled with a great and interesting variety of herbaceous plants, beautifully designed and maintained. There is a substantial rock garden with alpines and unusual plants and a very pretty pond. There is a short walk to three cairns by Andy Goldsworthy, through an evolving woodland garden.

Open: Sunday 27 June, 2pm - 5pm, admission £5.00, children free.

Directions: From Dunscore, follow the road to Corsock. About one-and-a-half miles further on, turn right at the post box, still on the road to Corsock and at small crossroads half a mile on, turn left.

Opening for: Alzheimer Scotland

Dumfriesshire

9 GLENAE
Amisfield DG1 3NZ
Victoria and Charlie Rotheroe
E: tottsrotheroe@gmail.com

A beautiful, well-established walled garden, well-stocked with interesting plants. Four lawns are surrounded by colourful herbaceous borders and apple trees. There is a lovely sunken garden with a tranquil water feature and the pink poppies (Mrs Perry) featured throughout the garden are a stunning sight in June. Visitors may also walk through a newly-cleared woodland, enjoying the mature trees and peaceful atmosphere.

Open: Sunday 13 June, noon - 6pm, admission £5.00, children free.

Directions: One and-a-half miles north of Amisfield on the A701. Turn left to Duncow and Auldgirth and one mile on right.

Opening for: All proceeds to SGS Beneficiaries

10 LEAP COTTAGE
West Cluden, Dumfries DG2 9UW
Mr Raymond Nelson
T: 07906 022 632 E: nelson_nomad@yahoo.com.au

Leap Cottage sits on the site of a former mill dating back to the 1600s. It is situated in the most amazing setting, right down on the banks of the Cluden Water, a tributary of the River Nith with wonderful views of the river's twists and turns. The tiny and enchanting garden is filled to the brim with a variety of plants and colour. There is a lovely walk through the trees right down to the river's edge, just beside the cottage.

Open: Sunday 6 June, 2pm - 5pm, admission £5.00, children free. Bonerick House is also open the same day and it is easily possible to visit both gardens as they are very close to one another.

Directions: Take the A76 Dumfries/Thornhill Road. Turn left to Irongray Industrial Estate/Park on the outskirts of Dumfries. Follow Irongray Road, past all the houses until barn on the right. Turn in here and park – access and parking to the cottage is difficult and limited so parking is at the farm. From there, following the yellow signs, walk to the T-junction, turn right and keep going to the end of the road. About 150 yards walk.

Opening for: All proceeds to SGS Beneficiaries

Leap Cottage © Stuart Littlewood

Dumfriesshire

11 **PEILTON**
Moniaive DG3 4HE
Mrs A Graham
T: 01848 200363 E: amgatpeilton@gmail.com

This really very special and attractive woodland garden has a great variety of interesting rhododendrons, shrubs and flowering trees. Peilton is of particular interest for the real plantsman.

Open: By arrangement 1 April - 31 May, admission £5.00, children free. Homemade teas may be arranged, if required, at the time of making the appointment. Please note that this is not included in the entry cost.

Directions: Off A702 between Kirkland of Glencairn and Moniaive.

Opening for: Marie Curie

12 **PORTRACK, THE GARDEN OF COSMIC SPECULATION**
Holywood DG2 0RW
John Jencks
W: www.gardenofcosmicspeculation.com

Forty major areas, gardens, bridges, landforms, sculpture, terraces, fences and architectural works. Covering 30 acres, The Garden of Cosmic Speculation, designed by the late Charles Jencks, uses nature to celebrate nature, both intellectually and through the senses, including the sense of humour.

Open: Sunday 30 May. Please check the Scotland's Gardens Scheme website and our social media channels nearer the date for further details. Entrance to this popular garden opening is by pre-paid ticket only, bookable online. Given the current circumstances, tickets will only be available from March 29th. There will be a reduced number of tickets available to keep visitors safe. We regret that there is no wheelchair access.

Directions: Portrack is one-and-a-half miles off the A76, five miles north of Dumfries.

Opening for: Maggie's

13 **SHAWHEAD**
7 Vendace Drive, Lochmaben DG11 1QN
Mr and Mrs Ian Rankine
T: 01387 811273 E: srankine298@btinternet.com

A relatively young garden situated on the edge of Lochmaben with delightful views overlooking Mill Loch. It has immaculately maintained lawns and well-furnished borders bursting with colour and a great collection of hardy perennials and grasses with conifers, shrubs and trees providing all year round interest.

Open: Saturday/Sunday, 7/8 August & Sunday 19 September, 1pm - 5pm, admission £5.00, children free. The walk around Mill Loch takes about 30-40 minutes from the House. Wear suitable walking shoes. For keen walkers, the nearby Castle Loch also has a lovely walk of 3 miles.

Directions: From Dumfries, turn left opposite The Crown Hotel, turn left at give way and then sharp left. From Lockerbie, take the right fork beside the Town Hall and after half a mile, take left turn.

Opening for: Castle Loch Lochmaben Community Trust

Dumfriesshire

14 WATERSIDE GARDEN
Waterside, Moffat, Dumfriesshire DG10 9LF
Ronnie Cann
T: 01683 221583 E: waterside-garden@holestone.net
W: www.holestone.net

Set in beautiful Moffat Dale and bounded on one side by the Moffat Water, Waterside Garden is home to woods, riverside walks and three acres of cultivated garden. There are many mature trees including oak, birch, beech and much more. Collections of species and hybrid rhododendrons and azaleas, bamboos, and other flowering shrubs give year-round interest. There are herbaceous beds, giving colour in spring and summer, alpines, mixed plantings, spring bulbs, especially daffodils, and wildflower meadows.

Open: By arrangement 15 April - 18 October, admission £5.00, children free. Open on Mondays to Thursdays between 10.30am and 5pm.

Directions: Three miles north of Moffat on the A708 opposite Craigieburn Forest Car Park. From Selkirk the garden is about 14.5 miles south of St Mary's Loch.

Opening for: Moffat Water Hall & Moffat & District Men's Shed

Waterside Garden

Dumfriesshire

15 **WESTWATER FARM**
Langholm DG13 0LU
Mr and Mrs Charlie Clapperton
T: 01387 381004 E: charlieclapperton@hotmail.com

In a wonderful, remote and romantic setting, the interesting walled garden adjacent to the house has both herbaceous plants and shrubs. There is also a woodland garden with a variety of bamboos and interesting trees. Dotted around the house and steadings are some fabulous pots.

Open: Sunday 18 July, 2pm - 5pm, admission by donation.

Directions: Thirteen miles from Lockerbie on the B7068 Lockerbie to Langholm road (five miles from Langholm). Entrance is signposted *Westwater* on the left coming from Lockerbie. Keep to left fork for the house.

Opening for: All proceeds to SGS Beneficiaries

16 **WHITESIDE**
Dunscore DG2 0UU
John and Hilary Craig
T: 01387 820501 E: hjcraig19@gmail.com

The garden, which extends to several acres, is 600 feet above sea level on a north-facing slope with views across to Queensberry and the Lowther Hills. There are some mature trees around the house but the rest of the garden is relatively new, having been created from a bare hillside over the last 20 years. There are shrubs, young trees, a rowan avenue, a walled vegetable garden, orchard and courtyard garden. Several burns run through the property and there is a pond and an enclosure for runner ducks.

Open: Sunday 11 July, noon - 5pm. Also open by arrangement 1 May - 31 May. Admission £5.00, children free.

Directions: From Dunscore, take the Corsock road. Continue two miles on, turn right opposite the postbox. Continue for one and three quarter miles, over the humpback bridge and past the white farmhouse on the left. *Whiteside* is signed on the left.

Opening for: Music in Dumfries

Whiteside

Whiteside

Dunbartonshire

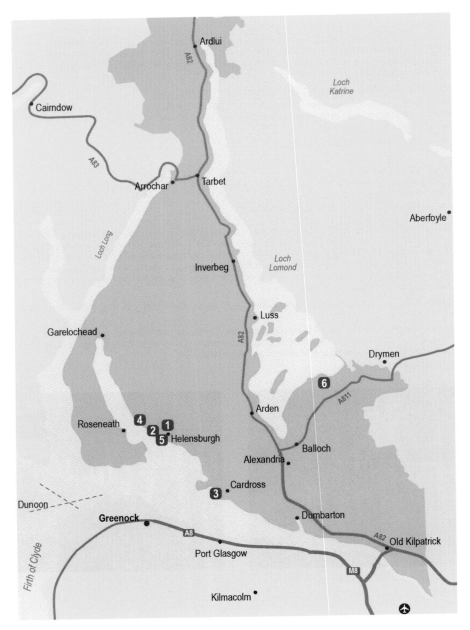

Dunbartonshire

OUR VOLUNTEER ORGANISERS

District Organiser:	Tricia Stewart	High Glenan, 24a Queen St, Helensburgh G84 9LG E: dunbartonshire@scotlandsgardens.org
Area Organisers:	Graham Greenwell Kathleen Murray Lesley and Norman Quirk	Avalon, Shore Road, Garelochhead G84 0EN 4 Cairndhu Gardens, Helensburgh G84 8PG Glenard, Upper Torwoodhill Road G84 8LE
District Photographer:	Stephen Skivington	157 Strathleven Drive, Alexandria G83 9PH
Treasurer:	Claire Travis	54 Union Street, Alexandria G83 9AH

GARDENS OPEN ON A SPECIFIC DATE

18 Duchess Park with High Glenan and Westburn, Helensburgh	Sunday, 16 May
Ross Priory, Gartocharn	Sunday, 23 May
Geilston Garden, Main Road, Cardross	Sunday, 6 June
4 Cairndhu Gardens, Helensburgh	Sunday, 20 June
James Street Community Garden Plant Sale, Helensburgh	Sunday, 5 September

GARDENS OPEN REGULARLY

Glenarn, Glenarn Road, Rhu, Helensburgh	21 March - 21 September

Dunbartonshire

1 18 DUCHESS PARK WITH HIGH GLENAN AND WESTBURN
18 Duchess Park, Helensburgh G84 9PY
Stewart and Sue Campbell

18 Duchess Park (NEW) Helensburgh G84 9PY (Stewart and Sue Campbell): The garden is small, 40 years old, and is still being developed. The site was originally a paddock on the edge of Duchess Wood, which backs on to the garden and forms a 'borrowed landscape'. The rear garden is sloping with two sets of steps to get to the upper garden. It is a woodland garden with two large oak trees, many species and hybrid rhododendrons, and other woodland shrubs and plants.
High Glenan Helensburgh G84 9LG (Tom and Tricia Stewart): A secluded garden with burn and waterside plants, gravel garden, herb and herbaceous borders and kitchen garden with selection of fruit and vegetables. Extensive programme of hard-landscaping has been undertaken over the last ten years.
Westburn 50 Campbell Street G84 9NH (Professor and Mrs Baker): A woodland garden of just over two acres. The Glenan Burn runs through a woodland of oak and beech trees with bluebells in the springtime. Some of the paths are steep, but there are bridges over the burn and handrails in places. There is also an air raid shelter, and the remains of a kiln, where James Ballantyne Hannay manufactured artificial diamonds in the 1800s. A lawn is surrounded by rhododendrons and azaleas, and there is a vegetable garden.

Open: Sunday 16 May, 1pm - 5pm, admission £5.00, children free. Short guided wildflower walks in Duchess Wood will be offered during the afternoon by the Friends of Duchess Wood. The bluebells should be in bloom. If the weather is poor, stout shoes are recommended. There will be homemade teas at High Glenan and a plant stall at Westburn.

Directions: 18 Duchess Park – Travel west along Queen Street about half a mile from High Glenan and it becomes Duchess Park, a cul de sac. Number 18 is at the far end on the right.
High Glenan – Approximately half a mile along Queen Street from its junction with Sinclair Street on the right-hand side.
Westburn – Proceed along West Montrose Street from Sinclair Street and take the fourth turn on the right. The entrance to Westburn is 100 yards up Campbell Street on the right-hand side.

Opening for: Rhu and Shandon Parish Church of Scotland, Friends of Duchess Wood & St Michael & All Angels Church

2 4 CAIRNDHU GARDENS
Helensburgh G84 8PG
Mrs Kathleen Murray

Kathleen took over this garden in 2019 when she moved from Shandon to Helensburgh. The borders were already well-stocked with interesting perennials and shrubs although growing beyond their space. Kathleen has installed a greenhouse and is currently redesigning the borders and introducing her favourite plants. Come to see the work in progress. There will be a large plant sale, including locally grown plants.

Open: Sunday 20 June, 2pm - 5pm, admission by donation.

Directions: 4 Cairndhu Gardens is one-third of a mile west from the Commodore Hotel on the A814. Please follow signs. Please park in Cairndhu Avenue.

Opening for: Macular Society

Dunbartonshire

3 **GEILSTON GARDEN**
Main Road, Cardross G82 5HD
The National Trust for Scotland
T: 01389 849187 E: geilstongarden@nts.org.uk
W: www.nts.org.uk/visit/places/Geilston-Garden/

Geilston Garden has many attractive features including the walled garden with herbaceous border providing summer colour, tranquil woodland walks and a large working kitchen garden. This is the ideal season for viewing the Siberian iris in flower along the Geilston Burn and the Japanese azaleas.

Open: Sunday 6 June, 1pm - 5pm, admission details can be found on the garden's website.

Directions: On the A814, one mile from Cardross towards Helensburgh.

Opening for: *The National Trust for Scotland: Geilston Garden*

Geilston Garden © NTS

Dunbartonshire

4 GLENARN
Glenarn Road, Rhu, Helensburgh G84 8LL
Michael and Sue Thornley
T: 01436 820493 E: masthome@btinternet.com
W: www.gardens-of-argyll.co.uk

Glenarn survives as a complete example of a ten-acre garden which spans from 1850 to the present day. There are winding paths through miniature glens under a canopy of oaks and limes, sunlit open spaces, a vegetable garden with beehives, and a rock garden full of surprise and season-long colour, with views over the Gareloch. The famous collections of rare and tender rhododendrons and magnolias give way in midsummer to roses rambling through the trees and climbing hydrangeas, followed by the starry white flowers of hoherias and eucryphias to the end of the season. A new feature is our Silent Space at the top of the garden.

Open: Every day 21 March - 21 September, dawn - dusk. Admission £5.00, children free.

Directions: On the A814, two miles north of Helensburgh, up Pier Road. Cars to be left at the gate unless passengers are infirm.

Opening for: Donation to SGS Beneficiaries

Glenarn

Glenarn

5 JAMES STREET COMMUNITY GARDEN PLANT SALE
Helensburgh G84 8EY
The Gardeners of James Street

Developed from a derelict children's play ground, the Community Garden is a relaxed area for contemplation with mixed herbaceous beds, maze and young trees. The plant sale will include a wide selection of nursery-grown perennials and locally grown trees, shrubs, herbaceous, alpine and house plants.

Open: Sunday 5 September, noon - 4pm, admission by donation.

Directions: Travel west along Princes Street from Sinclair Street through Colquhoun Square, turn right up James Street and the Community Garden is on the left. Park on the street.

Opening for: James Street Community Garden

Dunbartonshire

6	**ROSS PRIORY**

Gartocharn G83 8NL
University of Strathclyde

Mansion house with glorious views over Loch Lomond with adjoining garden. Wonderful rhododendrons and azaleas are the principal plants in the garden, with a varied selection of trees and shrubs throughout. Spectacular spring bulbs, border plantings of herbaceous perennials, shrubs and trees. Extensive walled garden with glasshouses, pergola and ornamental plantings. Children's play area and putting green beside the house.

Open: Sunday 23 May, 2pm - 5pm, admission £5.00, children free. Please note that the house is not open to view. Dogs on leads are welcome but not in the Walled Garden. Homemade Teas and Plant Stall in the Walled Garden.

Directions: Gartocharn one-and-a-half miles off the A811. Bus from Balloch to Gartocharn.

Opening for: Friends Of Loch Lomond & The Trossachs & CHAS

James Street Community Garden Plant Sale © Stephen Skivington

East Lothian

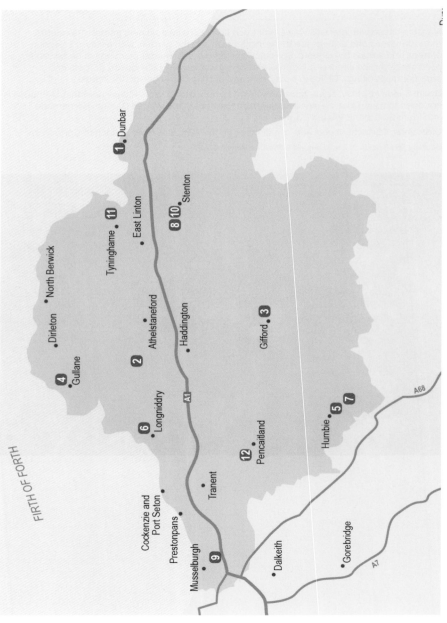

East Lothian

OUR VOLUNTEER ORGANISERS

District Organiser:	Joan Johnson	The Round House, Woodbush, Dunbar EH42 1HB E: eastlothian@scotlandsgardens.org
Area Organisers:	Frank Kirwan	Humbie Dean, Humbie EH36 5PW
	Ian Orr	6 Grannus Mews, Inveresk EH21 7TT
	Judy Riley	The Old Kitchen, Tyninghame House, Tyninghame, nr Dunbar EH42 1XW
District Photographer:	Malcolm Ross	2 Dall Hollow, North Berwick EH39 5FN
Treasurers:	Colin Wilson	5 Tenterfield Drive, Haddington, EH41 3JF

GARDENS OPEN ON A SPECIFIC DATE

Shepherd House, Inveresk, Musselburgh	Saturday/Sunday, 20/21 February
Longwood, Humbie	Thursday, 8 April
Humbie Dean, Humbie	Thursday, 8 April
Winton Castle, Pencaitland	Sunday, 18 April
Humbie Dean, Humbie	Thursday, 22 April
Shepherd House, Inveresk, Musselburgh	Saturday/Sunday, 24/25 April
Tyninghame House and The Walled Garden, Tyninghame House	Sunday, 9 May
Longwood, Humbie	Thursday, 13 May
Humbie Dean, Humbie	Thursday, 13 May
Stenton Village, Stenton, Dunbar	Sunday, 6 June
Humbie Dean, Humbie	Thursday, 10 June
Belhaven House, Edinburgh Road, Belhaven, Dunbar	Saturday, 26 June
Longniddry Gardens, Longniddry	Sunday, 27 June
Camptoun House, Camptoun, East Lothian	Saturday/Sunday, 3/4 July
Tyninghame House and The Walled Garden, Dunbar	Sunday, 4 July
Longwood, Humbie	Thursday, 8 July
Humbie Dean, Humbie	Thursday, 8 July
Gifford Village and Broadwoodside, Gifford	Sunday, 11 July
Greywalls, Gullane	Saturday, 31 July
Longwood, Humbie	Thursday, 5 August
Humbie Dean, Humbie	Thursday, 5 August
Longwood, Humbie	Thursday, 9 September
Humbie Dean, Humbie	Thursday, 9 September
Humbie Dean, Humbie	Thursday, 7 October

GARDENS OPEN REGULARLY

Shepherd House, Inveresk, Musselburgh	9 February - 25 February (Tues & Thurs)
Shepherd House, Inveresk, Musselburgh	20 April - 22 July (Tues & Thurs)

East Lothian

5 HUMBIE DEAN
Humbie EH36 5PW
Frank Kirwan
E: frank.kirwan@gmail.com

A two-acre ornamental and woodland garden sandwiched between two burns at 600 feet with interest throughout a long season. A limited palette of plants with hosta, hellebores, perennial geranium, primula, meconopsis, martagon lilies, spring bulbs, ground cover, herbaceous and shrub planting, bluebell meadow, mature and recent azalea and rhododendron planting. A short woodland walk has been created, only accessible by a series of steps.

Open: Thursday 8 April, 22 April, 13 May, 10 June, 8 July, 5 August, 9 September, 7 October, 10am - 2pm. Admission £5.00, children free.

Directions: Enter Humbie from the A68, pass the school and the village hall on the left then immediately turn right just before the Humbie Hub. Take the second left and Humbie Dean is on the left between two small bridges. Limited parking.

Opening for: Mamie Martin Fund

Humbie Dean

6 LONGNIDDRY GARDENS
Longniddry EH32 0LF
The Gardeners of Longniddry

Longniddry is an attractive village with extensive green spaces and outstanding sea views. Our gardens are tended by enthusiastic gardeners some of whom are old hands and some recent converts to gardening. The gardens exhibit a wonderful variety of size, layout and planting ensuring something for every visitor to enjoy. One of the smaller gardens is modern and shows what can be achieved with attractive and innovative hard landscaping. This contrasts with a fabulous lush garden including a water feature — small can be beautiful! Larger gardens include new and mature trees and herbaceous planting ranging from self-seeding cottage style to more formal. There are veggie plots and potagers, containers of all sorts, alpine beds and ponds. Outbuildings range from working greenhouses to summer houses and gazebos.

East Lothian

A new addition this year is professionally designed and though aimed at attracting wildlife, is anything but wild with a large modern swathe of varied grasses. Lots to see so please join us!

Open: Sunday 27 June, 1pm - 5pm, admission £7.00, children free. Tickets and maps will be available at the gardens at the entrances to Longniddry. These gardens will be well signposted.

Directions: On the A198 from North Berwick (east) or Edinburgh (west). Access also from the B1348 (the coast road from Port Seton/Cockenzie) and the B1377 (from Drem). Longniddry is also on the North Berwick train line from Edinburgh Waverley.

Opening for: St. Columba's Hospice Limited & Maggie's

---

7 LONGWOOD
Humbie EH36 5PN
Linda Flockhart and Sandra Gentle

....

An extensive, long-established country garden at 800 feet, undergoing renewal. There are ducks and hens, stream and ponds as well as areas of wild garden and borders including roses, vegetables, lawns and woodlands. Stunning views over the Forth.

Open: Thursday 8 April, 13 May, 8 July, 5 August, 9 September, 10am - 2pm. Admission £5.00, children free.

Directions: From the B6368 (Humbie to Haddington road) about one mile east of Humbie take the direction south to *Blegbie Farm* (signposted). Follow the road for circa two miles, passing Humbie Mains Farm as you go. You will find Blegbie Farm at a hard right-hand bend. The drive for Longwood will be straight in front of you, right beside Blegbie. Go straight up the drive and park at the bottom of the cottages. Do not turn right or left.

Opening for: Médecins Sans Frontières

---

8 RUCHLAW HOUSE

....

Ruchlaw House, is an impressive 17th century laird's house built by Archibald Sydserff. The walled garden has a south-facing aspect with well-maintained rubble walls and a thick holly hedge creating a monastic ambience. The garden is divided into four lawns separated by hedging, pleached fruit trees and herbaceous borders which have been restored and enhanced by the current owner. The garden is in its prime between April and June when the tulips, alliums and catmint form a riot of colour and are arranged to great effect. Within the garden are two sundials; one of particular historic note has an octagonal shaft. Visitors can also enjoy a number of walks around the grounds.

Open: Please check Scotland's Gardens Scheme website.

Directions: From the A199 at East Linton, follow the signs to *Stenton*, taking the left-hand turn after passing under the A1. Follow the road for three miles, passing through Ruchlaw Mains Farm; Ruchlaw House is then the next property on the left. From the A1 at the West Barns roundabout, follow the B6370 south, to and through Stenton towards Garvald, taking the first right turn after crossing the bridge at the bottom of the village. Ruchlaw House is a quarter-of-a-mile on the right.

Opening for: · Who Cares? Scotland

Edinburgh, Midlothian & West Lothian

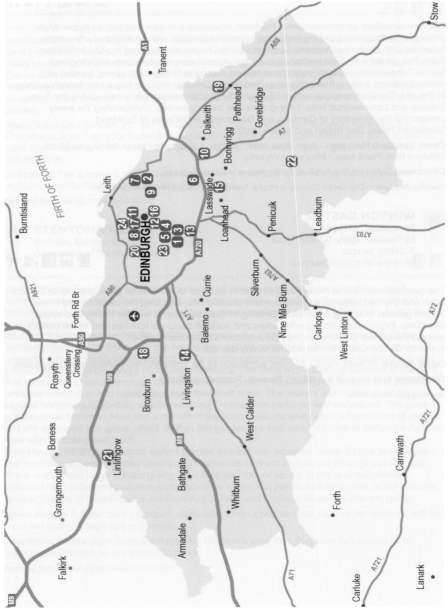

Edinburgh, Midlothian & West Lothian

OUR VOLUNTEER ORGANISERS

District Organiser:	Victoria Reid Thomas	Riccarton Mains Farmhouse, Currie EH14 4AR E: edinburgh@scotlandsgardens.org
Area Organisers:	Jerry & Christine Gregson	101 Greenbank Crescent, Edinburgh EH10 5TA
	Caroline Pearson	42 Pentland Avenue, Edinburgh EH13 0HY
	Michael Pearson	42 Pentland Avenue, Edinburgh EH13 0HY
	Gillian Polley	3 Swanston Road, Edinburgh EH10 7BB
Treasurers:	Michael Pearson	42 Pentland Avenue, Edinburgh EH13 0HY

GARDENS OPEN ON A SPECIFIC DATE

Jupiter Artland & Bonnington House, Wilkieston	Saturday/Sunday, 24/25 April
Dr Neil's Garden, Duddingston Village	Saturday/Sunday, 1/2 May
41 Hermitage Gardens, Edinburgh	Saturday, 1 May
Greentree, 18 Green Hill Park	Sunday, 9 May
The Gardens of Glenlockhart Valley, Glenlockhart Valley	Sunday, 9 May
Redcroft, 23 Murrayfield Road, Edinburgh	Saturday/Sunday, 15/16 May
101 Greenbank Crescent, Edinburgh	Saturday/Sunday, 22/23 May
Moray Place and Bank Gardens, Edinburgh	Sunday, 23 May
Rivaldsgreen House, 48 Friars Brae, Linlithgow	Saturday, 29 May
Hunter's Tryst, 95 Oxgangs Road, Edinburgh	Sunday, 30 May
Temple Village Gardens, Temple	Sunday, 6 June
Preston Hall Walled Garden, Pathhead	Sunday, 6 June
Dean Gardens, Edinburgh	Sunday, 6 June
89 Ravenscroft Street, Edinburgh	Saturday, 12 June
Eskbank Village Gardens, 23 Lasswade Road, Eskbank	Sunday, 13 June
14 East Brighton Crescent, Portobello, Edinburgh	Sunday, 13 June
The Glasshouses at the RBGE, 20A Inverleith Row, Edinburgh	Sunday, 13 June
89 Ravenscroft Street, Edinburgh	Wednesday, 16 June
89 Ravenscroft Street, Edinburgh	Saturday, 19 June
Even More Gardens of the Lower New Town, Edinburgh	Sunday, 20 June
Meadow Place, 19 Meadow Place	Sunday, 20 June
5 Greenbank Crescent, Edinburgh	Sunday, 27 June
2 Pentland Crescent, Edinburgh	Sunday, 18 July
Craigentinny Telferton Allotments, Edinburgh	Sunday, 25 July

Edinburgh, Midlothian & West Lothian

14 EAST BRIGHTON CRESCENT
Portobello, Edinburgh EH15 1LR
Mr and Mrs Jim & Sue Hurford

Roughly two-thirds of an acre suburban garden, developed over 35 years. People have said the following about it: 'A little bit of countryside in the town', 'Booming with green', 'A bosky bower' and 'There is such a wide range of plant material and every little corner holds a new gem'. There are some new features since the last opening.

Open: Sunday 13 June, 2pm - 5pm, admission £4.00, children free. Plant sale by Macplants. Apple press demonstration.

Directions: Buses 21, 42 and 49 to Brighton Place, and 15, 26, 40 and 45 to Portobello High Street. Brighton Place intersects Portobello High Street just east of the bus stops.

Opening for: The Trussell Trust

2 Pentland Crescent

2 PENTLAND CRESCENT
Edinburgh EH10 6NP
Jan Polley
T: 07801 439299 E: jpolley@blueyonder.co.uk

A colourful urban garden that contains a wide variety of shrubs and herbaceous planting, including roses, peonies, cranesbill, geums, azaleas, clematis, camellias, delphiniums and cotoneasters. The garden surrounds the house on four sides with planting designed to provide colour all year round, and to cope with varying degrees of sun and shade. It includes a rockery, herbaceous borders, archway, raised beds, various sitting areas and a pergola framed 'gin and tonic' patio from which to enjoy sunsets.

Edinburgh, Midlothian & West Lothian

Open: Sunday 18 July, 2pm - 5pm, admission £4.00, children free.

Directions: From the city centre take the A702 through Morningside, continue uphill and turn right at Comiston Springs Avenue. Pentland Crescent is first left. Bus 11 (get off at the Comiston Springs Avenue stop).

Opening for: Marie Curie

 4 | **41 HERMITAGE GARDENS**
Edinburgh EH10 6AZ
Dr and Mrs Tony Toft
E: toft41@hotmail.com

This relatively large city garden on the corner of Hermitage Gardens and Hermitage Drive is at its best in spring with its rock garden, rhododendrons, camellias, acers, tulips and mature trees.

Open: Saturday 1 May, 2pm - 5pm, admission £5.00, children free. There will be a plant stall.

Directions: Buses 5, 11, 15, 16, 23.

Opening for: Chest Heart & Stroke Scotland

5 | **5 GREENBANK CRESCENT**
Edinburgh EH10 5TE
Sandy Corlett
T: 0131 447 1119 E: sandycorlett@hotmail.co.uk

South-facing, newly designed, sloping terraced garden with views over Braidburn Valley Park to the Pentlands. Colourful chaos of herbaceous plants, shrubs, roses and small trees. Hard features include a gazebo, pergola, greenhouse and water feature.

Open: Sunday 27 June, 2pm - 5pm, admission £4.00, children free.

Directions: From the city centre take the A702 through Morningside, continue uphill on Comiston Road, turn right at Greenbank Church on to Greenbank Crescent. Buses 5, 16, 11.

Opening for: Parkinsons UK

6 | **89 RAVENSCROFT STREET**
Edinburgh EH17 8QS
Andrew and Alex Gray Muir

A large walled garden, full of surprises, in the old mining village of Gilmerton. Planting includes mature trees, roses and herbaceous borders. There is also a potager. Andrew and Alex Gray Muir have been there for over 50 years but say the garden is still a work in progress. There are plenty of seats so bring a thermos and sit and enjoy the garden.

Open: Saturday 12 June, Wednesday 16 June & Saturday 19 June, 2pm - 5pm, admission £4.00, children free.

Directions: Buses 29 and 3 come to the end of the street – look out for *Tanz* on the left and get off at the next stop. It is a nine-minute walk up Ravenscroft Street. Buses 7 and 11 come to Hyvots Bank. A short walk up Ravenscroft Place will bring you to Ravenscroft Street, where you turn right up a short stretch of unmetalled road. If you come by car, park on the public road and walk up the last 50 yards. If necessary, passengers can be dropped off in the yard in front of the house.

Opening for: Scottish Association For Mental Health

Edinburgh, Midlothian & West Lothian

7 **CRAIGENTINNY TELFERTON ALLOTMENTS**
Telferton Road, off Portobello Road, Edinburgh EH7 6XG
The Gardeners of Craigentinny and Telferton
W: ctallotments@gmail.com

Established in 1923, this independent allotment site is a tranquil and charming space, hidden away in a built-up area, where the local community benefit from growing their own vegetables and fruit. Yarn bombing of allotments, and display of scarecrows. Come and enjoy tea, home baking and a chat with our friendly plot-holders.

Open: Sunday 25 July, 2pm - 5pm, admission £3.00, children free.

Directions: Park on Telferton Road. Buses 15, 26, 45.

Opening for: Craigentinny Telferton Allotments

Craigentinny Telferton Allotments © Philip Gillespie

8 **DEAN GARDENS**
Edinburgh EH4 1QE
Dean Gardens Management Committee
W: www.deangardens.org

Nine acres of semi-woodland garden with spring bulbs on the steep banks of the Water of Leith in central Edinburgh. Founded in the 1860s by local residents, the Dean Gardens contain part of the great structure of the Dean Bridge, a Thomas Telford masterpiece of 1835. Lawns, paths, trees, and shrubs with lovely views to the weir in the Dean Village and to the St Bernard's Well. There is also a children's play area.

Open: Sunday 6 June, 2pm - 5pm, admission £4.00, children free.

Directions: Entrance at Ann Street or Eton Terrace.

Opening for: Macmillan Cancer Support

Edinburgh, Midlothian & West Lothian

9 **DR NEIL'S GARDEN**
Duddingston Village EH15 3PX
Dr Neil's Garden Trust
E: info@drneilsgarden.co.uk
W: www.drneilsgarden.co.uk

Wonderful, secluded, landscaped garden on the lower slopes of Arthur's Seat including conifers, heathers, alpines, a physic garden, herbaceous borders and ponds. Also Thompson's Tower with the Museum of Curling and beautiful views across Duddingston Loch.

Open: Saturday/Sunday, 1/2 May, 2pm - 5pm, admission £3.00, children free.

Directions: Park at the kirk car park on Duddingston Road West and then follow signposts through the manse garden.

Opening for: Dr. Neils Garden Trust

10 **ESKBANK VILLAGE GARDENS**
23 Lasswade Road, Eskbank EH22 3EE
Kate Fearnley and Maruska Greenwood
T: 07500 932953 E: kate@katefearnley.co.uk

A trail offering a range of varied gardens, large and small, in the village of Eskbank.
23 Lasswade Road (NEW) EH22 3EE (Kate Fearnley and Maruska Greenwood): A third of an acre, with beautiful mature planting including a range of trees, rhododendrons and azaleas. There is something in bloom every month of the year, with bearded irises and peonies a feature of early summer. We take an environmentally aware approach, encouraging bees and insects with lots of colour, and growing vegetables and fruit.
18 Dundas Road (NEW) EH22 3EL (Edward and Mary McMillan): A detached bungalow surrounded by an attractive front and back garden featuring a variety of trees, shrubs and vegetables.
39 Lasswade Road (NEW) EH22 3EG (Robert and Elizabeth Fairlie): An unusual suburban garden with a variety of statues, seating areas and summer colour.
48 Eskbank Road (NEW) EH22 3BX (David Binnie): An attractive raised house with a front and hidden rear garden featuring various shrubs, clipped hedges, fruit trees, roses and vegetables.
53 Eskbank Road (NEW) EH22 3BU (Geoffrey and Tish Alderson): One-and-a-half acres of trees, herbaceous and wonderful roses. Children's animal hunt.
61 Eskbank Road (NEW) EH22 3BU (Tim Rideout): A small garden with a flavour of the Western cape with plants and trees from South Africa.

Open: Sunday 13 June, 1pm - 5pm, admission £7.00, children free. Tickets and Trail maps will be available from 23 Lasswade Road EH22 3EE. Maps can also be downloaded from Scotland's Gardens Scheme website. Teas will be available at Gilston Lodge, 53 Eskbank Road EH22 3BU.

Directions: By bus: LRT buses 3, 49 from Edinburgh, 149 from Musselburgh or Penicuik; Borders bus X95 from Edinburgh or the borders. By train: to Eskbank station and a 15 minute walk. By car: from the A7 take A 768 (Lasswade Road) towards Dalkeith, No.23 Lasswade Road is on the right after Larkfield Road; from Dalkeith take the A768 from Justinlees roundabout, No.23 Lasswade Road is on the left after Dundas Crescent. Street parking is unrestricted for all gardens.

Opening for: One Dalkeith

Edinburgh, Midlothian & West Lothian

11 **EVEN MORE GARDENS OF THE LOWER NEW TOWN**
North West Northumberland Street Lane & 14 Logie Green Gardens EH7 4HE
Gardeners of Lower New Town
E: jw.homeoffice@gmail.com

Not to be missed – an even wider variety of horticultural creations than last year bringing fresh air and wildlife into the heart of the city. Comprises a steeply-terraced town garden, densely-planted courtyard gardens, imaginative back lane, patio and basement gardens, a traditional tenement green and a hidden roof garden, glorious mews lane planting and spectacular pot gardens, and newly landscaped front and back in a cul-de-sac. The collection provides lots of creative solutions to gardening in the city with year-round interest through a mix of seasonal planting and structural evergreens which the gardeners will be on hand to talk about.

Open: Sunday 20 June, 1pm - 5pm, admission £7.00, children free. Garden trail runs between Logie Green Gardens and Great King Street. Main trail tickets and maps points will be at North West Northumberland Street Lane and 14 Logie Green Gardens. A trail map will also be available from the Scotland's Gardens Scheme website.

Directions: Buses 23, 27 to Dundas Street and Canonmills, 8 to Rodney Street and Canonmills, 36 to Hamilton Place and Broughton Road.

Opening for: Shelter Scotland & Médecins Sans Frontières

12 **GREENTREE**
18 Green Hill Park EH10 4DW
Alison Glen
T: 0131 477 4151 E: alisonhmglen@gmail.com

The garden at No 18 was started 33 years ago when the house was built in the grounds of No 16. The garden is on two levels. At the drive level, there are fruit and vegetables in raised beds. Inspired by a visit to Japan, the Owner has created a little Japanese garden at the back of the house. Climb up the bank crossing a little stream, and you will find yourself on a viewing or turning point for her little buggy. Wander through trees and rhododendrons to the front of the house. Apart from the magnificent copper beech tree everything has been planted in the last 30 years. The tall Assisi pine was grown from a seed from Assisi and the rowan at the front door was planted by a bird! There is a little path down to the drive, or you may prefer the wheelchair friendly path between the two herbaceous borders, back to the house.

Open: Sunday 9 May, 10am - 5pm, admission £5.00, children free.

Directions: Buses 11, 16, 15, 23, 5. By car: from the east – Chamberlain Road, Strathearn Road, from the north – Morningside Road, from the west – Colinton Road.

Opening for: Alzheimer Scotland

Edinburgh, Midlothian & West Lothian

| 13 | **HUNTER'S TRYST** |

95 Oxgangs Road, Edinburgh EH10 7BA
Jean Knox
T: 0131 477 2919 E: jean.knox@blueyonder.co.uk

Well-stocked and beautifully designed, mature, medium-sized town garden comprising herbaceous and shrub beds, lawn, fruit and some vegetables, water features, seating areas, trees and an example of cloud pruning. This is a wildlife-friendly garden that has been transformed from a wilderness 35 years ago and continues to evolve. In 2017 two raised beds were added to the front garden. This hidden treasure of a garden was featured on *The Beechgrove Garden* in June 2015 and on *The Instant Gardener* in June 2016.

Open: Sunday 30 May, 2pm - 5pm. Also open by arrangement 1 April - 30 September. Admission £5.00, children free.

Directions: From Fairmilehead crossroads head down Oxgangs Road to Hunter's Tryst roundabout and it's the last house on the left. Buses 4, 5, 27, 400. The bus stop is at Hunter's Tryst and the garden is opposite.

Opening for: St. Columba's Hospice Limited & Lothian Cat Rescue

Hunter's Tryst

Edinburgh, Midlothian & West Lothian

18 ### NEWLISTON
Kirkliston EH29 9EB
Mr and Mrs R C Maclachlan
T: 0131 333 3231 E: newliston@gmail.com

A well preserved 18th-century parkland/designed landscape rather than a garden as such, full of mature rhododendrons and azaleas, fine vistas and allées of trees. The walk around the woods and lake is a carpet of wild garlic and bluebells in the spring. The wood to the east of the house is in the pattern of the Union Jack, best appreciated by standing in the centre where all the radiating paths meet. The house, designed by Robert Adam, is also open.

Open: 1 May - 4 June (not Mondays & Tuesdays), 2pm - 6pm, admission £5.00, children free.

Directions: Four miles south of the Forth Road Bridge, entrance off the B800.

Opening for: CHAS

19 ### PRESTON HALL WALLED GARDEN
Pathhead EH37 5UG
William and Henrietta Callander
T: 07971 028697 E: henrietta@prestonhall.co.uk
W: www.prestonhall.co.uk

Preston Hall Walled Garden is a beautiful example of an 18th-century walled garden. The current restoration began in 2011 and wonderfully demonstrates what can be achieved in a few years. An imposing brick wall surrounds the two-acre garden, which features two impressive gazebo structures that give spectacular views of the garden, a rose garden, a partly restored Victorian greenhouse, fruit and vegetable patches, and a stunning flower garden.

Open: Sunday 6 June, 2pm - 5pm, admission £6.00, children free.

Directions: Located 12 miles south of Edinburgh on the A68, one mile east of Pathhead village.

Opening for: My Name's Doddie Foundation

Preston Hall Walled Garden © Fiona Mackintosh

Edinburgh, Midlothian & West Lothian

Redcroft © Anna Buxton

20 REDCROFT
23 Murrayfield Road, Edinburgh EH12 6EP
James and Anna Buxton
T: 0131 337 1747 E: annabuxtonb@aol.com

Redcroft is a mature walled garden surrounding an attractive Arts and Crafts house. It is a hidden haven off a busy road with a variety of different features and habitats: an orchard, a rockery, a pond, shrubberies, a large lawn and contrasting longer grass. It is well maintained with many clipped shrubs and some cloud pruning. Early May is very colourful with rhododendrons and many other flowering shrubs and wall plants, and the greenhouse is full of tender plants. There will be tulips in pots and many other bulbs. Children are very welcome and there will be plenty of activities. We hope older children will enjoy our treehouse.

Open: Saturday/Sunday, 15/16 May, 2pm - 5pm, admission £5.00, children free. A bumper SGS plant sale.

Directions: Murrayfield Road runs north from Corstorphine Road to Ravelston Dykes. There is easy free parking available. Buses 12, 26, 31, get off at Murrayfield Stadium, bus 38 goes down Murrayfield Road.

Opening for: Fresh Start: Edinburgh

21 RIVALDSGREEN HOUSE
48 Friars Brae, Linlithgow EH49 6BG
Dr Ian Wallace
T: 01506 845700 E: Ianwjw1940@gmail.com

Mature two-acre garden with lovely mixed herbaceous, rose and tree planting.

Open: Saturday 29 May, 2pm - 5pm, admission £5.00, children free.

Directions: From the west end of the High Street turn into Preston Road, after crossing the canal turn left into Priory Road and at the T junction turn left down Friars Brae. There is car parking available.

Opening for: St John Scotland

Edinburgh, Midlothian & West Lothian

22 TEMPLE VILLAGE GARDENS
Temple EH23 4SQ
Temple Village Gardeners
T: 01875 830253 E: delapsandy@gmail.com

Temple Village is situated on the east bank of the River South Esk, to the south west of Gorebridge and is one of Midlothian's most attractive and historic conservation villages. Between the 12th and 14th centuries Temple was the headquarters of the Knights Templar. More recently the village has been home to Sir William Gillies the famous Scottish painter. A number of village gardens will be open, from the charming riverside garden of The Mill House, to the delightful front and rear gardens of some of the village houses on the Main Street. Planted in a variety of different styles, they display contrasting designs and plant combinations, reflecting the villagers' many distinctive horticultural interests.

Open: Sunday 6 June, 2pm - 5pm, admission £6.00, children free. Tickets and maps will be available from various points, including the parking field beside the play park (will be signposted – it is a single lane left turn in the middle of the village) and the Temple Village Hall. Teas will be available at the Temple Village hall. Parking also possible in the village.

Directions: On the B6372, three miles off the A7 from Gorebridge.

Opening for: Temple Village Halls Association

23 THE GARDENS OF GLENLOCKHART VALLEY
Glenlockhart Valley EH14 1DE
Jamie and Monica Wylie
T: 07703 184044 E: moniwylie@gmail.com

A cul-de-sac with five suburban gardens of individual character in an area once known as 'Happy Valley'. All are very different and have been in development for up to forty years, often on steep contours. They take in a walkway around paths and steps caressed by spring bulbs and choice woodlands, a level garden with Mediterranean and southern hemisphere plants, a tranquil space in a loop of the road, steep terraces on whinstone boulders planted with alpines and a large garden with mature trees and rhododendrons bordering Easter Craiglockhart Hill – 'rus in urbe'.

Open: Sunday 9 May, 2pm - 5pm, admission £7.00, children free. These gardens are not suitable for people with mobility problems. Young children must be closely supervised.

Directions: Glenlockhart Valley is off the Colinton Road. Buses 27 and 10 stop at Craiglockhart Tennis Centre and it is a short walk up from there. Bus 4 if alighting from Napier University Campus. Buses 36, 45. By car: Please park on Colinton Road. By bicycle: Use NCR75 Route.

Opening for: All proceeds to SGS Beneficiaries

Edinburgh, Midlothian & West Lothian

24 THE GLASSHOUSES AT THE ROYAL BOTANIC GARDEN EDINBURGH

20A Inverleith Row, Edinburgh EH3 5LR
Royal Botanic Garden Edinburgh
T: 0131 248 2909
W: www.rbge.org.uk

The Glasshouses with their ten climatic zones are a delight all year round. The Orchids and Cycads House brings together primitive cycads which dominated the land flora some 65 million years ago, and a diverse range of orchids, the most sophisticated plants in the world. In summer, giant water lilies, *Victoria amazonica*, are the star attraction in the Tropical Aquatic House. Plants with vibrant flowers and fascinating foliage thrive in the Rainforest Riches House and the complex ecosystems of life in the world's deserts are explored in the Arid Lands House. A large collection of gingers, *Zingiberaceae*, one of the largest collections of vireya rhododendrons in the world and a case housing carnivorous plants are among other attractions.

Open: Sunday 13 June, 2pm - 5pm, admission details can be found on the Garden's website.

Directions: Located off the A902, one mile north of the city centre. Entrances at Inverleith Row and Arboretum Place. Lothian Buses 8, 23 and 27 stop close to the East Gate entrance on Inverleith Row. *The Majestic Tour Bus* stops at Arboretum Place.

Opening for: *Donation to SGS Beneficiaries*

The Glasshouses at Royal Botanic Garden Edinburgh

Fife

Sponsored by

⊕ Investec

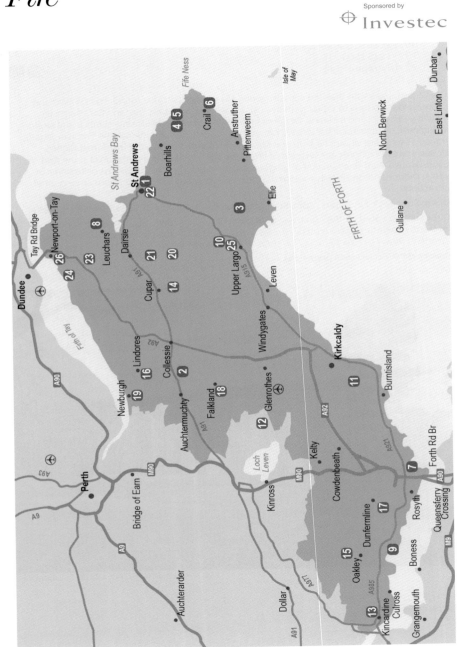

Fife

OUR VOLUNTEER ORGANISERS

District Organisers:	David Buchanan-Cook	Helensbank, 56 Toll Road, Kincardine FK10 4QZ
	Julia Young	South Flisk, Blebo Craigs, Cupar KY15 5UQ
		E: fife@scotlandsgardens.org
Area Organisers:	Alison Aiton	Craigview Cottage, Blebo Craigs KY15 5UQ
	Jeni Auchinleck	2 Castle Street, Crail KY10 3SQ
	Oenone Baillie	
	Pauline Borthwick	96 Hepburn Gardens, St Andrews KY16 9LP
	Lorna Duckworth	The Old Coach House, Dunbog KY14 6JF
	Anne Lumgair	Falside Cottage, Falside Mill, Kingsbarns KY16 8PT
	Barbara Pickard	Straiton Farmhouse, Balmullo KY16 0BN
	Fay Smith	37 Ninian Fields, Pittenweem KY10 2QU
Treasurer:	David Buchanan-Cook	Helensbank, 56 Toll Road, Kincardine FK10 4QZ

GARDENS OPEN ON A SPECIFIC DATE

Lindores House, by Newburgh	Sunday, 21 February
Cambo Farmhouse, Kingsbarns	Wednesday, 24 February
Willowhill, Forgan, Newport-on-Tay	Fri/Sat/Sun, 26/27/28 March
The Tower, 1 Northview Terrace, Wormit	Saturday, 27 March
Cambo Spring Plant & Garden Market, Kingsbarns	Saturday/Sunday, 10/11 April
Willowhill, Forgan, Newport-on-Tay	Wednesday, 14 April
South Flisk, Blebo Craigs, Cupar	Sunday, 25 April
Straiton Farmhouse, Straiton Farm, Balmullo	Sunday, 23 May
Kirklands, Saline	Sunday, 23 May
South Flisk, Blebo Craigs, Cupar	Sunday, 23 May
Lindores House, by Newburgh	Sunday, 23 May
Earlshall Castle, Leuchars	Sunday, 30 May
Straiton Farmhouse, Straiton Farm, Balmullo	Sunday, 13 June
Balcarres, Colinsburgh	Sunday, 13 June
St Andrews Botanic Garden, Canongate, St Andrews, Fife	Saturday/Sunday, 19/20 June
46 South Street, St Andrews	Sunday, 20 June
Backhouse at Rossie Estate, by Collessie	Saturday, 26 June
Whinhill, Lahill Mains, Upper Largo	Sunday, 27 June
Newburgh – Hidden Gardens, Newburgh	Sunday, 27 June
Earlshall Castle, Leuchars	Sunday, 27 June
Gilston House, By Largoward, Leven	Sunday, 11 July
Crail: Gardens in the Burgh, 2 Castle Street, Crail	Saturday/Sunday, 24/25 July
Dalgety Bay Gardens, Western Approach Road, Dalgety Bay	Saturday/Sunday, 24/25 July
Lindores House, by Newburgh	Sunday, 25 July
Greenhead Farmhouse, Greenhead of Arnot, Leslie	Sunday, 26 September
Hill of Tarvit Plant Sale and Autumn Fair, Hill of Tarvit, Cupar	Sunday, 3 October

Fife

GARDENS OPEN REGULARLY

Millfield Garden, Millfield House, Falkland, Fife	7 February - 28 February (Suns only)
Glassmount House, by Kirkcaldy	1 April - 30 September (not Suns)
Willowhill, Forgan, Newport-on-Tay	17 April - 8 May (Mons & Sats)
The Tower, 1 Northview Terrace, Wormit	1 May - 15 May (Sats only)
Willowhill, Forgan, Newport-on-Tay	19 June - 17 July (Mons & Sats)
The Tower, 1 Northview Terrace, Wormit	3 July - 17 July (Sats only)
Willowhill, Forgan, Newport-on-Tay	2 August - 30 August (Mons & Sats)
The Tower, 1 Northview Terrace, Wormit	7 August - 21 August (Sats only)

GARDENS OPEN BY ARRANGEMENT – BOOK A VISIT WITH THE GARDEN OWNER

The Tower, 1 Northview Terrace, Wormit	1 April - 30 September
Kirklands, Saline	1 April - 30 September
Rosewells, Pitscottie	1 April - 30 September
46 South Street, St Andrews	1 May - 31 July
Straiton Farmhouse, Straiton Farm, Balmullo	1 May - 30 September
Gardener's Cottage, Crombie Point, Shore Road, Crombie	1 May - 31 July (Thurs & Fris)
Logie House, Crossford, Dunfermline	1 May - 30 Sept. (not Weds, Sats & Suns)
Helensbank, Kincardine	1 June - 30 September

Fife

1 46 SOUTH STREET
St Andrews KY16 9JT
Mrs June Baxter
T: 01334 474 995 E: ejbaxter986@gmail.com

Renowned town garden in medieval long rig, with orchard underplanted with wildflowers and bulbs. Many unusual flowering shrubs will be looking their best. Roses and other climbers clothe the surrounding high walls. Shrub roses planted in a delightful central parterre fill the air with scent. An historic and unique feature in St Andrews, but also a wonderfully planted space where different styles of planting complement the range of plants used. Historic doocot.

Open: Sunday 20 June, 2pm - 5pm. Also open by arrangement 1 May - 31 July. Admission £5.00, children free.

Directions: Entry for the garden is off Greenside Place. Parking is available at the Boys Brigade Hall, on the corner of Kinnessburn Road and Langlands Road, KY16 8BW.

Opening for: Friends of Craigtoun (Sunday 20 June) & St Andrews Preservation Trust Limited (1 May - 31 July)

2 BACKHOUSE AT ROSSIE ESTATE
by Collessie KY15 7UZ
Andrew and Caroline Thomson
E: info@backhouserossie.co.uk
W: www.backhouserossie.co.uk

The longest interrupted rose archway in Scotland smothered by rambling roses over a DNA pathway form the heart of the walled garden. A formal pond, water feature, grass labyrinth, yew-backed herbaceous borders with wispy grasses and unusual perennials, parterre filled with roses, cut flowers, soft fruits and herbs. Old espalier fruit trees trained against the walls, new orchard and Victorian glasshouse complete the walled garden. Alpine scree and gravel plantings, walk to a covenanter's tomb, short Bear Walk for little children, nine hole family putting. Heritage and Education Centre Exhibition.
National Plant Collection: *Narcissus* (Backhouse cvs.).

Open: Saturday 26 June, 2pm - 5pm, admission £5.00, children free.

Directions: On A91, between Auchtermuchty and Collesie, and one-and-a-quarter miles east of Auchtermuchty, at the Backhouse Rossie banner and the single sign to *Charlottetown*, 300 yards down single track road, turn right into Backhouse Rossie estate.

Opening for: The Suzy Lamplugh Trust – National Stalking Helpline

Backhouse at Rossie Estate

Fife

3 BALCARRES
Colinsburgh KY9 1HN
Lord and Lady Balniel
T: 01333 340205 (Estate Office)

Balcarres House has been owned by the Lindsay family since the late 16th century and each generation has made their mark on the house and gardens. The formal gardens with their magnificent yew hedges and terraces were laid out by Sir Coutts Lindsay in the 1870s. Since then other changes have been made but the largest impact has come from Lady Crawford (aged 96). She has been the inspiration for the garden and the driving force of much of what has been created in the past fifty years. The gardens come into their own in early summer with the Rose Garden in full bloom with a variety of Hybrid Teas and climbing roses such as Blairii No.2, Shropshire Lad & Lady Hillingdon. Herbaceous borders are bursting into life with a variety of Geranium, Astrantia, Viola, oriental poppies and Aquilegia. The Woodland & Chapel Walks will also be at their best with many different Hostas, Smilacina, and other diverse plants, shrubs and trees. Enjoy the walks to the Sawmill Pond planting, the Den and the Balcarres Craig.

Open: Sunday 13 June, 2pm - 5pm, admission £6.00, children free.

Directions: Half-a-mile north of Colinsburgh off A942. Bus to Colinsburgh.

Opening for: Colinsburgh Community Trust Ltd

Balcarres

4 CAMBO FARMHOUSE
Kingsbarns KY16 8QD
Sir Peter and Lady Erskine

A new walled garden in development. Started in a derelict garden in 2015 with nothing but two mature plum trees and all weeds known to gardeners. In 2021 it will be showing signs of maturity and with the adjacent mill pond and woodlands it has promise!

Open: Wednesday 24 February, 11am - 4pm for Snowdrops and Winter Walks, admission £5.00, children free. Tickets should be pre-booked online via the SGS website listing.

Directions: On A917 between Kinsgbarns and Cambo House.

Opening for: Unicorn Preservation Society

5 CAMBO SPRING PLANT & GARDEN MARKET

Kingsbarns KY16 8QD
Trustees of Cambo Heritage Trust
T: 01333 451040 E: hello@camboestate.com
W: www.cambogardens.com

Pop in to Cambo to freshen up your garden for Spring. We will have a unique selection of plants and bulbs from visiting nurseries, garden goods and local crafts to browse. Outdoor café open all day. Gardens, woodlands and play area to visit. National Plant Collection: Galanthus.

Open: Saturday/Sunday, 10/11 April, 11am - 4pm, admission details can be found on the garden's website. Entry to the Spring Market is free but normal admission charges to Cambo Gardens apply.

Directions: A917 between Crail and St Andrews.

Opening for: Cambo Heritage Trust

6 CRAIL: GARDENS IN THE BURGH

2 Castle Street, Crail KY10 3SQ
Sue Jerdan
T: 01333 450538 E: sueellen.jerdan@gmail.com
W: www.crailfestival.com

Take an enjoyable stroll around this quintessential East Neuk village and explore its many beautiful gardens in varied styles: cottage, historic, plantsman's and bedding. The stunning coastal location of the gardens presents some challenges for planting but also allows for a great range of more tender species to flourish.

Open: Saturday/Sunday, 24/25 July, 1pm - 5pm, admission £6.00, children free. Tickets and maps are available on the day from Mrs Jeni Auchinleck, 2 Castle Street or from Mrs Sue Jordan, 74 Bow Butts.

Directions: Approach Crail from either St Andrews or Anstruther via the A917. Parking available in Marketgait.

Opening for: Crail Preservation Society

7 DALGETY BAY GARDENS

Western Approach Road, Dalgety Bay KY11 9SA
Mrs Sybil Cobban, Dalgety Bay Horticultural Society
T: 01383 825 349 E: michaeljg@btinternet.com

17 Inchview Gardens This compact garden was designed and created by Sybil, who won *Fife Garden Competition* in 2006. Having held seven annual garden parties for Marie Curie Nurses and three for her local church, Sybil is now opening for SGS! The garden has a selection of herbaceous and bedding plants. She does not have a favourite flower, but top of her list are heucheras, acers and hostas.

DBHS Allotments The allotment site has grown and developed over the last 45+ years. All allotments are taken and it is really nice to see them in production in the month of July. The Annual Show is in September and a lot of the produce you see will be on the show benches. Allotment holders will be on site to chat and you may get the secret of the huge marrow or gigantic cabbage.

Open: Saturday/Sunday, 24/25 July, 2pm - 5pm, admission £5.00, children free.

Directions: Inchview Gardens are accessed off Moray Way South. The allotments are behind Peter Vardy Vauxhall, Western Approach Road, Dalgety Bay.

Opening for: Marie Curie

Fife

8 EARLSHALL CASTLE
Leuchars KY16 0DP
Paul and Josine Veenhuijzen
T: 01334 839205

Extensive, exquisitely designed garden, which perfectly complements the Castle also restored by Sir Robert Lorimer in the 1890s. Fascinating topiary lawn, the finest in Scotland and for which Earlshall is renowned, rose terrace, croquet lawn with herbaceous borders, shrub border, box garden, orchard, kitchen and herb garden. Spectacular spring bulbs.

Open: Sunday 30 May, 2pm - 5pm. Also open Sunday 27 June, 2pm - 5pm. Admission £5.00, children free.

Directions: On Earlshall Road, three-quarters of a mile east of Leuchars Village (off A919). Bus/train to Leuchars.

Opening for: Royal Scots Dragoon Guards Regimental Trust (Sunday 30 May) & Leuchars St Athernase Parish Church (Sunday 27 June)

9 GARDENER'S COTTAGE
Crombie Point, Shore Road, Crombie, Dunfermline KY12 8LQ
Fay Johnstone and Jamie Andrews
T: 07921174212 E: fay.johnstone@gmail.com

Originally part of the Craigflower Estate, the garden was transformed by the late Scottish-German botanist Ursula McHardy to demonstrate models of natural vegetation patterns of the Southern Hemisphere. Within the walled garden you will find an Australian eucalyptus forest and a South American forest with southern beeches and monkey-puzzles. There is also a South African area and a New Zealand section with five pools as well as traditional mixed borders. What remains of the original botanical collection is maintained by the current owners in an informal manner in line with Fay's work with plants supporting holistic health and wellbeing.

Open: By arrangement 1 May - 31 July (Thursdays & Fridays), admission £5.00, children free.

Directions: Park at, or get the bus to, the Ness in Torryburn then walk 15 minutes along Shore Road.

Opening for: Scottish Wildlife Trust Ltd & Marine Conservation Society

Gardener's Cottage

Fife

10 GILSTON HOUSE

By Largoward, Leven KY8 5QP
Mr and Mrs Edward Baxter
T: 07754857739 E: catherine@cathbrown.com
W: www.eastneukestates.co.uk

Large garden with mixed borders and mature trees in a beautiful park with wildflower meadow and woodland surrounding an early 19th c. house. Older, established shrubs sit with abundant new planting of trees and perennials. *Betula albosinensis* 'Pink Champagne' and 'Fascination' stand with *Sorbus hupehensis* 'Pink Pagoda' above an Oudolf-inspired mix including grasses, foxgloves and verbascums. Acid loving plants thrive here too with meconopsis on repeat throughout our deep borders. Enjoy your tea and cake on the main terrace alongside the central rectangle of catmint, wild swan anemones and *Sedum karfunkelstein* with their beautiful dusty dark purple leaves. Beyond the borders around the house is a walled garden, a work in progress and a short walk through the woods will take you to our pond (used for curling from 1898) planted with bulbs, meadow flowers, and the beginnings of woodland planting. Far reaching views.

Open: Sunday 11 July, 1pm - 5pm, admission £5.00, children free.

Directions: 15 mins by car from St Andrews on A915 (buses from Leven and St Andrews request stop) one hour north of Edinburgh

Opening for: Royal Highland Education Trust

11 GLASSMOUNT HOUSE

by Kirkcaldy KY2 5UT
Peter, James and Irene Thomson
T: 01592 890214 E: mcmoonter@yahoo.co.uk

Densely planted walled garden with surrounding woodland. An A-listed sun dial, Mackenzie & Moncur greenhouse and historical doocot are complemented by a number of newer structures. Daffodils are followed by a mass of candelabra and cowslip primula, meconopsis and *Cardiocrinum giganteum*. Hedges and topiary form backdrops for an abundance of bulbs, clematis, rambling roses and perennials, creating interest through the summer into September. The garden is now extending beyond the walls, with new areas of naturalistic planting blending the boundary between the surrounding fields and the woodland.

Open: 1 April - 30 September (not Sundays), 2pm - 5pm, admission £5.00, children free.

Directions: From Kirkcaldy, head west on the B9157. Turn left immediately after the railway bridge on the edge of town. Follow the single track road for one-and-a-half miles and cross the crossroads. Glassmount House is the first turning on your right.

Opening for: Parkinsons UK

Fife

 12 **GREENHEAD FARMHOUSE**
Greenhead of Arnot, Leslie KY6 3JQ
Mr and Mrs Malcolm Strang Steel
T: 01592 840459
W: www.fife-bed-breakfast-glenrothes.co.uk

....

The south-facing garden combines a sense of formality in its symmetrical layout, with an informal look of mixed herbaceous and shrub borders. The garden is constantly evolving with new themes and combinations of plants, all unified by a fantastic use of colour. There is also a well-stocked polytunnel which is used to augment the highly productive fruit and vegetable garden.

Open: Sunday 26 September, 2pm - 5pm, admission £5.00, children free.

Directions: A911 between Auchmuir Bridge and Scotlandwell.

Opening for: Scotland's Charity Air Ambulance

13 **HELENSBANK**
Kincardine FK10 4QZ
David Buchanan-Cook and Adrian Miles
T: 07739 312912 E: Helensbank@aol.com
W: www.helensbank.com

....

Hidden away from public view, this is an 18th-century walled garden, with main feature a Cedar of Lebanon, reputedly planted in 1750 by the sea captain who built the house. The tree is registered as a 'Notable Tree' and while it provides challenges for planting, in terms of shade and needle fall, the microclimate it provides has encouraged the owners' passion for pushing boundaries and growing unusual and exotic plants. Distinctive garden 'rooms' in part of the garden comprise a perennial blue and white cottage garden, a formal rose garden and an Italian double courtyard with citrus trees in pots. A 'hot' courtyard contains exotics including varieties of banana, acacia, iochroma, impatiens, melianthus and brugmansia. A shaded walk along the bottom of the garden leads to a Japanese themed area including a pagoda. A large glasshouse houses various exotic and climbing plants. The garden has well over a hundred roses, including a National Collection. National Plant Collection: Portland Roses.
Champion Trees: The garden has a "notable" Cedar of Lebanon – 2nd largest in Fife.

Open: By arrangement 1 June - 30 September, admission £5.00, children free. Cream teas and light lunches available for groups.

Directions: The garden is down a lane off the main Toll Road. *SGS* signs.

Opening for: Scottish Veterans Residences

14 **HILL OF TARVIT PLANT SALE AND AUTUMN FAIR**
Hill of Tarvit, Cupar KY15 5PB
The National Trust for Scotland/Scotland's Gardens Fife
W: scotlandsgardens.org or www.nts.org.uk

....

This long established plant sale is a fantastic opportunity to purchase bare root and potted plants from an enormous selection on offer. We also welcome donations of plants on the Friday and Saturday prior to the sale and also on the day – so do please 'Bring and buy'! Hill of Tarvit is one of Scotland's finest Edwardian mansion houses. Surrounding the mansion house are spectacular gardens designed by Robert Lorimer, There are also woods, an open heath, golf course and parkland to explore.

Open: Sunday 3 October, 10:30am - 2:30pm, admission £2.00, children free.

Directions: Two miles south of Cupar off A916.

Opening for: Scotland's Gardens Scheme SCIO

Fife

15 KIRKLANDS

Saline KY12 9TS
Peter and Gill Hart
T: 07787 115477 E: gill@i-comment360.com
W: www.kirklandshouseandgarden.co.uk

Kirklands, built in 1832, has been the Hart family home for 41 years. Over the years we have reinstated the walled garden from a paddock and constructed terraces with raised beds. There are 18 espalier apple trees against the walls and box hedging with a display of tulips. The woodland garden starts with snowdrops and bluebells, then rhododendrons, trilliums, fritillaries, meconopsis, erythroniums and candelabra primulas follow. The rockery displays dwarf rhododendrons and azaleas. The herbaceous borders reach their peak in the summer. The bog garden by the Saline Burn is home to giant *Gunnera manicata*. Over the bridge we have 20 acres of woodland with a pathway by the burn. To keep the grandchildren occupied, Peter built a tree house, climbing frame and rope swing, though we hope they will take an interest in gardening too!

Open: Sunday 23 May, 2pm - 5pm. Also open by arrangement 1 April - 30 September. Admission £5.00, children free.

Directions: Junction 4, M90, then B914. Parking in the centre of the village, then a short walk to the garden. Limited disabled parking at Kirklands.

Opening for: Saline Environmental Group

Helensbank

Fife

16 LINDORES HOUSE
by Newburgh KY14 6JD
Robert and Elizabeth Turcan & John and Eugenia Turcan
T: 01337 840369

Lindores House overlooks the loch. Woodland walk beside the loch and stunning views from the garden. Herbaceous borders, wonderful snowdrops, leucojums, trilliums, primulae, rhododendrons and species trees including *Nothofagus* and *Davidia involucrata*, the handkerchief tree. Don't miss the 17th-century yew, believed to be the largest in Fife, which you can walk inside!

Open: Sunday 21 February, 11:30am - 2pm for Snowdrops and Winter Walks. Also open Sunday 23 May, 2pm - 5pm. And open Sunday 25 July, 2pm - 5pm. Admission £5.00, children free.

Directions: Off A913 two miles east of Newburgh. Bus from Cupar.

Opening for: RED SQUIRREL SURVIVAL TRUST LTD (Sunday 21 February) & Lindores Parish Church of Scotland (Sunday 23 May & Sunday 25 July)

17 LOGIE HOUSE
Crossford, Dunfermline KY12 8QN
Mr and Mrs Hunt
T: 07867 804020

Central to the design of this walled garden is a path through a double mixed border. Long rows of vegetables and fruit also contribute to colour and design when seen from the house and terrace. A long border of repeat flowering plants and rose and annual beds contribute to an extended season of colour and interest. There is a magnificent and very productive Mackenzie & Moncur greenhouse in excellent condition with fully working vents and original benches and central heating system. The garden abuts a developing woodland garden.

Open: By arrangement 1 May - 30 September (not Wednesdays, Saturdays & Sundays), admission £5.00, children free.

Directions: M90 exit 1 for Rosyth and Kincardine Bridge (A985). After about two miles turn right to Crossford. At traffic lights, turn right and the drive is on the right at the end of the village main street.

Opening for: Scottish Veterans Residences

18 MILLFIELD GARDEN
Millfield House, Falkland, Fife KY15 7BN
Sarah & Aaron Marshall
T: 07584620534

Millfield is set on the edge of the beautiful and historic village of Falkland. Falkland Gardening Group is developing a snowdrop trail in the village. Millfield has a walled garden, bulb meadows, woodland paths, all with snowdrops. There are also over 100 different snowdrop species set around the driveway area at waist height, for ease of viewing! The garden also houses a selection of hellebores and winter flowering shrubs.

Open: 7 February - 28 February (Sundays only), 11am - 3pm for Snowdrops and Winter Walks, admission £5.00, children free.

Directions: From the A912 turn into the village, travel straight past the central fountain. Follow the road until it makes a sharp left – Millfield is straight ahead.

Opening for: to be confirmed

Fife

19 **NEWBURGH – HIDDEN GARDENS**
Newburgh KY14 6AH
The Gardeners of Newburgh
T: 07763340362 E: judilaugh@gmail.com

Hidden behind the 18th century facades of Newburgh High Street lies a jumble of wonderful old gardens, some of them dating back centuries. Many have spectacular views of the Tay estuary. This year our gardens will include some that have previously opened, which have been developed since their former opening, and some opening for the first time. As before, there will be a wide mix of flowers, vegetables, herbaceous borders, orchards and a fair few hens and ducks!

Open: Sunday 27 June, noon - 5pm, admission £5.00, children free. Admission includes tea/coffee with home baking (with optional additional donation). Newburgh, at the northern end of the Fife coastal path, sits on a hill, and access to some of the gardens is up closes and down vennels. Some are suitable for disabled access but not all.

Directions: On the A913 between Perth and Cupar. There is a car park at each end of the town, with tickets and teas available nearby.

Opening for: *Newburgh Community Trust*

Millfield Garden

Fife

20 ROSEWELLS
Pitscottie KY15 5LE
Birgitta and Gordon MacDonald
E: g.macdonald54@hotmail.co.uk

Rosewells, designed by the garden owners, has developed over the last 25 years with an underlying theme that each part of the garden should work in relation to the rest, to create one overall effect. The design centres on texture and foliage to provide a lively effect with structure and shape all year. The winter 'bones' are provided with trees and shrubs with features such as contorted stems and peeling or coloured bark. In spring and summer, texture and coloured foliage of shrubs and perennials add to the overall design. Birgitta sees flowers as an added bonus with scent and colour being important and combinations of yellow, blue and white colour schemes are preferred. The garden has many varieties of cornus, magnolias, trilliums, meconopsis, agapanthus, rhododendrons, primulas, auriculas, fritillaries, erythroniums, peonies and acers, which are favourites.

Open: By arrangement 1 April - 30 September, admission £5.00, children free.

Directions: B940 between Pitscottie and Peat Inn, one mile from Pitscottie. Rosewells is the ochre-coloured house.

Opening for: Save the Children UK

21 SOUTH FLISK
Blebo Craigs, Cupar KY15 5UQ
Mr and Mrs George Young
T: 01334 850859 E: southfliskgarden@gmail.com
W: www.standrewspottery.co.uk

The spectacular views over Fife to Perthshire and Angus and the large flooded quarry full of fish (and the occasional otter) and planted with impressive marginals make the garden at South Flisk very special in the area. Flights of old stone steps, cliffs, huge boulders, exotic ferns and mature trees form a backdrop for carpets of primroses, bluebells, spring bulbs and woodland plants like trilliums, camassia and colourful primulas. There are different rhododendrons in flower in the garden from March until July. In front of the house is a charming, mature walled garden with traditional cottage-garden planting and next to the house is the St Andrews Pottery where George will be demonstrating his pottery skills for those who need a break from the garden!

Open: Sunday 25 April & Sunday 23 May, 2pm - 5pm, admission £5.00, children free.

Directions: Six miles west of St Andrews off the B939 between Strathkinness and Pitscottie. There is a small stone bus shelter opposite the road into the village and a small sign saying *Blebo Craigs*. Or check out the map on our website. Bus to Blebo Craigs.

Opening for: Book Aid International

Fife

22 **ST ANDREWS BOTANIC GARDEN**
Canongate, St Andrews, Fife KY16 8RT
T: 01334 461200 E: info@standrewsbotanic.org
W: http://standrewsbotanic.org

The original Botanic Garden was founded by the University of St. Andrews in 1889 in the precincts of St. Mary's College. Originally a small garden, it now covers 7.5ha (18.5 acres) and not only provides a wonderful space in which to relax and enjoy its beauty and atmosphere, but also provides a scientific garden for teaching and research. Highlights include borders showcasing many fascinating plants including those from China and Chile, the pinetum featuring Wollemi Pine, strong collections of woody genera (eg Sorbus), alpines and bulbs as well as family friendly garden trails, natural play area, pond and plenty of wildlife to be spotted. A new feature opening in the spring includes a gradient of habitats found in Fife from wood pasture to sand dune, and has been designed to study how naturalised plant communities will respond to climate change and biosecurity threats.
Champion Trees: A number of rare species.

Open: Saturday/Sunday, 19/20 June, 10am - 6pm, admission details can be found on the garden's website.

Directions: The garden is located on Canongate and is a 10/15 minute walk from the centre of St Andrews. Follow the signs from the town down Viaduct walk, which is a shared path for bikes and walkers. The 99C bus route goes past the garden and takes 5 minutes from the bus stop in St Andrews. The nearest train station is Leuchars on the 99 bus route. There is a free car park at the garden.

Opening for: *Friends Of St Andrews Botanic Garden*

St Andrews Botanic Garden

Fife

23 STRAITON FARMHOUSE
Straiton Farm, Balmullo KY16 0BN
Mrs Barbara Pickard
T: 01334 870203 E: barbarapickard46@gmail.com

A profusion of cottage garden favourites – including poppies, foxgloves and lupins – together with unusual and varied herbaceous and tree peonies, *Grevillea*, *Cornus*, *Crinodendron*, *Baptisia*, etc. There is also a rose garden with 27 varieties of David Austin roses interplanted with shrubs and herbaceous plants.

Open: Sunday 23 May & Sunday 13 June, 11am - 2pm. Also open by arrangement 1 May - 30 September. Admission £5.00, children free.

Directions: From Cupar enter Balmullo via A914 from Dairsie, pass the phone box and shop, leave the village and take the second exit left on a sharp right hand bend. From Dundee approach Balmullo on A914, go under the railway bridge and take the second right, signposted Lucklawhill. At the T junction, turn right and follow road straight on past the telephone box and down the hill to the farm visible in the distance. If using a SatNav please ignore if directions are given to Logie and down the quarry road as it is disused and unsafe. You should approach Straiton from the St Michaels, Balmullo Road which will be well signposted.

Opening for: To be confirmed

24 THE TOWER
1 Northview Terrace, Wormit DD6 8PP
Peter and Angela Davey
T: 01382 541635 M: 07768 406946 E: adavey541@btinternet.com

Situated four miles south of Dundee, this one-acre Edwardian landscaped garden has panoramic views over the River Tay. Set on a hill, a series of paths meander around ponds and a small stream, rockeries featuring hellebores and low-level planting, a curved lawn and larger borders. Original woodland paths lead to a granite grotto with waterfall pool. At the rear of the house the vegetable garden features raised beds made from granite sets. Rhododendrons have recently been removed to create more space for seating and flower beds. The garden is colourful throughout the summer, with many architectural plants accentuating the clever hard landscape design.

Open: Saturday 27 March, 12:30pm - 4pm. Also open 1 May - 15 May (Saturdays only), 3 July - 17 July (Saturdays only) & 7 August - 21 August (Saturdays only), 2pm - 4:30pm and open by arrangement 1 April - 30 September. Admission £5.00, children free. The March opening is for Hellebores, and coincides with the similar opening at nearby Willowhill on the same date.

Directions: From B946 park on Naughton Road outside Spar shop and walk up path on left following signs.

Opening for: Dundee Chamber Music Club

25 WHINHILL
Lahill Mains, Upper Largo KY8 5QS
Sue and Jeremy Eccles

Whinhill is a south-facing hillside garden overlooking the Forth, created over 25 years from fields and farm steadings. The walled garden, formed from the old cattle-court, is packed with shrubs, perennials and bulbs, many grown from seed or cuttings. The lower, more recent section, features a reflecting pool and a collection of peonies and roses. The five-acre garden has a woodland edge with cut paths and huts to explore and the old horses' field, now divided by a serpentine beech hedge, is currently being planted out with trees, shrubs and fruit trees.

Fife

Open: Sunday 27 June, 10am - 5pm, admission £5.00, children free.

Directions: Whinhill is on the right on the A915 , approximately one mile north of Upper Largo. There is a green *Whinhill* sign at the end of the drive. The X97 bus from Leven to St Andrews passes the gate and will stop on request.

Opening for: Cystic Fibrosis Trust

26 WILLOWHILL

Forgan, Newport-on-Tay DD6 8RA
Eric Wright and Sally Lorimore
T: 01382 542890 E: e.g.wright@dundee.ac.uk
W: www.willowhillgarden.weebly.com

An evolving three-acre garden. The house is surrounded by a series of mixed borders designed with different vibrant colour combinations for effect all season. Spectacular mix of roses, herbaceous perennials and annuals planted through the wide borders are a highlight in mid to late summer. A new 'no dig' 160-foot border in shades of white, blue, purple and pale yellow has been created in 2019/2020. Come and see!

Open: The weekend of 26 March - 28 March, 11:30am - 3pm. Wednesday 14 April, 2pm - 5pm. Open Mondays and Saturdays, 17 April - 8 May, 19 June - 17 July, 2 August - 30 August, 2pm - 5pm. Admission £5.00, children free. March openings for hellebores and early Spring flowering; April & May for late Spring bulbs and flowers; June & July for roses and high Summer colour; August for late Summer colour. The 27 March Hellebore opening coincides with the similar opening at nearby The Tower, Wormit on the same date.

Directions: One-and-a-half miles south of Tay Road Bridge. Take the B995 to Newport off the Forgan roundabout. Willowhill is the first house on the left-hand side next to the Forgan Arts Centre.

Opening for: Rio Community Centre & Rhet Fife Countryside Initiative Limited

Willowhill

Glasgow & District

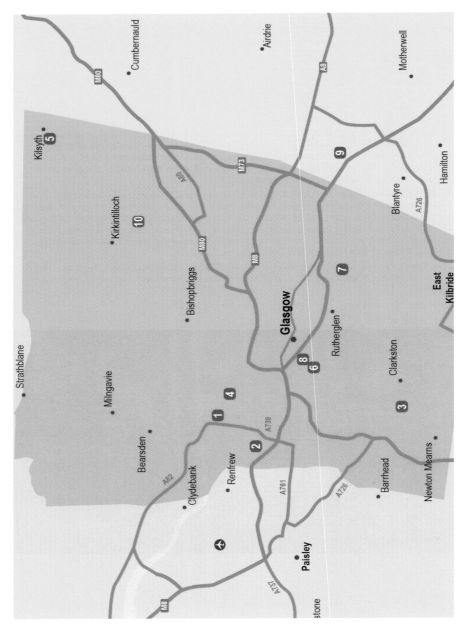

Glasgow & District

OUR VOLUNTEER ORGANISERS

District Organiser:	Heidi Stone	E: glasgow@scotlandsgardens.org
Area Organisers:	Caroline Anderson	64 Partickhill Road, Glasgow G11 5NB
	Ian Angus	
	Audrey Mason	Hillend House, Drakemyre, Dalry KA24 5JR
	Anne Murray	44 Gordon Road, Netherlee, Glasgow G44 3TW
	Jim Murray	44 Gordon Road, Netherlee, Glasgow G44 3TW
	Michelle Stewart	20 Kierhill Road, Balloch, Glasgow G68 9BH
District Photographer:	Stephen Kelly	E: stephenkelly008@gmail.com
Treasurer:	James Shearer	Heathfield, 6 Oldfold Walk, Milltimber AB13 0JG

GARDENS OPEN ON A SPECIFIC DATE

Gartnavel Secret Garden, Gartnavel Royal Hospital, 1055 Great Western Road, Glasgow	Sunday, 2 May
Kilsyth Gardens, Allanfauld Road, Kilsyth	Sunday, 30 May
The Good Life Garden, 12 Chatelherault Avenue, Glasgow	Sunday, 13 June
The Hidden Gardens, 25 Albert Drive, Glasgow	Sunday, 20 June
Woodbourne House, Seven Sisters, Lenzie, Glasgow	Sunday, 4 July
Viewpark Gardens and Allotments, Bairds Avenue, Viewpark	Sunday, 11 July
Kamares, 18 Broom Road, Newton Mearns, Glasgow	Sunday, 18 July
Strathbungo Garden, March Street, Glasgow	Sunday, 25 July
Horatio's Garden, National Spinal Injuries Unit, Queen Elizabeth University Hospital, 1345 Govan Road, Glasgow	Sunday, 22 August
Gartnavel Secret Garden, Gartnavel Royal Hospital, 1055 Great Western Road, Glasgow	Sunday, 29 August

GARDENS OPEN BY ARRANGEMENT – BOOK A VISIT WITH THE GARDEN OWNER

Kilsyth Gardens, Allanfauld Road, Kilsyth	1 April - 31 August

Glasgow & District

1 **GARTNAVEL SECRET GARDEN**
Gartnavel Royal Hospital, 1055 Great Western Road, Glasgow G12 0XH
Gartnavel Royal Hospital Growing Spaces Volunteers
T: 0141 211 3681

Gartnavel Royal's hidden walled garden forms part of the original 200-year-old hospital and was the private garden of the hospital's superintendent. The basic infrastructure was restored six years ago by the Green Exercise Partnership with new raised beds and growing spaces being installed. It is cared for by a group of loyal volunteers and is an oasis of calm for hospital patients, staff, visitors and the public. We do a little bit of everything at Gartnavel; in collaboration with our TCV friends, we grow both edibles and ornamentals and, as a hospital garden, we feature lots of sensory and medicinal plants too.

Open: Sunday 2 May & Sunday 29 August, 2pm - 5pm, admission £6.00, children free.

Directions: From Great Western Road (car, bus or foot): Enter Gartnavel Hospital site and turn right at the traffic lights onto Shelley Road. Follow yellow *SGS Open* signs, continue past pond and beyond car park on your left; at the fork bear left up the hill. Pass The Calman Centre on your left as you enter a wooded area. Continue up the hill to T junction, turn right along the front of West House and park in the spaces there. Once parked continue to follow the signs to the gardens at the rear of West House.

Opening for: *The Charity for Gartnavel Royal Hospital*

Gartnavel Secret Garden © Bryony White

Gartnavel Secret Garden

2 **HORATIO'S GARDEN**
National Spinal Injuries Unit, Queen Elizabeth University Hospital, 1345 Govan Road, Glasgow G51 4TF
Horatio's Garden
E: sallie@horatiosgarden.org.uk
W: Horatiosgarden.org.uk

Opened in 2016, the award-winning Horatio's Garden at the Scottish National Spinal Injuries Unit was designed by acclaimed garden designer and RHS judge, James Alexander-Sinclair. This fully accessible garden creates a peaceful sanctuary using planting, with a wealth of variety, colour and seasonality in every corner. Visit to see how this high-profile national charity has created a beautiful, cleverly designed, contemporary and accessible garden in the heart of a Greater Glasgow and Clyde NHS hospital, for the benefit of patients, relatives and staff.

Glasgow & District

Open: Sunday 22 August, 2pm - 5pm, admission £7.00, children free.

Directions: From the east or west of the city: On the M8 motorway to Junction 25, follow signs for the *Clyde Tunnel* (A739) for three-quarters of a mile, then follow signs for the *Queen Elizabeth Hospital*. Turn left into Govan Road and the hospital is on the left. From north of the River Clyde: go through the Clyde Tunnel (A739) and follow signs for the hospital. Please look at our website for the hospital estate map for directions to the garden and available parking.

Opening for: Horatio's Garden

3 KAMARES

18 Broom Road, Newton Mearns, Glasgow G77 5DN
Derek and Laura Harrison
E: laurah6367@gmail.com

Sitting in two-thirds of an acre, Kamares is a hacienda-style house surrounded by mature trees and a beautiful beech hedge. The garden has much of interest including a well-established pond, acers, Japanese grasses, colourful mixed shrubs, herbaceous borders and rare US sequoias. There are several patio gardens and a delightful courtyard with a rockery and miniature waterfall. Sculptures and topiary can be found around the garden where you are also welcome to visit the garden shed known as 'Owl Cottage'. The artist owner and her husband have had fun playing with spaces, colour and contrasting textures as an alternative canvas.

Open: Sunday 18 July, 2pm - 5pm, admission £7.00, children free. A very well-stocked plant stall with home-grown established plants will be available.

Directions: From the A77 heading south, turn left into Broom Estate and sharp left again into Broom Road. Kamares is the last house on the left near the top of the hill. On road parking is available beyond the house on Broom Road, Broomcroft Road, Sandringham Road and Dunvegan Avenue.

Opening for: Jewish Care Scotland

4 KEW TERRACE GARDENS: BACK TO FRONT

Kew Terrace G12 0TE
The Gardeners of Kew Terrace

Last year [2020], the importance of having gardens for relaxation and enjoyment has been recognised. The Terrace gardens along Great Western Road, between Byres Road and Gartnavel, were compulsorily purchased as part of the closing-off of side roads. With increasing demands on Glasgow City Council Parks Department, maintenance has declined with grass cutting currently being their main contribution. About ten years ago, the opportunity was taken in Kew Terrace, to develop the area between the grass and the main road hedge as a colourful woodland garden. This was fully supported by the local councillors. As this woodland garden has matured and its use as a walk has increased, the influence has stimulated others, including the Belhaven Terraces and Lowther Terrace, to do the same. The rear gardens to Kew and adjacent terraces have also flourished and been used more than ever, with many determined to learn from their experience to have an even better display in 2021.

Open: Date to be advised, check Scotland's Garden Scheme's website.

Directions: From the M8 take junction 17 and turn west onto Great Western Road. Drive to the traffic lights at Kirklee and turn left into Horselethill Road. Parking spaces are usually available. Many buses which travel along Great Western Road are available.

Opening for: Friends Of Glasgow West

Glasgow & District

5 KILSYTH GARDENS
Allanfauld Road, Kilsyth G65 9DE
Mr and Mrs George Murdoch & Mr and Mrs A Patrick
T: 07743 110908 E: alan.patrick3@googlemail.com

Aeolia (Mr and Mrs George Murdoch): A third-of-an-acre woodland garden developed since 1960 and designed to have something in flower every month of the year. The garden contains a large variety of mature specimen trees and shrubs, maples, primulas, hardy geraniums and herbaceous plants. Spring bulbs provide early colour and lilies and dahlias provide late season interest. There are a couple of small ponds for wildlife, two greenhouses and a fruit production area. The owners are members of the *Scottish Rhododendron Society* and have a collection of over 100 specimens, some grown from seed. Areas of the garden are often under development to provide something new to see and provide material for the extensive plant sale, which is all home grown.

Blackmill (Mr and Mrs A Patrick): Across the road from Aeolia is Blackmill through which the Garrel Burn flows. The garden includes the magnificent seven-metre waterfall with its ever-changing moods throughout the year. On one side of the property, on the site of an old water-powered sickle mill, is an acre of mature specimen trees, rhododendrons and shrubs with an ornamental pond and a rock pool built into the remains of the mill building. Across the burn there are a further two acres of woodland glen with paths along the waterside offering glimpses of the many cascading waterfalls. A large area of wildflowers has been newly introduced alongside the burn. A micro-hydro scheme is on view, along with many different examples of dry stone walls. Visitors remark on the sense of tranquillity and peace they experience in the garden and appreciate the works of art created from repurposed stone and salvaged material.

Open: Sunday 30 May, 2pm - 5pm. Also open by arrangement 1 April - 31 August. Admission £7.00, children free.

Directions: Turn off the A803 into Parkburn Road up to the crossroads (parking attendant will advise on parking). The 89 bus Glasgow – Kilsyth has a stop at the crossroads a couple of minutes walk to the gardens. The nearest station is Croy, then take the bus 147 or 344 to Kilsyth.

Opening for: Strathcarron Hospice

Kilsyth Gardens, Blackmill

Glasgow & District

6 **STRATHBUNGO GARDEN**
March Street, Glasgow G41 2PX
Frank Burns
W: facebook.com/strathbungogarden

Nestled behind Glasgow's busy main road artery to the Southside, you will happen upon a hidden walled terrace garden which marks the historical boundary to Strathbungo. It's an unexpected cottage-style city garden, showing how a piece of ground can be turned into a lovely colourful space for all the occupants of the terrace to enjoy. Inventive container planting is a key feature of this distinct urban retreat, which holds year-round interest. There's a range of fruit trees, some of which are trained as minarettes and stepovers. Why not visit Strathbungo Garden on Facebook and see what's been happening in the garden over the past months?

Open: Sunday 25 July, 2pm - 5pm, admission £4.00, children free.

Directions: From the south take the M74 to Junction 1A Polmadie. Turn left onto Polmadie Road, then turn right at the next traffic lights onto Calder Street. Proceed to Nithsdale Drive, then turn left into March Street where ample parking can be found. From the north take the M8 and join the M74, turn right into Polmadie Road at Junction 1A.

Opening for: ALVO Rural South Lanarkshire

7 **THE GOOD LIFE GARDEN**
12 Chatelherault Avenue, Cambuslang, Glasgow G72 8BJ
Paul and Sheona Brightey

The front garden is split into a gravel garden and a small white woodland garden. Go through the gate and you will find a garden, the aim of which is to grow as many different edibles as possible, including herbs, fruit arches, vegetable beds and edible hedging. There are herbaceous perennials and a cut-flower bed, a wildlife pond, a pizza oven and around the corner, a food smoker.

Open: Sunday 13 June, 2pm - 5pm, admission £6.00, children free.

Directions: M74 Glasgow to Cambuslang at junction two, exit onto Cambuslang Road/A724 towards Rutherglen. At the roundabout, take the first exit and stay on Cambuslang Road/A724. Continue to follow A724. Turn right onto Buchanan Drive, then right onto Richmond Drive, which turns left and becomes Chatelherault Avenue. M74 Glasgow to Cambuslang at Junction Two, exit onto Cambuslang Road/A724 towards Rutherglen. At the roundabout, take the first exit and stay on Cambuslang Road/A724. Continue to follow A724. Turn right onto Buchanan Drive, then right onto Richmond Drive, which turns left and becomes Chatelherault Avenue.

Opening for: Simon Community Scotland

Glasgow & District

8 THE HIDDEN GARDENS
25 Albert Drive, Glasgow G41 2PE
The Hidden Gardens Trust
T: 0141 433 2722 E: info@thehiddengardens.org.uk
W: thehiddengardens.org.uk

The Hidden Gardens has been designed to reflect the legacy of this historic site as well as the ever-changing character and needs of the local area. The north to south borders echo the layout of the site when it was a tree nursery in the 1800s, whilst the retained tramlines and the chimney reflect its industrial past. A number of artworks are integrated into the overall design, for example the Xylotheque, a library of wooden books detailing native Scottish trees. The Hidden Gardens is an independent charity offering learning and social activities and opportunities for the whole community to participate in its development. It is a calm, green space where you can relax away from the busy city streets: take a walk around the formal lawn; brush past the aromatic herb border; admire the white wall border with its herbaceous plantings and espalier fruit trees; stroll through the wildlife area; connect with nature in the woodland glade; and enjoy the naturalistic planting of the grassy meadow.

Open: Sunday 20 June, 1pm - 4pm, admission £6.00, children free; includes a guided tour led by our knowledgeable Head Gardener, and demonstrations focusing on the challenges of gardening in a changing climate. Tours hourly, beginning at 1pm. Please feel free to bring along a picnic and allow time to visit our plant sale kiosk.

Directions: Free street parking on Albert Drive is available if coming by car. The Hidden Gardens are very accessible by public transport; the 3, 4, 5, 6, 7, 38, 57 and 59 buses take you within walking distance; enter either through Tramway or from Pollokshaws Road. Trains to Pollokshields East station are every 15 minutes from Glasgow Central Station. At the top of the stairs at Pollokshields East station turn right and enter the Hidden Gardens through Tramway.

Opening for: The Hidden Gardens Trust

The Hidden Gardens © Paula Murdoch

Glasgow & District

9 **VIEWPARK GARDENS AND ALLOTMENTS**
Bairds Avenue, Viewpark G71 6HJ
Viewpark Allotments Association
T: 07967 153798
W: viewparkgardensallotmentsassociation.btck.co.uk

Viewpark is a thriving community of contemporary allotments. These not only provide the opportunity to garden and grow but also offer enjoyment, education and therapy for local groups, families and individuals. Each plot has its own character. Crops grown range from potatoes to peaches, godetia to grapes. Inspiration can be found everywhere, from planting combinations, irrigation methods, use of small spaces, unusual crops, etc. Environmental awareness is high on the agenda with a stunning wildflower meadow, sensory garden, delightful fairy garden, hedgehog houses, bug hotels, group orchard, two large polytunnels and the use of recyclable materials.

Open: Sunday 11 July, 2pm - 5pm, admission £6.00, children free. Excellent plant stall with a great range of perennials, annuals and vegetables.

Directions: On the A721, New Edinburgh Road between Bellshill and Viewpark.

Opening for: Viewpark Gardens Trust

10 **WOODBOURNE HOUSE**
Seven Sisters, Lenzie, Glasgow G66 3AW
Alice May

This is a landscaped garden on several levels; about the size of half-a-football-pitch and roughly triangular with a traditional Victorian villa at its centre. It features a wildlife pond and a 'wigloo' – an igloo made from living willow and climbers – alongside rare and unusual perennials. These include cold-hardy tropicals and colourful tender ones. On one side a woodland-style border gives way to a bog garden and exotic slope, while paths and steps lead up to decking and gravel planting along the rear drive.

Open: Sunday 4 July, 2pm - 5pm, admission £6.00, children free.

Directions: From the M80 exit Junction 3 onto A806. After two mini-roundabouts turn left onto Woodilee Road at the Old Gatehouse pub. Park in the pub. Walk back onto Woodilee Road and turn left along it, then left again onto Seven Sisters and continue right to the very end to Woodbourne House.

Opening for: David Sheldrick Wildlife Trust

Inverness, Ross, Cromarty & Skye

Sponsored by

⊕ Investec

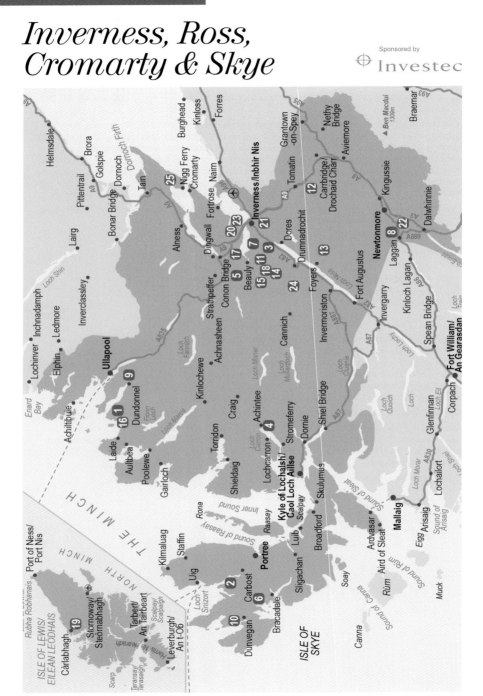

Inverness, Ross, Cromarty & Skye

OUR VOLUNTEER ORGANISERS

District Organisers:	Lucy Lister-Kaye	House of Aigas, Aigas, Beauly IV4 7AD E: inverness@scotlandsgardens.org
Area Organiser:	Emma MacKenzie	Glenkyllachy, Tomatin IV13 7YA
Treasurer:	Sheila Kerr	Lilac Cottage, Struy, By Beauly IV4 7JU

GARDENS OPEN ON A SPECIFIC DATE

Dundonnell House, Little Loch Broom, Wester Ross	Thursday, 15 April
House of Gruinard, Laide, by Achnasheen	Wednesday, 26 May
Gorthleck House Garden, Stratherrick	Friday - Monday, 28 - 31 May
Dundonnell House, Little Loch Broom, Wester Ross	Thursday, 3 June
Old Allangrange, Munlochy	Saturday, 5 June
Field House, Belladrum, Beauly	Sunday, 6 June
White Rose Cottage, Pitcalnie, Tain	Sunday, 6 June
Craig Dhu House, Laggan	Sunday, 20 June
House of Aigas and Field Centre, by Beauly	Sunday, 27 June
2 Durnamuck, Little Loch Broom, Wester Ross	Saturday, 10 July
House of Aigas and Field Centre, by Beauly	Sunday, 25 July
Dundonnell House, Little Loch Broom, Wester Ross	Thursday, 12 August
Kiltarlity Gardens, Kilarlity	Sunday, 15 August
2 Durnamuck, Little Loch Broom, Wester Ross	Saturday, 21 August
Old Allangrange, Munlochy	Saturday, 4 September

GARDENS OPEN REGULARLY

Highland Liliums, 10 Loaneckheim, Kiltarlity	1 January - 31 December
Oldtown of Leys Garden, Inverness	1 January - 31 December (not open Thurs & Fris 1 April - 31 October)
Abriachan Garden Nursery, Loch Ness Side	1 February - 30 November
Attadale, Strathcarron	1 April - 30 October
Dunvegan Castle and Gardens, Isle of Skye	Check the garden's website
Glenkyllachy, Tomatin	1 April - 30 October (Mons & Tues)
Balmeanach House, Balmeanach, nr Struan, Isle of Skye	1 May - 1 October
Leathad Ard, Upper Carloway, Isle of Lewis	1 May - 30 September (not Suns)
5 Knott, Clachamish, Portree, Isle of Skye	27 June - 19 Sept. (Mons, Fris & Suns)
Torcroft, Balnain, Glenurquhart	1 July - 31 July (Mons only)

Inverness, Ross, Cromarty & Skye

2 5 KNOTT

Clachamish, Portree, Isle of Skye IV51 9NZ
Brian and Joyce Heggie
T: 01470 582213 E: jbheggie@hotmail.co.uk
W: knottcottageselfcatering.co.uk

An informal, organic garden on a gently sloping half acre site. Perimeter hedging has enabled a sheltered and tranquil oasis to be created. Winding paths meander through the densely planted borders filled with a diverse range of perennials, annuals and shrubs. There is also a vegetable area with raised beds and a large polytunnel. A developing wild flower meadow with sea loch views leads onto a sheltered bay and a shoreside walk to the headland. There are regular sightings of seals, otters, sea eagles and harbour porpoises. Garden seating in several locations. The garden is situated in an easily reached, particularly quiet and scenic area of Skye.

Open: 27 June - 19 September (Mondays, Fridays & Sundays), 2pm - 5pm. Also open by arrangement 1 June - 30 September. Admission £3.00, children free.

Directions: From Portree, take the A87 to Uig/Dunvegan. After approximately three miles, take the A850 towards Dunvegan. Six miles on, past the *Treaslane* sign, look for the red phone box on the right. Turn right on the bend at the signpost for *Knott.*

Opening for: *Crossroads Care Skye & Lochalsh*

5 Knott

Inverness, Ross, Cromarty & Skye

3 ABRIACHAN GARDEN NURSERY

Loch Ness Side IV3 8LA
Mr and Mrs Davidson
T: 01463 861232 E: info@lochnessgarden.com
W: www.lochnessgarden.com

This is an outstanding garden with over four acres of exciting plantings with winding paths through native woodlands. Seasonal highlights include snowdrops, hellebores, primulas, meconopsis, hardy geraniums and colour-themed summer beds. Views over Loch Ness.

Open: 1 February - 30 November, 9am - 7pm, admission £3.00, children free.

Directions: On the A82 Inverness/Drumnadrochit road, about eight miles south of Inverness.

Opening for: *Highland Hospice*

4 ATTADALE

Strathcarron IV54 8YX
Mr Ewen Macpherson
T: 01520 722603 E: info@attadalegardens.com
W: www.attadalegardens.com

The Gulf Stream, surrounding hills and rocky cliffs create a microclimate for 20 acres of outstanding water gardens, old rhododendrons, unusual trees and a fern collection in a geodesic dome. There is also a sunken fern garden developed on the site of an early 19th-century drain, a waterfall into a pool with dwarf rhododendrons, sunken garden, peace garden and kitchen garden. Other features include a conservatory, Japanese garden, sculpture collection and giant sundial.

Open: 1 April - 30 October, 10am - 5:30pm, admission £10.00, children £1.00, Seniors £8.00

Directions: On the A890 between Strathcarron and South Strome.

Opening for: *The Howard Doris Centre*

Attadale

Inverness, Ross, Cromarty & Skye

5 AULTGOWRIE MILL
Aultgowrie, Urray, Muir of Ord IV6 7XA
Mr and Mrs John Clegg
T: 01997 433699 E: john@johnclegg.com

Aultgowrie Mill is an 18th century converted water mill set in gardens, river and woodlands of 13 acres. Features include a wooded island, a half-acre wildflower meadow and a large wildlife pond, all with views of the surrounding hills. The maturing gardens have terraces, lawns, two mixed orchards and raised vegetable beds with glasshouse and a third of a mile river walk. *The Beechgrove Garden* featured this garden in July 2014. Well behaved dogs on leads welcome.

Open: By arrangement 1 April - 30 September, admission £4.50, children free.

Directions: From the south, turn left at Muir of Ord Distillery, Aultgowrie Mill is then about three miles. From the north and west, after Marybank Primary School, Aultgowrie Mill is about one-and-a-half miles up the hill.

Opening for: RNLI

6 BALMEANACH HOUSE
Balmeanach, nr Struan, Isle of Skye IV56 8FH
Mrs Arlene Macphie
T: 01470 572320 E: info@skye-holiday.com
W: www.skye-holiday.com

Approximately a third of an acre of open croft land was fenced and a garden started, some 30 years ago. Now well established, there are glorious herbaceous borders, with a small azalea and rhododendron walk, a rose garden, arbour area, a small sunken pond and a well established woodland, complete with statues and fairies. Two additional ponds and a small shrubbery provide shelter for wildlife. Visitors are welcome to sit, or even picnic, in the numerous seating areas provided – remembering to take all litter away, please.

Open: 1 May - 1 October, 10am - 3:30pm, admission £3.00, children free.

Directions: A87 to Sligachan, turn left, Balmeanach is five miles north of Struan and five miles south of Dunvegan.

Opening for: Scottish SPCA

7 BERRYFIELD HOUSE
Lentran, Inverness IV3 8RJ
Lynda Perch-Nielsen
T: 01463 831346 M: 07547 960341 E: lyndazpn@gmail.com

An open garden of trees and bushes with views across the Beauly Firth to Ben Wyvis. There are large swathes of bulbs: crocus, dogs tooth violets and heritage daffodils. A three-acre wildflower meadow with meandering paths adjoins the garden giving interest until the start of autumn foliage and crocus.

Open: By arrangement 1 April - 1 August, admission by donation.

Directions: Halfway between Inverness and Beauly on the A862. From Inverness – four and a quarter miles on the left from crossing over the Clachnaharry railway bridge. From Beauly – one and a quarter miles on the right from The Old North Inn.

Opening for: Action Medical Research

Inverness, Ross, Cromarty & Skye

8	**CRAIG DHU HOUSE**
	Laggan PH20 1BS
	Mrs Valerie Macpherson
	T: 07885 168601

Craig Dhu sits above the river Spey with a dramatic rockface background and surrounded by magnificent trees including Silver and Douglas fir, Western Hemlock, Wellingtonia, aspen and birch. There are stunning views. Flower and shrub border, rhododendron path, woodland walks, vegetable patch and an orchard – all at nearly 1000 feet.

Open: Sunday 20 June, 2pm - 5pm, admission £4.00, children free. Homemade teas £4.00

Directions: On the A86 between Newtonmore and Laggan. If you are coming from Newtonmore, it is on the left just after the Lochans.

Opening for: Laggan and Newtonmore Church of Scotland: Laggan Church

Balmeanach

9	**DUNDONNELL HOUSE**
	Little Loch Broom, Wester Ross IV23 2QW
	Dundonnell Estates
	T: 07789 390028

Camellias, magnolias and bulbs in spring, rhododendrons and laburnum walk in this ancient walled garden. Exciting planting in new borders gives all year colour centred around one of the oldest yew trees in Scotland. A new water sculpture, midsummer roses, recently restored unique Victorian glass house, riverside walk, arboretum – all in the valley below the peaks of An Teallach. Champion Trees: Yew and Holly.

Open: Thursday 15 April, Thursday 3 June and Thursday 12 August, 2pm - 5pm. Also open by arrangement 1 April - 31 October. Admission £5.00, children free. Homemade teas only available on 3rd June.

Directions: Turn off the A835 at Braemore on to the A832. After 11 miles take the Badralloch turn for a half mile.

Opening for: The Wild Camel Protection Foundation & Population Matters

Inverness, Ross, Cromarty & Skye

10 DUNVEGAN CASTLE AND GARDENS
Isle of Skye IV55 8WF
Hugh Macleod of Macleod
T: 01470 521206 E: info@dunvegancastle.com
W: www.dunvegancastle.com

Five acres of formal gardens dating from the 18th century. In contrast to the barren moorland of Skye, the gardens are an oasis featuring an eclectic mix of plants, woodland glades, shimmering pools fed by waterfalls and streams flowing down to the sea. After the water garden with its ornate bridges and islands replete with a rich and colourful plant variety, wander through the elegant surroundings of the formal round garden. The walled garden is worth a visit to see its colourful herbaceous borders and recently added Victorian-style glasshouse. In what was formerly the castle's vegetable garden, there is a garden museum and a diverse range of plants and flowers which complement the features including a waterlily pond, a neoclassical urn and a larch pergola. Replanting and landscaping have taken place over the last 30 years to restore and develop the gardens.

Open: Opening details can be found on the garden's website.

Directions: One mile from Dunvegan village, 23 miles west of Portree. Follow the signs for *Dunvegan Castle.*

Opening for: *Donation to SGS Beneficiaries*

11 FIELD HOUSE
Belladrum, Beauly IV4 7BA
Mr and Mrs D Paterson
W: www.dougthegarden.co.uk

An informal country garden in a one-acre site with mixed borders, ponds and some unusual plants – a plantsman's garden. Featured on the *The Beechgrove Garden.*

Open: Sunday 6 June, 2pm - 4:30pm, admission £4.00, children free.

Directions: Four miles from Beauly on the A833 Beauly to Drumnadrochit road, then follow the signs to *Belladrum.*

Opening for: *Highland Disability Sport Lochaber: Swim Team*

12 GLENKYLLACHY
Tomatin IV13 7YA
Mr and Mrs Philip Mackenzie
E: emmaglenkyllachy@gmail.com

In a magnificent Highland glen, at 1200 feet above sea level, Glenkyllachy offers a glorious garden of shrubs, herbaceous plants, rhododendrons, trees and spectacular views down the Findhorn River. There are some rare specimens and a newly planted arboretum. Rhododendrons and bulbs flower in May/June, herbaceous plants bloom through July/August with glorious autumn colours from September. Original sculptures and a Highgrove-inspired wall provide year-round interest. Featured on the *Beechgrove Garden* in 2018. We took advantage of Lockdown in 2020 to re-assess existing plant schemes and create new borders and paths. We have also extended the garden with a 'wild area' blending the garden into the beautiful birch and juniper natural hillside.

Open: 1 April - 30 October (Mondays & Tuesdays), 2pm - 5pm. Also open by arrangement 1 January - 31 December. Admission £5.00, children free.

Inverness, Ross, Cromarty & Skye

Directions: Turn off the A9 at Tomatin and take the Coignafearn/Garbole single-track road down the north-side of the River Findhorn, there is a cattle grid and gate on the right 500 yards AFTER the humpback bridge and the sign to *Farr*.

Opening for: Marie Curie

13 GORTHLECK HOUSE GARDEN
Stratherrick IV2 6UJ
Steve and Katie Smith
T: 07710 325903 E: gorthleckgarden@gmail.com

Gorthleck is an unusual 20-acre woodland garden built in an unlikely place, on and around an exposed rocky ridge which offers long views of the surrounding countryside in the 'borrowed landscape' tradition of Japanese gardens. The layout of the garden works with the natural features of the landscape with numerous paths, hedges and shelter belts creating clearly defined areas where a large collection of trees and shrubs are thriving. The garden includes over 400 different varieties of rhododendrons, half of which are species, and a large variety of bamboos. It is a large garden so allow sufficient time to see it properly.

Open: Friday - Monday, 28 - 31 May, 10am - 6pm, admission £5.00, children free.

Directions: From the A9, take the B851 towards Fort Augustus to join the B862. Go through the village of Errogie where there is a sharp left-hand bend on the road. After approximately one mile, there is a small church on the left. The Gorthleck drive is directly opposite the church and the house can be seen on the hill to the left as you follow the drive to the left of the new house. Visitors can park on the verges at the top of the drive.

Opening for: Maggie's

14 HIGHLAND LILIUMS
10 Loaneckheim, Kiltarlity IV4 7JQ
Neil and Frances Macritchie
T: 01463 741365 E: accounts@highlandliliums.co.uk
W: www.highlandliliums.co.uk

Highland Liliums is a working retail nursery with spectacular views over the Beauly valley and Strathfarrar hills. A wide selection of home-grown plants available including alpines, ferns, grasses, herbaceous, herbs, liliums, primulas and shrubs.

Open: 1 January - 31 December, 9am - 5pm. Also open as part of the Kiltarlity Gardens on Sunday 15 August.

Directions: Signposted from Kiltarlity village, which is just off the Beauly to Drumnadrochit road (A833), approximately 12 miles from Inverness.

Opening for: Donation to SGS Beneficiaries

Inverness, Ross, Cromarty & Skye

15 HOUSE OF AIGAS AND FIELD CENTRE

by Beauly IV4 7AD
Sir John and Lady Lister-Kaye
T: 01463 782443 E: info@aigas.co.uk
W: www.aigas.co.uk

The House of Aigas has a small arboretum of named Victorian specimen trees and modern additions. The garden consists of extensive rockeries, herbaceous borders, ponds and shrubs. Aigas Field Centre rangers lead regular guided walks on nature trails through woodland, moorland and around a loch.
Champion Trees: Douglas fir, Atlas cedar and *Sequoiadendron giganteum*.

Open: Sunday 27 June, 2pm - 5pm & Sunday 25 July, 2pm - 5pm. Also open by arrangement 1 April - 31 October. Admission £4.00, children free.

Directions: Four and a half miles from Beauly on the A831 Cannich/Glen Affric road.

Opening for: Highland Hospice: Aird branch

16 HOUSE OF GRUINARD

Laide, by Achnasheen IV22 2NQ
The Hon Mrs A G Maclay
T: 01445 731235 E: office@houseofgruinard.com

Superb hidden and unexpected garden developed in sympathy with stunning west coast estuary location. Wide variety of interesting herbaceous and shrub borders with water garden and extended wild planting.

Open: Wednesday 26 May, 2pm - 5pm, admission £4.00, children free.

Directions: On the A832 12 miles north of Inverewe and nine miles south of Dundonnell.

Opening for: Macmillan Cancer Support

17 KILCOY CASTLE

Redcastle, by Muir of Ord IV6 7RX
Kilcoy Castle Estate
T: 07766 445511

To the front of the castle are steps which lead on to grass terraces surrounded by shrubs and trees: the walled garden leads off to the east. The area farthest from the castle has been restyled based on the poem *Solitude* by Thomas Merton. The shape is rhomboid with a central point taken from which the design radiates planted with pleached hornbeam, underplanted with willow. Box holly and yew hedges are still to grow to fruition. Work is ongoing with new herbaceous border and different planting using annuals and herbaceous plants; the garden will host a further vibrant display of colourful plants within the walled garden along with a greenhouse in full production.

Open: By arrangement 16 August - 23 August, admission £6.50, children free.

Directions: From the Tore roundabout, take the A832, go past Fettes Sawmill on the left. Turn right at Kilcoy Kindergarten (an old church) heading towards Kilcoy. Go along the single road for about a quarter of a mile and you will see the Kilcoy Castle entrance on the left.

Opening for: Nansen Highland

Inverness, Ross, Cromarty & Skye

18 KILTARLITY GARDENS

Kilarlity IV4 7JH
Sheila Ross, Sue Mullins, Neil and Frances Macritchie
T: 01463 741365 E: accounts@highlandliliums.co.uk
W: www.highlandliliums.co.uk

Aird View 30a Camault Muir, Kiltarlity IV4 7JH (Sheila Ross): The garden at Aird View offers a mix of borders, a water feature, an arbour and a newly added herbaceous border. There are also fruit trees and vegetable beds.

Foinaven Loaneckheim, Kiltarlity, Beauly IV4 7JQ (Sue Mullins): Foinaven is approximately half an acre in size, and is blessed with several mature Scots pine trees. This is a 'plantaholics' garden with many different varieties of shrubs, trees and herbaceous plants. There is a natural pond and the garden has untamed areas for wildlife and pollinators. Wildlife is well catered for by the selection of plants with flowers for pollinators, and the birds are fed well by the resultant berries.

Highland Liliums 10 Loaneckheim, Kiltarlity IV4 7JQ (Neil and Frances Macritchie): Highland Liliums is a working retail nursery with spectacular views over the Beauly valley and Strathfarrar hills. A wide selection of home-grown plants available including alpines, ferns, grasses, herbaceous, herbs, liliums, primulas and shrubs.

Open: Sunday 15 August, noon - 5pm, admission £3.00, children free. Admission tickets available at any of the gardens. Teas £3.00 and discounted plants at Highland Liliums.

Directions: Aird View Take the A833 Beauly to Drumnadrochit road, pass Brockies Lodge. Turn right at the bus shelter and follow the single track road to junction at school. Turn left up the hill to the top at junction. Aird View is on the right.

Foinaven Turn up Post Office Brae in Kiltarlity then turn right after the Free Church. Follow the road towards Highland Liliums. Foinaven is about a half mile from the church (sixth house on the right-hand side).

Highland Liliums Signposted from Kiltarlity village, which is just off the Beauly to Drumnadrochit road (A833), approximately 12 miles from Inverness.

Opening for: Highland Hospice: Aird branch

19 LEATHAD ARD

Upper Carloway, Isle of Lewis HS2 9AQ
Rowena and Stuart Oakley
T: 01851 643204 E: stuart.oakley1a@gmail.com
W: www.leathadard.org.uk

A one-acre sloping garden with stunning views over East Loch Roag. It has evolved along with the shelter hedges that divide the garden into a number of areas giving a new view at every corner. With shelter and raised beds, the different conditions created permit a wide variety of plants to be grown. Features include herbaceous borders, cutting borders, bog gardens, grass garden, exposed beds, patios, a pond and vegetables and fruit grown both in the open ground and the Keder greenhouse. Some of the vegetables are grown to show standards.

Open: 1 May - 30 September (not Sundays), 10am - 6pm. Also open by arrangement 1 April - 30 April (not Sundays). Admission £4.00, children free.

Directions: On the A858 Shawbost-Carloway, first right after the Carloway football pitch, and the first house on the right. By bus take the Westside circular bus, exit Stornoway, head for Carloway football pitch.

Opening for: British Red Cross

Inverness, Ross, Cromarty & Skye

20 OLD ALLANGRANGE
Munlochy IV8 8NZ
J J Gladwin
T: 01463 811304 E: office@blackislebeegardendesign.com

The garden surrounds an 18th-century orange lime-washed house. There is a formalish parterre in front of the house with loose planting in the individual beds, a terrace garden, lime pom pom bed planted with roses, herb garden, mound, orchard, all linked with various styles of hedges – pleached lime, yew, beech, box, holly, mixed and more recently, we have started to remove perimeter wire fences and replace with log hedges and brash bunds. The hedges are treated with different degrees of formality. There is a five-acre organic vegetable garden with two large Keder greenhouses. We have a keen interest in gardening for all wildlife with a particular focus on planting for invertebrates. No chemicals have been used since arrival in 1995. The development and improvement of the garden is on-going.
Champion Trees: Yew and sweet chestnut.

Open: Saturday 5 June, 2pm - 5pm and Saturday 4 September, 2pm - 5pm. Also open by arrangement for groups (minimum 10 people). Admission £6.50, children free.

Directions: From Inverness head four miles north on the A9, and follow the directions for *Black Isle Brewery*. Park up at the Brewery and walk down to the garden. Directions will be given in the shop.

Opening for: Black Isle Bee Gardens

21 OLDTOWN OF LEYS GARDEN
Inverness IV2 6AE
David and Anne Sutherland
T: 01463 238238 E: ams@oldtownofleys.com

Large garden established in 2003 on the outskirts of Inverness and overlooking the town. Herbaceous beds with lovely rhododendron and azalea displays in spring. There are specimen trees, three ponds surrounded by waterside planting and a small woodland area. A new rockery area was created in 2015 and is still developing.

Open: 1 January - 31 December (not open Thursdays & Fridays from 1 April - 31 October) dawn - dusk, admission by donation.

Directions: Turn off southern distributor road (B8082) at Leys roundabout towards Inverarnie (B861). At the T-junction turn right. After 50 yards turn right into Oldtown of Leys.

Opening for: Donation to SGS Beneficiaries

22 SHANVALL
Glentruim, Newtonmore PH20 1BE
George and Beth Alder
T: 01540 673213 E: beth.alder@yahoo.co.uk

The garden is two-thirds of an acre at 900 feet above sea level, surrounding a 19th-century cottage. On the south side of the River Spey, it has lovely views of the Creag Dubh and Creag Meagaidh mountains. There are ruined buildings of an old township within the garden. To the south is a garden of roses and perennials. Within a stone wall, there are fruit cages, a small orchard and organic vegetable beds which have been cultivated for about 200 years. The garden on the north slopes has trees, shrubs, herbaceous border, wildflowers, a pond and is rich with wildlife, including woodpeckers and red squirrels.

Open: By arrangement 1 July - 31 August, admission by donation.

Directions: Shanvall is on the minor road running along the south side of the Spey, linking the A9 south of Newtonmore at Glentruim and the A889 at Catlodge. The garden gate is on the right about one-and-a-half miles from the A9. Further details on request.

Opening for: Laggan and Newtonmore Church of Scotland

Inverness, Ross, Cromarty & Skye

23 **THE LOOKOUT**
Kilmuir, North Kessock IV1 3ZG
David and Penny Veitch
T: 01463 731489 E: david@veitch.biz

A three-quarter-acre elevated coastal garden with incredible views over the Moray Firth which is only for the sure-footed. This award-winning garden, featured on the *The Beechgrove Garden* has been created out of a rock base with shallow pockets of ground, planted to its advantage to encourage all aspects of wildlife. There is a small sheltered courtyard, raised bed vegetable area, pretty cottage garden, scree and rock garden, rose arbour, rhododendrons, flowering shrubs, bamboos, trees and lily pond with waterside plants.

Open: By arrangement 1 April - 30 September (not Sats & Suns), admission £4.00, children free.

Directions: From Inverness, take the North Kessock left turn from the A9, and third left at the roundabout to go on the underpass, then sharp left onto Kilmuir Road. From Tore, take the slip road for North Kessock and immediately right for Kilmuir. Follow signs for *Kilmuir* (three miles) until you reach the shore. The Lookout is near the far end of the village with a large palm tree in front, surrounded by gravel.

Opening for: Alzheimer Scotland

24 **TORCROFT**
Balnain, Glenurquhart IV63 6TJ
Barbara Craig
T: 01456 476717

This garden is about three-quarters of an acre on a hillside overlooking Loch Meiklie in Glen Urquhart. It is a wild garden, with its own character and style. There are weeds and cardamine for the orange tip butterflies, but most of all there are plants in profusion from acer, anemone and astrantia to veronicastrum, verbascum, weigela and water lilies. A natural stream comes into the garden and meanders into various small ponds. In the spring there are masses of bog primula of all types and colours. There is a fern bed, a rockery, herbs, wooded area. New in 2018 was a stumpery, beds and another pond.

Open: 1 July - 31 July (Mondays only), 2pm - 5pm. Also open by arrangement 1 April - 31 October. Admission £3.00, children free.

Directions: From Inverness turn right at Drumnadrochit and go towards Cannich. After four miles, sign *Balnain*, there is a very sharp right-hand bend with a high retaining wall on the right. At the end of the wall take the turning to the right signposted *Torcroft Lodges*.

Opening for: Munlochy Animal Aid & Send a Cow

25 **WHITE ROSE COTTAGE**
Pitcalnie, Tain IV20 1XJ
Mr and Mrs S Miles
T: 01862 851292 E: lambdon@hotmail.co.uk

A garden full of surprises from secret dens to hidden gems. Colourful rhododendron displays plus unusual trees, shrubs and flowers in woodland, seaside and traditional settings.

Open: Sunday 6 June, 2pm - 5pm, admission £4.00, children free.

Directions: Turn right at Nigg roundabout over the railway crossing, through Nigg Station and Arabella. Turn left to Shandwick up a slight hill (the cemetery is on the left). White Rose Cottage is immediately after the Old Schoolhouse on the left opposite junction to Pitcalnie. Stagecoach Buses from Tain, 30A or 30C. Request stop.

Opening for: Nigg Old Trust & Cromarty Firth Men's Shed

Kincardine & Deeside

Sponsored by
Investec

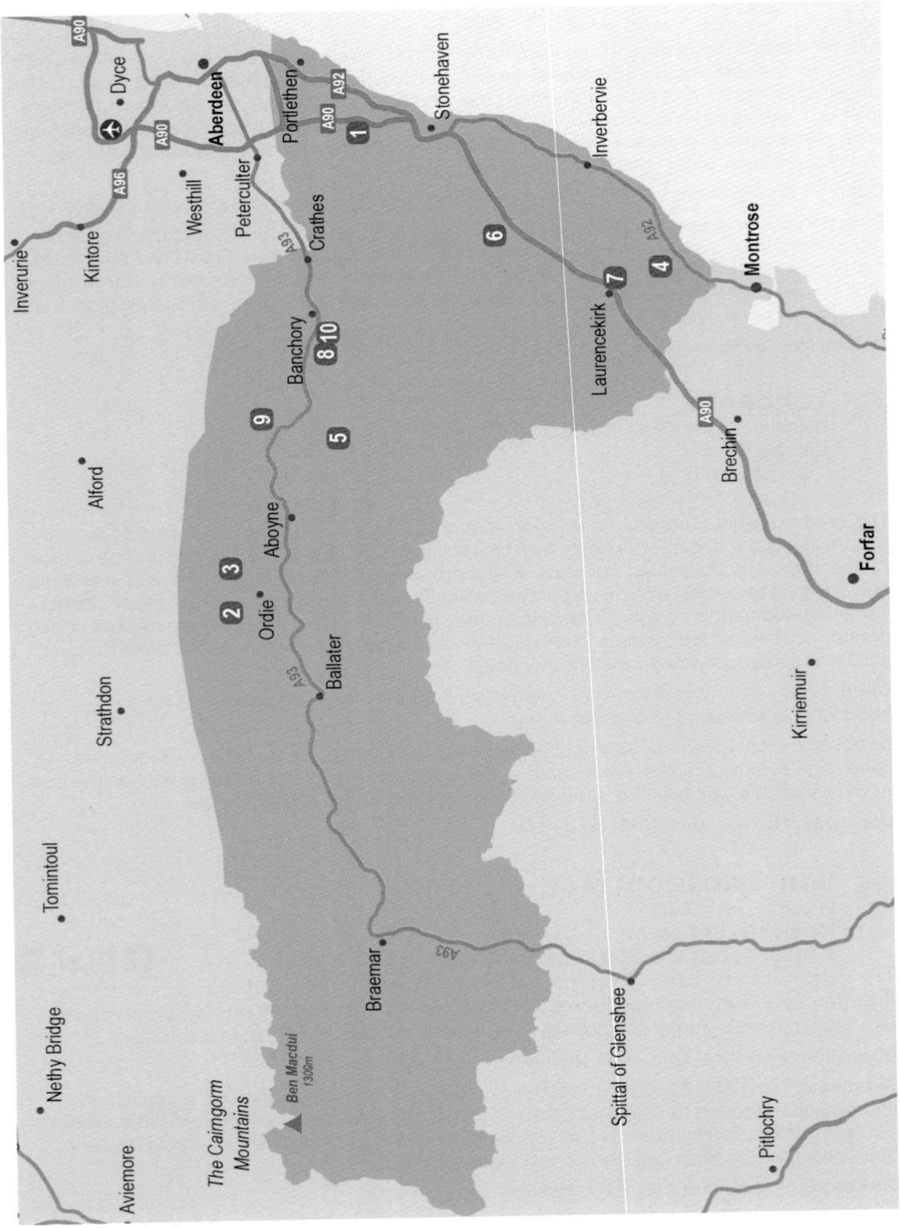

Kincardine & Deeside

OUR VOLUNTEER ORGANISERS

District Organisers:	Catherine Nichols	Westerton Steading, Dess, Aboyne AB34 5AY
	Julie Nicol	Cedarwood Lodge, Aboyne AB34 5JB
		E: kincardine@scotlandsgardens.org
Area Organisers:	Wendy Buchan	Inneshewen, Dess, Aboyne AB34 5BH
	Gavin Farquhar	Ecclesgreig Castle, St Cyrus DD10 0DP
	Tina Hammond	Sunnybank, 7 Watson Street, Banchory AB31 5UB
	Liz Inglesfield	2 Earlspark Circle, Bieldside, Aberdeen AB15 9BW
	David & Patsy Younie	Bealltainn, Ballogie, Aboyne AB34 5DL
Treasurer:	Michael Buchan	Inneshewen, Dess, Aboyne AB34 5BH

GARDENS OPEN ON A SPECIFIC DATE

Ecclesgreig Castle, St Cyrus	Sunday, 7 March
Inchmarlo Retirement Village Garden, Inchmarlo, Banchory	Sunday, 23 May
Kincardine Castle, Kincardine O'Neil	Sunday, 13 June
Dallachy, Logie Coldstone, Aboyne, Aberdeenshire	Saturday/Sunday, 19/20 June
Finzean House, Finzean, Banchory	Sunday, 27 June
Lumphanan Gardens, Brucelea, by Lumphanan	Sunday, 4 July
Douneside House, Tarland	Sunday, 11 July
Glenbervie House, Drumlithie, Stonehaven	Sunday, 1 August
Clayfolds, Bridge of Muchalls, Stonehaven	Sunday, 8 August
Glensaugh, Glensaugh Lodge, Fettercairn, Laurencekirk	Sunday, 12 September

GARDENS OPEN BY ARRANGEMENT – BOOK A VISIT WITH THE GARDEN OWNER

Glenbervie House, Drumlithie, Stonehaven	1 May - 15 September

Kincardine & Deeside

1 CLAYFOLDS
Bridge of Muchalls, Stonehaven AB39 3RU
Andrea Sinclair
E: andreaysinclair@outlook.com

An informal country garden extending to a half acre, with a further six acres of wildflowers, native trees and a pond. The main garden is laid out with lawn and mixed borders, which are filled with shrubs and a wide range of hardy perennials and includes a 'hot' border with various flaxes and a variety of hot-coloured plants. Small, cottage-style garden to the front of the house. Follow the tracks through the recently developed six-acre Wilderness Garden and see what native fauna and flora you can spot.

Open: Sunday 8 August, 2pm - 5pm, admission £4.00, children free.

Directions: SatNav – AB39 3RU but travel inland a further one-and-a-half miles to Clayfolds. Travelling in either direction on the A92, three miles north of Stonehaven, take the road signposted *Netherley 3*, continue travelling inland for approximately one-and-a-half miles and you will then be directed where to park.

Opening for: Scottish SPCA

2 DALLACHY
Logie Coldstone, Aboyne, Aberdeenshire AB34 5PQ
Graeme Law and Toby Johns
E: gandt5755@sky.com

A half-acre garden at 200m, with views to Morven and the hills, which has been developing from a blank canvas since 2016. It features several different areas including lawns with mixed borders, courtyard garden, scree garden, pond, small orchard/fruit garden and summer house. All are planted with a mixture of hardy trees, shrubs, perennials and bulbs to give year-round interest and to be wildlife friendly. There are several different seating areas to take advantage of the sun or shelter from the weather!

Open: Saturday/Sunday, 19/20 June, 10:30am - 4:30pm, admission £5.00, children free. Opening by timed bookings. Please email owners in advance to book a slot.

Directions: Take the A97 to Logie Coldstone, turn up the lane between the former church/war memorial and the old post office. Take the first left in front of 'Culharvie' onto unmade road, Dallachy is the third house on the right.

Opening for: Cancer Research UK & Alzheimer's Research UK

3 DOUNESIDE HOUSE
Tarland AB34 4UD
The MacRobert Trust
W: www.dounesidehouse.co.uk

Douneside is the former home of Lady MacRobert, who developed these magnificent gardens in the early to mid-1900s. Ornamental borders, an Arts and Crafts themed terraced garden and water gardens surround a spectacular infinity lawn overlooking the Deeside hills. A walled garden supplies organic vegetables and cut flowers to Douneside House, which is now a multi-award winning hotel, and also houses a large ornamental greenhouse. A new arboretum displays over 130 trees amongst mown grass paths and there are many walking trails behind Douneside offering breathtaking views across the Howe of Cromar and beyond.

Open: Sunday 11 July, 2pm - 5pm, admission £5.00, concessions £3.00, children free. There will be a local pipe band and raffle.

Directions: On the B9119 towards Aberdeen. Tarland one mile.

Opening for: Perennial

Kincardine & Deeside

4 ECCLESGREIG CASTLE
St Cyrus DD10 0DP
Mr Gavin Farquhar
T: 01224 214301 E: enquiries@ecclesgreig.com
W: www.ecclesgreig.com

Ecclesgreig Castle, Victorian Gothic on a 16th-century core, is internationally famous as an inspiration for Bram Stoker's *Dracula*. The snowdrop walk (over 150 varieties of snowdrop) starts at the castle, meanders around the estate, along woodland paths and the pond, ending at the garden. In the Italian balustraded gardens, there is a 140-foot-long herbaceous border, classical statues and stunning shaped topiary with views across St Cyrus to the sea. Started from a derelict site, development continues. Also to be found in the grounds is the well of St Cyrus.

Open: Sunday 7 March, 1pm - 4pm for Snowdrops and Winter Walks, admission £4.00, children free.

Directions: *Ecclesgreig* will be signposted from the A92 Coast Road and from the A937 Montrose/Laurencekirk Road.

Opening for: Girlguiding Montrose District

Dallachy

5 FINZEAN HOUSE
Finzean, Banchory AB31 6NZ
Mr and Mrs Donald Farquharson

Finzean House was the family home of Joseph Farquharson, the Victorian landscape painter, and the garden was the backdrop for several of his paintings. The garden has lovely views over the historic holly hedge to the front of Clachnaben. There is a spring woodland garden, extensive lawns with herbaceous and shrub borders and a working cut-flower garden for late summer, alongside a recently restored pond area. A new vegetable garden was created in 2020.

Open: Sunday 27 June, 2pm - 5pm, admission £5.00, children free, OAPs £4.00.

Directions: On the B976, South Deeside Road, between Banchory and Aboyne.

Opening for: The Forget-Me-Not Club

Kirkcudbrightshire

Sponsored by

Investec

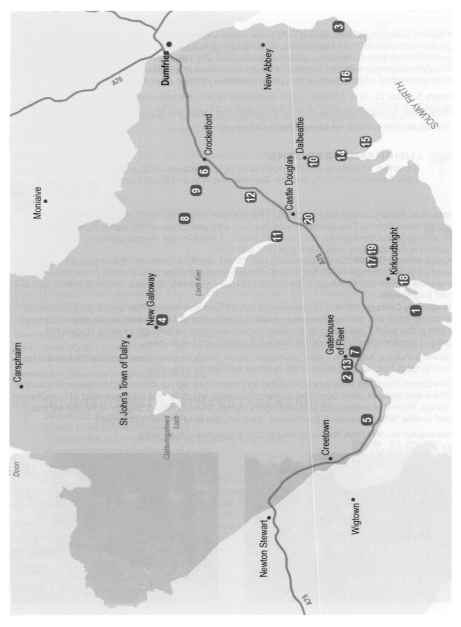

SOLWAY FIRTH

Dumfries

A76

New Abbey

Crocketford

Dalbeattie

Castle Douglas

Moniaive

Loch Ken

New Galloway

Kirkcudbright

Carsphairn

St John's Town of Dalry

Gatehouse of Fleet

Clatteringshaws Loch

Creetown

Doon

Newton Stewart

Wigtown

A75

A75

Kirkcudbrightshire

OUR VOLUNTEER ORGANISERS

District Organisers:	Julian Stanning	Seabank, Merse Road, Dalbeattie DG5 4QH
	Theodora Stanning	Seabank, Merse Road, Dalbeattie DG5 4QH
		E: kirkcudbrightshire@scotlandsgardens.org
Area Organisers:	Hedley Foster	Deer Park, Gatehouse of Fleet DG7 2DN
	May Lockhart	25 Victoria Park, Kirkcudbright DG6 4EN
	Norman McClure	142 Cotton Street, Castle Douglas DG7 1DG
	Lesley Pepper	Anwoth Old Schoolhouse DG7 2EF
	Audrey Slee	Holmview, New Galloway DG7 3RN
	George Thomas	Savat, Meikle Richorn, Dalbeattie DG5 4QT
District Photographer:	Stuart Littlewood	stu@f8.eclipse.co.uk
Treasurer:	Russell Allan	Braeburn, 6 Barcloy Mill, Rockcliffe DG5 4QL

GARDENS OPEN ON A SPECIFIC DATE

Danevale Park, Crossmichael	Sunday, 14 February
The Limes, Kirkcudbright	Sunday, 28 March
3 Millhall, Shore Road, Kirkcudbright	Sunday, 18 April
Balmaclellan House, Balmaclellan, Castle Douglas	Sunday, 25 April
The Limes, Kirkcudbright	Saturday, 1 May
Cally Gardens, Cally Avenue, Gatehouse of Fleet	Sunday, 9 May
Arbigland House, Kirkbean, Dumfries	Sunday, 16 May
The Limes, Kirkcudbright	Sunday, 23 May
Corsock House, Corsock, Castle Douglas	Sunday, 30 May
Threave Garden, Castle Douglas	Friday/Saturday/Sunday, 4/5/6 June
Seabank, The Merse, Rockcliffe	Sunday, 13 June
Southwick House, Southwick	Sunday, 4 July
Dalbeattie Community Allotments Association, Port Road, Dalbeattie	Sunday, 18 July
Crofts, Kirkpatrick Durham, Castle Douglas	Sunday, 25 July
Cally Gardens, Cally Avenue, Gatehouse of Fleet	Sunday, 1 August
3 Millhall, Shore Road, Kirkcudbright	Sunday, 5 September

Kirkcudbrightshire

GARDENS OPEN BY ARRANGEMENT – BOOK A VISIT WITH THE GARDEN OWNER

Stockarton, Kirkcudbright	1 January - 31 December
The Limes, Kirkcudbright	1 January - 31 December
Barholm Castle, Gatehouse of Fleet	1 February - 31 October
Anwoth Old Schoolhouse, Anwoth, Gatehouse of Fleet	15 February - 15 November
Kings Grange House, Castle Douglas	27 March - 11 April & 10 July - 8 August
Corsock House, Corsock, Castle Douglas	1 April - 30 June
Luckie Harg's, Anwoth, Gatehouse of Fleet, Castle Douglas	1 April - 31 August
Savat, Meikle Richorn, Dalbeattie	1 April - 31 October (not Tues & Thurs)
Brooklands, Crocketford	1 May - 30 September
The Waterhouse Gardens at Stockarton, Kirkcudbright	1 May - 30 September
Seabank, The Merse, Rockcliffe	29 May - 12 June

Kirkcudbrightshire

1 **3 MILLHALL**
Shore Road, Kirkcudbright DG6 4TQ
Mr Alan Shamash
T: 01557 870352 E: shamash@freeuk.com

Impressive five-acre garden with a large collection of mature shrubs, including over 200 rhododendron species, many camellias, perennials, over 300 hydrangeas and many rare Southern Hemisphere plants. The garden has several interesting paths and is on a hillside running along the rocky shore of the Dee Estuary in Kirkcudbright Bay.

Open: Sunday 18 April, 2pm - 5pm & 5 September, 2pm - 5pm. Admission £5.00, children free.

Directions: On the B727 between Kirkcudbright and Borgue on the west shore of the Dee Estuary. Parking at Dhoon beach public car park, about three miles south of Kirkcudbright. There is a five-minute walk to the house.

Opening for: Kirkcudbright Hospital League Of Friends & Alzheimer's Research UK

3 Millhall

2 **ANWOTH OLD SCHOOLHOUSE**
Anwoth, Gatehouse of Fleet DG7 2EF
Mr and Mrs Pepper
T: 01557 814444 E: lesley.pepper@btinternet.com

Two acres of delightful cottage-style gardens behind the old schoolhouse and cottage in a picturesque setting opposite Anwoth Old Church (in ruins) and graveyard. Winding paths alongside a burn, informally planted with unusual woodland perennials and shrubs. Wildlife pond, fish pond, rock garden, vegetable garden, wildflower area and viewpoint.

Open: By arrangement 15 February - 15 November, admission £3.00, children free.

Directions: Driving west on the A75, take the Anwoth turn off about half a mile after Gatehouse of Fleet. Anwoth Church is about half a mile along the road and Anwoth Old Schoolhouse is a little further along, opposite Anwoth Old Church (in ruins).

Opening for: Dogs for Good

Kirkcudbrightshire

3 **ARBIGLAND HOUSE**
Kirkbean, Dumfries DG2 8BQ
Alistair Alcock and Wayne Whittaker
T: 01387 880764 E: alcockalistair@gmail.com
W: www.arbiglandhouseandgardens.co.uk

Arbigland House is an Adam-style 18th-century mansion surrounded by 24 acres of woodland gardens running down to a beach on the Solway Firth. The gardens date from the 18th century but the more formal areas were developed in the late 19th and early 20th centuries and are currently undergoing a programme of restoration and development. There are 200 year old trees lining the Broad Walk which runs down to the Solway and a huge variety of rhododendrons and azaleas; within the woodland are a range of features including a stream-fed lake and a Japanese garden, with a more formal sundial garden and sunken rose garden, all in the process of renewal. Amongst these are a diverse collection of mature trees and shrubs.

Open: Sunday 16 May, 2pm - 5pm, admission £5.00, children free. Depending on restrictions, short tours may be available to parts of the house.

Directions: Take the A710 to Kirkbean. In the village turn off towards Carsethorn and, after 200 yards, turn right and follow signs to *John Paul Jones Cottage*. After a mile or so, turn left at the T junction through white gates and down the drive through ornamental gates to Arbigland House.

Opening for: Absolute Classics

4 **BALMACLELLAN HOUSE**
Balmaclellan, Castle Douglas DG7 3PW
Alan and Fiona Smith
T: 01644 420227 Mob: 07769680938
E: alan.smith12345@btinternet.com

The formal garden at Balmaclellan House sits within a six-acre woodland garden with many interesting maturing trees. This formal garden was created in 2011 on the site of a redundant tennis court. The design is based on the Balmaclellan Mirror, a very early iron age mirror made of bronze which was found nearby and is currently in the National Museum of Scotland. The mirror is represented by a raised pond with other decorative features on the original replicated by raised beds and granite setts. While the planting has been designed to give year round colour the use of daffodils and tulips brings a vibrancy to the garden in early spring. A small wooden building dates back to 1896 and is where the resident Minister is said to have written his sermons. The woodland walks and lawned areas have stone seats at appropriate points to take in the lovely views over the Rhins of Kells.

Open: Sunday 25 April, noon - 4pm, admission £5.00, children free.

Directions: On the B7075, just off the A712 approximately 14 miles north of Castle Douglas and two miles from New Galloway.

Opening for: Glenkens Community And Arts Trust Limited

5 **BARHOLM CASTLE**
Gatehouse of Fleet DG7 2EZ
Drs John and Janet Brennan
T: 01557 840327 E: barholmcastle@gmail.com

Barholm Castle, a 16th-century tower, was restored from a ruin in 2006. The gardens surrounding the tower have been mostly developed from scratch and are now mature. There is a recently extended walled garden, with a gate designed by the artist blacksmith Adam Booth; a courtyard garden; a wooded ravine with huge hybrid rhododendrons from Benmore,

Kirkcudbrightshire

a pond and a large fernery with over 90 varieties of fern, including very large tree ferns; a large Victorian style greenhouse filled with succulents and tender perennials; and a large open garden with island beds of shrubs and perennials and a pond. Directly around the castle are rockeries and shrub borders. Views over Wigtown Bay are magnificent. The garden is planted for year-round colour, from February, when the castle ravine is a river of snowdrops, to October, when autumn colour is splendid.

Open: By arrangement from 1 February to 31 October, including for Snowdrops and Winter Walks. Admission £5.00, children free.

Directions: Off the A75 at the Cairn Holy turn off, fork right three times up a steep narrow road for half-a-mile.

Opening for: *Home-Start Wigtownshire*

Balmaclellan House

6 BROOKLANDS
Crocketford DG2 8QH
Mr and Mrs Robert Herries
T: Gardener, Holly: 07525 755178

Large old walled garden with a wide selection of plants, including some interesting shrubs and climbers and a kitchen garden. Mature woodland with many established rhododendrons and azaleas, and carpeted with snowdrops in the early spring.

Open: By arrangement 1 May - 30 September, admission £5.00, children free.

Directions: Turn off the A712 Crocketford to New Galloway Road one mile outside Crocketford at the Gothic gatehouse (on the right travelling north).

Opening for: *All proceeds to SGS Beneficiaries*

Kirkcudbrightshire

7 CALLY GARDENS
Cally Avenue, Gatehouse of Fleet DG7 2DJ
Kevin Hughes
T: 01557 815228 E: info@callygardens.co.uk
W: www.callygardens.co.uk

Cally Gardens and Specialist Plant Centre is a treasure trove of exotic and rare hardy plants gathered from around the globe. The towering 18th-century walls of what was once the kitchen garden and pleasure garden of Cally House now provide shelter to thousands of rare and exotic plants. The informal garden, which was created by the famous plant collector Michael Wickenden, is now in the care of the plantsman Kevin Hughes. Kevin took ownership of Cally in 2018 and has since brought his own large collection of magnolias, daphnes and trilliums and has also added more collections including galanthus, paeonies and nerines. As an ecologist and environmentalist, Kevin has decided to make Cally a haven for birds, insects and all things wild.

Open: Sunday 9 May, 10am - 5pm & 1 August, 10am - 5pm. Admission £5.00, children free.

Directions: From Dumfries take the Gatehouse of Fleet turning off the A75, follow the B727 and turn left through the Cally Palace Hotel gateway from where the gardens are well signposted. A regular bus service will stop at the end of Cally Drive if requested.

Opening for: WWF-UK

8 CORSOCK HOUSE
Corsock, Castle Douglas DG7 3DJ
The Ingall family
T: 01644 440250

Corsock House garden includes an amazing variety of designed landscape, from a strictly formal walled garden, through richly planted woodlands full of different vistas, artfully designed water features and surprises to extensive lawns showing off the Bryce baronial mansion. This is an Arcadian garden with pools and temples, described by Ken Cox as 'perhaps my favourite of Scotland's many woodland gardens'.

Open: Sunday 30 May, 2pm - 5pm. Also open by arrangement 1 April - 30 June. Admission £5.00, children free.

Directions: Off the A75, Dumfries is 14 miles, Castle Douglas is ten miles, Corsock Village is half-mile on the A712.

Opening for: Corsock & Kirkpatrick Durham Church Of Scotland

9 CROFTS
Kirkpatrick Durham, Castle Douglas DG7 3HX
Mrs Andrew Dalton
T: 01556 650235 E: jenniedalton@mac.com

Victorian country-house garden with mature trees, a walled garden with fruit and vegetables and glasshouses, hydrangea garden and a pretty water garden. Delightful woodland walk, colourfully planted with bog plants, and a stream running through.

Open: Sunday 25 July, 2pm - 5pm, admission £5.00, children free.

Directions: A75 to Crocketford, then three miles on the A712 to Corsock and New Galloway.

Opening for: Corsock & Kirkpatrick Durham Church Of Scotland

Kirkcudbrightshire

10 DALBEATTIE COMMUNITY ALLOTMENTS ASSOCIATION

Port Road, Dalbeattie DG5 4AZ
Dalbeattie Community Allotments Association
T: 01556 612208

Dalbeattie Community Allotments Association was formed in 2008 and the site was officially opened in August 2010. A local landowner has leased the land for 25 years at £1 per year, initially providing for 47 plots. The initial results were so successful that the area is now increased to provide for 81 productive plots where local residents can grow their own fruit, vegetables and flowers. Come and enjoy a stroll around the site, chat to members or relax in one of the community areas. Information will be available and photos of the development of the site will be on display.

Open: Sunday 18 July, 2pm - 5pm, admission £3.00, children free.

Directions: The allotment site can be found on the Dalbeattie bypass (A710) next to Craignair Health Centre.

Opening for: Dalbeattie Community Initiative

Dalbeattie Community Allotments Association

11 DANEVALE PARK

Crossmichael DG7 2LP
Mrs M R C Gillespie
T: 01556 670223 E: danevale@tiscali.co.uk

First opening for snowdrops in 1951, these mature grounds have a wonderful display of snowdrops as well as aconites and many other wildflowers. Walks through the woods and alongside the River Dee make this a memorable afternoon. We will have snowdrops for sale, but as we will not be serving teas this year, you are very welcome to bring your own.

Open: Sunday 14 February, 10:30am - 3pm for Snowdrops and Winter Walks, admission £5.00, children free.

Directions: On the A713 two miles from Castle Douglas and one mile short of Crossmichael.

Opening for: Earl Haig Fund Poppy Scotland

Kirkcudbrightshire

12   KINGS GRANGE HOUSE

Castle Douglas DG7 3EU
Christine and Peter Hickman
T: 07787 535889

An extensive garden surrounded by mature trees and shrubberies, with views to the south west over the surrounding countryside. Originally Victorian, the garden is being restored by the present owners with a colourful variety of herbaceous mixed borders, beds and rockeries, mainly to the front of the house. There are banks of daffodils and a carpet of white narcissus in the lawns and around the pergola in springtime.

Open: By arrangement 27 March - 11 April & 10 July - 8 August, admission £5.00, children free.

Directions: Take the B794 north off the A75, two miles east of Castle Douglas. Kings Grange House is approximately one mile on the left.

Opening for: RNLI & Marie Curie

13   LUCKIE HARG'S

Anwoth, Gatehouse of Fleet, Castle Douglas DG7 2EF
Drs Carole and Ian Bainbridge
T: 01557 814141 E: luckiehargs@btinternet.com

A new and developing garden on the outskirts of Gatehouse. A rock and spring herbaceous garden with a wide range of alpines, Himalayan and New Zealand plants, rock garden, crevices, troughs, large alpine house and bulb frame. Under the extension new beds and woodland area are being developed. Small productive vegetable and fruit garden, plus a bluebell bank in May.

Open: By arrangement 1 April - 31 August, admission £5.00, children free.

Directions: From Gatehouse High Street, turn north onto Station Road, immediately west at the Fleet Bridge by The Ship Inn. After almost one mile turn left signed to *Anwoth Old Church*. Luckie Harg's is the first on the right after 400 yards. The nearest bus stop is on Gatehouse High Street, walk about 15 minutes to Luckie Harg's.

Opening for: Scottish Rock Garden Club

14   SAVAT

Meikle Richorn, Dalbeattie DG5 4QT
George Thomas
T: 01556 612863 Mob. 07866 392150 E: georgethomas6@icloud.com

A generally informal garden of about two-thirds of an acre with mature trees, exposed Dalbeattie granite and winding paths. The garden houses a unique summerhouse, artist Sue Thomas's studio and a greenhouse. Planting caters for sun to shade and dry to very moist, with shrubs – including rhododendrons, herbaceous and minimal summer bedding with an eye to keeping maintenance requirements to a minimum! There is a paved area around the house in which there are two water features, and may display potted plants.

Open: By arrangement 1 April - 31 October (not Tuesdays & Thursdays), admission £5.00, children free.

Directions: Leave Dalbeattie along the A710 south towards Kippford. After about 1.7 miles pass *Gorsebank* on the left and 200 yards further on turn right into a large lay-by on your left. If possible, park here and walk up the lane towards *Meiklebob Holiday Cottages* and continue straight ahead on the paved road for about 500 yards. Parking is limited at and near the property. Savat is the sixth house on the left.

Opening for: All proceeds to SGS Beneficiaries

Kirkcudbrightshire

15 **SEABANK**
The Merse, Rockcliffe DG5 4QH
Julian and Theodora Stanning
T: 01556 630244

This one-and-a-half-acre garden extends to the high water mark with westerly views across a wildflower meadow to the Urr Estuary, Rough Island and beyond. The house is flanked by raised beds, and overlooks a cottage style garden; peripheral plantings of mixed shrubs and perennials are interspersed with spring bulbs and summer annuals for all-year-round interest. There is a greenhouse with a range of succulents and tender plants. To the rear of the property is a new walled garden stocked with top and soft fruit, perennial vegetables (sea kale, asparagus and globe artichokes), a range of annual vegetables and flower borders. A further greenhouse is used for tomatoes and cucumbers, and has peaches growing against the back wall. A plantswoman's garden with a range of interesting and unusual plants.

Open: Sunday 13 June, 2pm - 5pm. Also open by arrangement 29 May - 12 June. Admission £5.00, children free.

Directions: Park in the public car park at Rockcliffe. Walk down the road about 50 yards towards the sea and turn left along The Merse, a private road. Seabank is the sixth house on the left.

Opening for: Marie Curie: DG5 Fundraising Group

Seabank

Lanarkshire

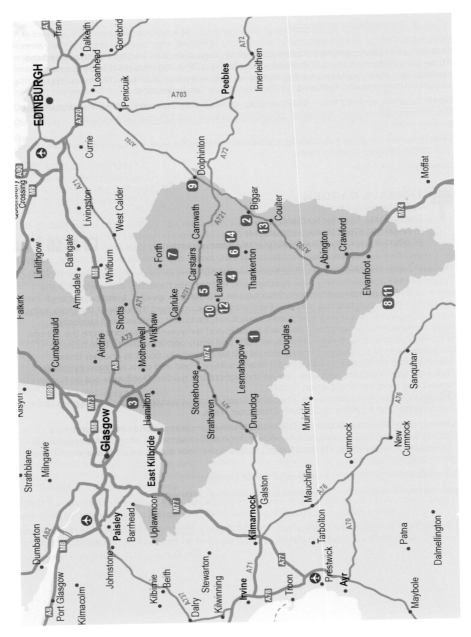

Lanarkshire

OUR VOLUNTEER ORGANISERS

District Organiser:	Vanessa Rogers	1 Snowberry Field, Thankerton ML12 6RJ E: lanarkshire@scotlandsgardens.org
Area Organiser:	Nicky Eliott Lockhart	Stable House, Cleghorn Farm, Lanark ML11 7RW
District Photographer:	Alistair McNeill	alistairmcneill@hotmail.com
Treasurer:	Sheila Munro Tulloch	Castlegait House, Castlegait ML10 6FF

GARDENS OPEN ON A SPECIFIC DATE

Cleghorn, Stable House, Cleghorn Farm, Lanark	Sunday, 28 February
Old Farm Cottage, The Ladywell, Nemphlar, Lanark	Saturday/Sunday, 20/21 March
Old Farm Cottage, The Ladywell, Nemphlar, Lanark	Saturday/Sunday, 10/11 April
Covington House, Covington Road, Thankerton, Biggar	Sunday, 25 April
Meadowhead, Dolphinton, West Linton	Sunday, 13 June
Dippoolbank Cottage, Carnwath	Sunday, 20 June
Symington House, By Biggar	Sunday, 4 July
Covington House, Covington Road, Thankerton, Biggar	Sunday, 18 July
Biggar's Gardens, Biggar	Sunday, 25 July
The Walled Garden, Shieldhill, Quothquan, Biggar	Sunday, 1 August
Bothwell Village Gardens, 30 Blantyre Road, Bothwell	Sunday, 8 August
Gardens of the Highest Villages, Leadhills & Wanlockhead	Saturday/Sunday, 21/22 August

GARDENS OPEN REGULARLY

Old Farm Cottage, The Ladywell, Nemphlar, Lanark	5 May - 1 September (Weds only)

GARDENS OPEN BY ARRANGEMENT – BOOK A VISIT WITH THE GARDEN OWNER

Carmichael Mill, Hyndford Bridge, Lanark	1 January - 31 December
Old Manse Wild Garden, Old Manse, Wanlockhead, Biggar	1 April - 31 October
St Patrick's House, Lanark	1 May - 30 June
Covington House, Covington Road, Thankerton, Biggar	1 June - 31 July
The Walled Garden, Shieldhill, Quothquan, Biggar	13 June - 12 September
Auchlochan Walled Garden, New Trows Road, Lesmahagow	20 June - 31 October (not Sats & Suns)
St Patrick's House, Lanark	1 October - 31 October

Lanarkshire

6 COVINGTON HOUSE
Covington Road, Thankerton, Biggar ML12 6NE
Angus and Angela Milner-Brown
T: 01899 308024 E: angela@therathouse.com

Set in seven acres, Covington House stands within both traditional and formal gardens, including an 18th-century walled garden with potager, fruit cages and alpine garden. A fernery and heather garden can be found within one of two small areas of broadleaved woodland. Recently, the original glebe lands have been acquired and will be managed as a wildflower meadow, with a delightful, easy meadow walk. Biodiversity is deliberately being allowed to flourish, in part to help the honeybee apiary near the house, but also to encourage moths, bumblebees and butterflies. A spring visit will be rewarded with a fine display of spring bulbs, particularly tulips. Covington, settled as a feudal estate by King David I, has been an important fortified location since at least the 11th century.

Open: Sunday 25 April, 1pm - 4pm. Also open Sunday 18 July, 1pm - 5pm. And open by arrangement 1 June - 31 July. Admission £5.00, children free. Visitors are welcome to picnic in the Glebe.

Directions: One mile along Covington Road from Thankerton on the left.

Opening for: Bumblebee Conservation Trust

7 DIPPOOLBANK COTTAGE
Carnwath ML11 8LP
Mr Allan Brash

Artist's intriguing cottage garden. Vegetables are grown in small beds. There are herbs, fruit, flowers and a pond in woodland area with a treehouse and summerhouse. This is an organic garden that was mainly constructed with recycled materials. The highlight of your visit will be the stunning display of Meconopsis cultivar, first discovered here a few years ago and now named Meconopsis 'Dippoolbank'.

Open: Sunday 20 June, 2pm - 6pm, admission £4.00.

Directions: Off the B7016 between Forth and Carnwath near the village of Braehead on the Auchengray road. Approximately eight miles from Lanark. Well signposted.

Opening for: The Little Haven (Forth)

8 GARDENS OF THE HIGHEST VILLAGES
Leadhills ML12 6XX and Wanlockhead ML12 6UR
The Gardeners of Leadhills and Wanlockhead
T: 07870 299293

Gardening in the highest villages in Scotland, at around 1500 feet, has its challenges, especially cold winds which burn much in their path. The growing season is short and the soil poor. Despite all this, our gardeners have created four delightful gardens: an ecological garden of 'rooms' dedicated to wildlife; a miniature village; a colourful, immaculate one, and a hillside country garden. The villages also boast the world's first working men's library instituted in 1741.

106 Main Street (NEW) Leadhills ML12 6XR (John McClafferty): In excess of a hundred containers packed with colour and inspiring planting give a stunning first impression of this garden. The hillside behind the cottage has been lovingly tended to make the most of its contours. There are a few surprises to be found here.

Gamblers' Cottage (NEW) 4 Curfew Place, Leadhills ML12 6XX (Mary Brearley): This hillside garden has an amusing history in that, years ago, it was twice extended by the owner by beating neighbours in games of poker. Today it is a great example of what can be achieved on a steep plot.

Lanarkshire

Old Manse Wild Garden (NEW) Old Manse, Wanlockhead ML12 6UR (Callum Gough): Gardening at 1530 feet is not easy but this fascinating garden is exceptional. Extending to one acre, it is divided into many intriguing and sometimes quirky rooms, each one very different from the next and hugely biodiverse. The owner has an interest in permaculture and the garden is dedicated to providing habitats for wildlife (the entire ecosystem for some species), in particular amphibians and all types of insects including butterflies and bees. The butterfly garden should not be missed during the late summer through into autumn, but the plantings designed to attract wildlife and the rest of the garden provide a highly enjoyable visit throughout the year.

Teddywood Bear Village (NEW) 104, Main Street, Leadhills ML12 6XR (Lee Gilmore): A quirky hillside garden featuring the homes of the Leadhills bears, paying homage to the many famous sons of Leadhills. This miniature village has been cleverly designed to incorporate paths, flowers and natural hillside mosses to great effect.

Open: Saturday/Sunday, 21/22 August, 1:30pm - 5pm, admission £5.00, children free. These gardens are not suitable for people with limited mobility. Stout shoes recommended. Leadhills Annual Flower Show takes place on Saturday 21st August. Teas will be served at the Scots Mining Company House, Leadhills. The Mining Museum in Wanlockhead has a visitors' mine and Visitor Centre.

Directions: Leave M74 at Junction 13 and follow signs to Abington, through the village signposted *Leadhills*. From Sanquhar/Thornhill on A76 take turn near Mennock signposted *Wanlockhead*. Buses available from Sanquhar and Lanark.

Opening for: *Leadhills Reading Society & Scottish Mountain Rescue*

Old Manse Wild Garden

9 MEADOWHEAD
Dolphinton, West Linton EH46 7AB
Andrew and Pam Taylor
E: pam.taylor1@btinternet.com

Water is a major feature of this eleven-and-a-half-acre garden with a lochan, river and many wildlife ponds. Wilderness areas provide valuable biodiversity with a wide variety of habitats for flora and fauna, including a family of swans. Many varieties of primula provide a mass of colour in the extensive bog garden and the rhododendrons and azaleas will still be in bloom. Steps from the walled garden with its Italianate ponds, waterfall, rill, fountain and sitooteries, lead up to a pleasant terrace with a small parterre. For the more energetic there are delightful woodland walks.

Open: Sunday 13 June, 2pm - 5pm, admission £4.00, children free. Stout shoes recommended. There will be a children's quiz and a variety of other activities for the young folk. Old and young alike will be fascinated by the live moths and butterflies collected from the garden and presented by a local lepidopterist.

Directions: The garden can be found just off the A702 in the village of Dolphinton.

Opening for: *Wateraid*

Lanarkshire

10 OLD FARM COTTAGE

The Ladywell, Nemphlar, Lanark ML11 9GX
Ian and Anne Sinclair
T: 01555 663345 M: 07833 204180 E: anniesinclair58@gmail.com

This delightful one-acre garden, which featured in Scotland on Sunday in 2019, has something of interest all year round. Open for two weekends in the spring, it has an extensive collection of daffodils, narcissi and other early flowering plants. The wildlife garden offers mown paths through grassed areas, there is a putting green, summerhouse, apiary and pond. Interesting shrubs and small trees, attractive for their flowers, are complemented by herbaceous plantings. Recently, attention has been paid to reducing windbreaks, redesigning borders and developing small alpine beds. The garden is also offered as a backdrop for small groups to take photographs for family birthdays or celebrations. Please contact the owners to arrange in advance.

Open: Saturday/Sunday, 20/21 March & Saturday/Sunday, 10/11 April, 11am - 3pm. May to September, 1st Wednesday of each month, 11am - 3pm. Admission £4.00, children free. Walkers and small groups welcome by arrangement. Visitors are welcome to bring a picnic.

Directions: Leave the A73 at Cartland Bridge (Lanark to Carluke Road) or the A72 (Clyde Valley Road) at Crossford. Both routes are well signposted. The garden is on the Nemphlar spur of the Clyde Walkway, just off the West Nemphlar Road on Ladywell Lane.

Opening for: *Guide Dogs*

11 OLD MANSE WILD GARDEN

Old Manse, Wanlockhead, Biggar ML12 6UR
Callum Gough
T: 07717768324 E: callum.gough@exel.net

Gardening at 1530 feet is not easy but this fascinating garden is exceptional. Extending to one acre, it is divided into many intriguing and sometimes quirky rooms, each one very different from the next and hugely biodiverse. The owner has an interest in permaculture and the garden is dedicated to providing habitats for wildlife (the entire ecosystem for some species), in particular amphibians and all types of insects including butterflies and bees. The butterfly garden should not be missed during the late summer through into autumn, but the plantings designed to attract wildlife and the rest of the garden provide a highly enjoyable visit throughout the year.

Open: By arrangement 1 April - 31 October, admission £5.00, children free. Not suitable for visitors with limited mobility. Stout shoes recommended. In an area of great interest, the Mining Museum in Wanlockhead has a visitors' mine, Visitor Centre and tearoom.

Directions: Leave M74 at Junction 13 follow signs to Abington, through the village signposted *Leadhills*. From Sanquhar/Thornhill, A76 take turn near Mennock signposted *Wanlockhead*. Buses available from Sanquhar and Lanark.

Opening for: *WLMT Hidden Treasures Museum of Lead Mining*

12 ST PATRICK'S HOUSE

Lanark ML11 9EH
Mr and Mrs Peter Sanders
T: 01555 663800 E: peterjeansanders@gmail.com

A May visit to St Patrick's House garden will be rewarded with a stunning display of rhododendrons, azaleas, heathers and shrubs. Created over a 50-year period, the grounds of this five-acre garden slope down to the River Clyde. Natural springs have been harnessed to create water features. A large contemporary pond with an arbour begs you to sit a while. Paths wind between beds of varied plantings and perennials, rockeries, and woodland plants, which all add to the magic of this unexpected gem.

Lanarkshire

Open: By arrangement 1 May - 30 June. Also open by arrangement 1 October - 31 October. Admission £5.00, children free.

Directions: A73 into Lanark, after the Police Station turn right into Friars Lane. At the bottom of the hill turn right onto St Patrick Road. The garden is a quarter of a mile on the left.

Opening for: Lanark Community Development Trust

St Patrick's House

13 SYMINGTON HOUSE
By Biggar ML12 6LW
Mr and Mrs James Dawnay

A traditional walled garden and greenhouses saved from dereliction 20 years ago. Now with beautiful herbaceous borders set off by a backdrop of yew hedges. The greenhouses have collections of fuchsias, geraniums and tender fruit. There are woodland and river walks to enjoy too.

Open: Sunday 4 July, 2pm - 5:30pm, admission £5.00, children free.

Directions: Entrance east of Symington Village on A72 between Biggar and Symington. Bus 191 or 91 Biggar to Lanark.

Opening for: Cancer Research UK

14 THE WALLED GARDEN, SHIELDHILL
Quothquan, Biggar ML12 6NA
Mr and Mrs Gordon
T: 01899 221961 E: nicolagord@gmail.com

This 200-year-old walled garden was completely redesigned and planted in 2014/15 with contemporary features within a classic design. The garden incorporates a modern rill and banks of colour with perennial flowers in a variety of borders. The resident bees enjoy the large area of traditional meadow flowers as well as the rose garden planted with lavenders, salvias and stocks. Outside the wall you will find mature woodland including a giant sequoia and a wildlife pond. If you are interested in fruit and vegetables, take a look at the raised beds and the peach tree and vine in the greenhouse. There are many secluded spots around the garden to sit and enjoy a cup of tea and a home-made cake.

Open: Sunday 1 August, 2pm - 5pm. Also open by arrangement 13 June - 12 September. Admission £5.00, children free.

Directions: Turn off the B7016 between Biggar and Carnwath towards Quothquan. After about a mile, look for signs and turn right at the lodge.

Opening for: Médecins Sans Frontières

Moray & Nairn

Sponsored by
⊕ Investec

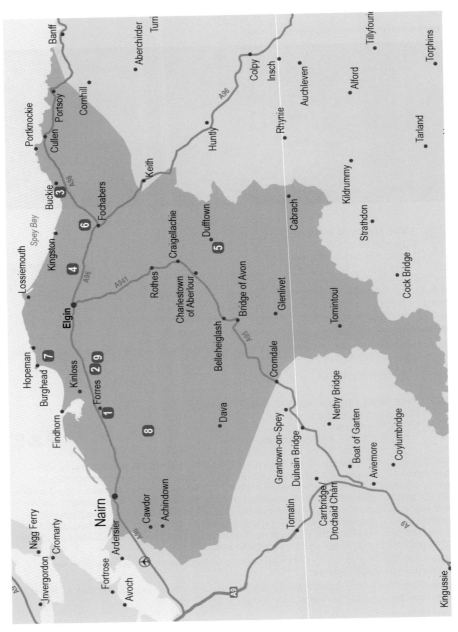

Banff
Aberchirder
Turri
Tillyfouri
Torphins
Portknockie
Portsoy
Cornhill
Colpy
Insch
Alford
Cullen
Auchleven
Tarland
A96
Buckie
Huntly
Rhynie
Strathdon
Kildrummy
3
Fochabers
Dufftown
Cabrach
Cock Bridge
Kingston
Craigellachie
5
6
4
A96
A941
Rothes
Bridge of Avon
Glenlivet
Lossiemouth
Charlestown
of Aberlour
Tomintoul
Elgin
A95
Belleheiglash
Cromdale
Hopeman
7
Burghead
Kinloss
2 9
Nethy Bridge
Forres
Dava
Boat of Garten
Findhorn
1
Grantown-on-Spey
Coylumbridge
8
Dulnain Bridge
Aviemore
Cawdor
Achindown
Carrbridge
Drochaid Chàrr
Nigg Ferry
Nairn
Tomatin
A9
Cromarty
Invergordon
Ardersier
Fortrose
Avoch
A9
Kingussie
Spey Bay

Moray & Nairn

OUR VOLUNTEER ORGANISERS

District Organiser:	James Byatt	Lochview Cottage, Pitgaveny, Elgin IV30 5PQ E: moraynairn@scotlandsgardens.org
Area Organisers:	Michael Barnett	Drumdelnies, Nairn IV12 5NT
	Lorraine Dingwall	10 Pilmuir Road West, Forres IV36 2HL
	David Hetherington	Haugh Garden, College of Roseisle IV30 5YE
	Gwynne Hetherington	Haugh Garden, College of Roseisle IV30 5YE
	Annie Stewart	33 Albert Street, Nairn IV12 4HF
Treasurers:	David Barnett	196 Findhorn, Forres IV36 3YN

GARDENS OPEN ON A SPECIFIC DATE

No 3 Mains of Burgie, by Forres	Sunday, 27 June
Gordon Castle Walled Garden, Fochabers	Sunday, 11 July
Glebe House, Main Street, Urquhart	Sunday, 18 July
Cuthberts Brae, 84 Seatown, Buckie	Saturday/Sunday, 24/25 July
Glenrinnes Lodge, Dufftown, Keith, Banffshire	Sunday, 25 July
No 3 Mains of Burgie, by Forres	Sunday, 8 August

GARDENS OPEN REGULARLY

Gordon Castle Walled Garden, Fochabers	1 January - 31 December
Logie House, Dunphail, Forres	1 January - 31 December
Burgie Arboretum, Between Forres and Elgin	1 April - 31 October

GARDENS OPEN BY ARRANGEMENT – BOOK A VISIT WITH THE GARDEN OWNER

10 Pilmuir Road West, Forres	25 January - 11 March
Haugh Garden, College of Roseisle	1 May - 31 August
10 Pilmuir Road West, Forres	1 June - 1 August

Moray & Nairn

1 **10 PILMUIR ROAD WEST**
Forres IV36 2HL
Mrs Lorraine Dingwall
T: 01309 674634 E: fixandig@aol.com

Plantswoman's small town garden with over 300 cultivars of hostas, an extensive collection of hardy geraniums together with many other unusual plants. Managed entirely without the use of artificial fertilisers or chemicals, the owner encourages hedgehogs, toads and wild birds to control slugs. In early spring there are approximately 150 named snowdrops to be seen, some of which are very rare.

Open: By arrangement 25 January - 11 March for Snowdrops. Also open by arrangement 1 June - 1 August. Admission £3.00, children free.

Directions: From Tesco roundabout at Forres continue along Nairn Road. Take the first left onto Ramflat Road, then go right at the bottom and first left onto Pilmuir Road West.

Opening for: Macmillan Cancer Support

2 **BURGIE ARBORETUM**
Between Forres and Elgin IV36 2QU
Hamish Lochore
T: 01343 850231 E: hamish@burgie.org

A rare opportunity to see a sizeable woodland garden/arboretum in its infancy. It has a good collection of rhododendrons, Sorbus, alder, birch and Tilia but also includes many unusual trees from around the world. The arboretum is zoned into geographic areas and species type. It includes a Japanese Garden, bog garden, bog wood, loch and quarry garden. First created in 2005 and is ongoing. Most plants are grown from hand-collected seed and propagated in the Georgian greenhouse.

Open: 1 April - 31 October, 8am - 5pm, admission £3.00, children free.

Directions: A96 between Forres and Elgin. Four miles east of Forres. Six miles west of Elgin. Sign to *Burgie Mains* along the A96 is set in wrought iron decorated with horses and cattle. South off the main road and one mile to the Woodland Garden car park.

Opening for: Sandpiper Trust & World Horse Welfare

Burgie Arboretum © Robbie Laing

Moray & Nairn

3 CUTHBERTS BRAE
84 Seatown, Buckie AB56 1JS
Elizabeth and Malcolm Schofield
T: 07878 486093 E: malcolmsgsp@gmail.com
W: https://www.instagram.com/cuthbertsbrae_garden/

Gardeners' World Magazine, Readers Garden of the Year 2020, Judges Choice Winner. *'In the small seaside town of Buckie in the north east Moray Coast, what was once a wild hill, overgrown with brambles, has now been transformed into a beautiful colourful haven for all to admire.'* – *Gardeners' World Magazine.* The garden is sited on a steep hill with a small flat terrace with gravel garden wrapping around the house. The path then takes you down the bank into a terraced cottage garden that is a magnet for bees, butterflies and other wildlife. As you continue into the newer section of the garden you discover the greenhouse, rabbit enclosure and veg beds. *'This garden is a really good lesson in what you can achieve in inhospitable conditions with limited knowledge and money.'* – Alan Titchmarsh.

Open: Saturday/Sunday, 24/25 July, 12:30pm - 5pm, admission £4.00, children free.

Directions: Arriving from the Tesco road turn left at the Town Square. Take the next right. Use the car park at the *Seatown* sign. Follow the signage to our garden. The garden is a short walk (five minutes) from the Town Square.

Opening for: *Scottish Association For Mental Health*

Cuthberts Brae

Moray & Nairn

4 GLEBE HOUSE
Main Street, Urquhart IV30 8LG
Melanie Collett

Early 19th-century formal walled garden of the former manse by Alexander Forteath, also incorporating a unique doocot in its construction of clay dab. The garden consists of colourful herbaceous borders within the walled garden and box hedge symmetry. A wide variety of roses together with an orchard and kitchen garden area to the south.

Open: Sunday 18 July, 2pm - 4:30pm, admission £5.00, children free.

Directions: Off the main street in Urquhart, find the walled entrance at the end of the street. Follow parking signs.

Opening for: The Royal Air Force Benevolent Fund

5 GLENRINNES LODGE
Dufftown, Keith, Banffshire AB55 4BS
Mrs Kathleen Locke
T: 01340 820384
W: www.glenrinnes.com

The garden and policies surrounding Glenrinnes Lodge are typical of a Victorian lodge. There is a semi-formal garden that lends itself to quiet reflection with stunning views up Glenrinnes. A walled kitchen garden, with a large heated greenhouse supplies plants, cut flowers and fruit and vegetables. There is also a newly-developed herbaceous border displaying vibrant colours through the use of perennial and half-hardy plantings. There are delightful walks in the meadow around the pond and into the woodland; watch out for red squirrels! Some major works have been undertaken recently and much of the garden is still a 'work in progress'. In keeping with the rest of the estate, Glenrinnes Lodge is gardened following organic principles.

Open: Sunday 25 July, 2pm - 5pm, admission £4.00, children free.

Directions: In the centre of Dufftown at the Clock Tower take the B9009 road to Tomintoul for about one mile. After passing Dufftown Golf Club on your right there is a lane to the left, which leads to two stone pillars to Glenrinnes Lodge.

Opening for: Alzheimer's Research UK

6 GORDON CASTLE WALLED GARDEN
Fochabers, Moray IV32 7PQ
Angus and Zara Gordon Lennox
T: 01343 612317 E: info@gordoncastlescotland.com
W: www.gordoncastle.co.uk

At almost eight acres in size, Gordon Castle has one of the oldest and largest walled gardens in Britain. Lovingly restored to its former glory with a modern design by award-winning designer Arne Maynard, this beautiful garden is overflowing with vegetables, fruit, herbs and cut flowers. The onsite café has a 'Plant, Pick, Plate' ethos using wonderful fresh produce grown in the garden. There is a children's natural play area and shop.

Open: Sunday 11 July, 2pm - 5pm. And open 1 April - 31 October, 10am - 4pm. Admission £7.00, children free. Open the rest of the year, 10am - 4pm. Admission £3.00, children free. £3.00 charge for the children's play area.

Directions: The main entrance is at the western end of the village of Fochabers, just off the A96, nine miles east of Elgin and 12 miles west of Keith.

Opening for: Gordon Lennox Fochabers Trust (Sunday 11 July) & Donation to SGS Beneficiaries

Moray & Nairn

7 HAUGH GARDEN
College of Roseisle IV30 5YE
Gwynne and David Hetherington
T: 01343 835790

Within our previously unmaintained two-acre garden, we have created four different environments. Our mature woodland, with informal pond and 18th century farmhouse ruin, is filled with birdsong, insects and wildlife. Walks meander through early flowering snowdrops followed by hellebores, tulips and narcissi. Extensive herbaceous borders enclosing the lawns and orchard display vibrant colours. Various paths wind their way through young pine and birch woodland underplanted with shrubs and meadow areas. Lastly, our organic vegetable beds, soft fruit and polytunnel keep us self-sufficient all year round.

Open: By arrangement 1 May - 31 August, admission £5.00, children free.

Directions: From Elgin take the A96 west, then the B9013 Burghead Road to the crossroads at the centre of College of Roseisle. The garden is on the right, enter from the Duffus Road.

Opening for: CHAS & Alzheimer Scotland

8 LOGIE HOUSE
Dunphail, Forres IV36 2QN
Alasdair and Panny Laing
E: panny@logie.co.uk
W: www.logie.co.uk

Originally a formal garden with a large area of vegetable production, Logie House garden has been developed since 1991 with emphasis on trees, shrubs and hardy perennials, giving all-year-round interest. The meandering burn and dry stone walls support the creation of a wide variety of planting habitats from dry sunny banks to damp shady areas. Many of the unusual plants are propagated for sale in the Garden Shop at Logie Steading. Also features woodland and river walks.

Open: 1 January - 31 December, 10am - 5pm, admission £2.00, children free.

Directions: Six miles south of Forres off the A940. Follow signs to *Logie Steading*.

Opening for: Donation to SGS Beneficiaries

9 NO 3 MAINS OF BURGIE
by Forres, Moray IV36 2QZ
Mandeigh Wells-Ali
E: mandeigh@gmail.com

The hidden garden behind the hedge where cultivated and wild meet. We have no 'weeds' in this garden which is managed as a pollinator's paradise. This small cottage garden also contains a sunny courtyard, a Japanese area leading into a tiny woodland garden and onto the mixed border. Both the fish pond and wildlife pond support toads, newts, frogs and dragonflies. The main beds are an immersion in nectar-rich plants and bright colours. Various species of cultivars mingle with wild plants such as ground elder to create a species-rich feast.

Open: Sunday 27 June, 10am - 4pm. Also open Sunday 8 August, 10am - 4pm. Admission £3.00, children free.

Directions: Located off the A96 between Forres and Elgin, four miles east of Forres – sign to *Burgie Mains/Arboretum*. Turn south off the main road and head up the hill, past the sign to *Arboretum*, keep left and up to hairpin bend right at the top. No 3 is the right-hand cottage. Parking in the field next door. Bus 10 stops on the main road at the bottom of the lane to the cottage/arboretum.

Opening for: All proceeds to SGS Beneficiaries

Peeblesshire & Tweeddale

1 8 HALMYRE MAINS
West Linton EH46 7BX
Joyce and Mike Madden
T: 07774 609547 E: agentromanno@gmail.com

A half-acre organic garden with colourful herbaceous borders and a number of raised vegetable beds. There is a greenhouse, Keder house and polytunnel leading to the wildlife pond with a summer house and viewing area. There are four large composting bins, with additional hot bin, wormery and the production of comfrey liquid fertiliser on display.

Open: Sunday 11 July, 2pm - 5pm, admission £5.00, children free.

Directions: Five miles south of Leadburn Junction on the A701 (Moffat).

Opening for: *Lamancha Hub*

8 Halmyre Mains © Kathy Henry

Peeblesshire & Tweeddale

2 ABBOTSFORD

Melrose TD6 9BQ
The Abbotsford Trust
T: 01896 752043 E: enquiries@scottsabbotsford.co.uk
W: www.scottsabbotsford.com

The garden was designed by Sir Walter Scott with advice from artists, architects and friends. It is a rare surviving example of a Regency garden layout and completely different from the English landscape garden style of Capability Brown. Scott's garden aims to provide a harmonious transition between the luxury and comfort of the interiors of the house with wonders of nature in the wider estate through a series of secluded, richly detailed and sheltered 'rooms'. In its day it would have showcased the latest plants discovered from around the globe, both in its borders and 'stove houses'. Regular tours are held exploring Scott's vision for the garden and the hidden meanings of its design. Check the Abbotsford website for details.

Open: 1 March - 31 March 10am - 4pm, 1 April - 31 October 10am - 5pm & 1 November - 30 November 10am - 4pm, admission details can be found on the garden's website.

Directions: Off the A6091 near Melrose. Buses X62 and 72 from Edinburgh and Peebles. Train from Waverley to Tweedbank. Minibus or one-mile walk from train station.

Opening for: *Donation to SGS Beneficiaries*

3 DAWYCK BOTANIC GARDEN

Stobo EH45 9JU
A Regional Garden of the Royal Botanic Garden Edinburgh
T: 01721 760254
W: www.rbge.org.uk/dawyck

Dawyck is a regional garden of the Royal Botanic Garden Edinburgh which had its 350th anniversary in 2020. Stunning collection of rare trees and shrubs. With over 300 years of tree planting, Dawyck is a world-famous arboretum with mature specimens of Chinese conifers, Japanese maples, Brewer's spruce, the unique Dawyck beech and sequoiadendrons from North America which are over 150 feet tall. Bold herbaceous plantings run along the burn. Range of trails and walks. Fabulous autumn colours.
National Plant Collection: *Larix* spp. and *Tsuga* spp.
Champion Trees: Numerous.

Open: Sunday 10 October, 10am - 5pm, admission details can be found on the garden's website.

Directions: Eight miles south west of Peebles on the B712.

Opening for: *Donation to SGS Beneficiaries*

Peeblesshire & Tweeddale

4 DRUMELZIER OLD MANSE
Drumelzier, nr Broughton ML12 6JD
Mr and Mrs Julian Birchall
T: 01899 830319 E: birchall@oldmanse.org.uk

A traditional Manse garden in the attractive Upper Tweed Valley. Colourful herbaceous border within a walled garden. Unusual selection of plants throughout the garden including many varieties of geraniums and rare *Meconopsis baileyi* 'Hensol Violet'. There is a rock border and kitchen garden. A wide variety of shrubs have been planted in the last 15 years in the lower garden leading down to the path along the burn with shade-loving plants and hostas. A beautiful setting and surrounding walks.

Open: By arrangement 15 June - 15 August, admission £5.00, children free.

Directions: On the B712, ten miles south west of Peebles, two miles east of Broughton.

Opening for: British Red Cross

5 GATTONSIDE VILLAGE GARDENS
Gattonside TD6 9NP
The Gardeners of Gattonside
T: 07500 869041 E: jenbarr@gmx.com

Gattonside is a pretty, south-facing village beside the River Tweed and opposite the town of Melrose. Traditionally the village was known for its fruit trees and was the garden for the monks of Melrose Abbey. Today it is a village with a variety of gardens. You can visit small, cottage type gardens with mixed herbaceous borders, Dahlia enthusiasts' gardens and even ponds with fish. There are new gardens and more established gardens – with mixed borders, vegetables, fruit cages as well as many beautiful trees, copper beech and oak to name but a few.

Open: Sunday 15 August, 1pm - 5pm, admission £5.00, children free. Tickets and maps available from village hall on Main Street.

Directions: Short walk from Melrose over the chain bridge. Twenty minute walk along the River Tweed from Tweedbank Railway Station. By car access off the A68 signposted *Gattonside*.

Opening for: Macmillan Cancer Support & The Fragile X Society

6 GLEN HOUSE
Glen Estate, Innerleithen EH44 6PX
The Tennant family
T: 01896 830210 E: info@glenhouse.com
W: www.glenhouse.com

Surrounding the outstanding Scots Baronial mansion designed by David Bryce in the mid-19th century, Glen House gardens are laid out on shallow terraces overhanging the glen itself, which offers one of the loveliest designed landscapes in the Borders. The garden expands from the formal courtyard through a yew colonnade, and contains a fine range of trees, long herbaceous border and a pool garden with pergola, all arranged within the curve of slopes sheltering the house.

Open: Sunday 4 July, 1pm - 4pm, admission £5.00, children free. Plant Stall provided by Quercus Garden Plants

Directions: Follow the B709 out of Innerleithen for approximately two-and-a-half miles. Right turn at signpost for *Glen Estate*.

Opening for: CDP Worldwide: sustainable finance sculpture

Peeblesshire & Tweeddale

7 **HAYSTOUN**
Peebles EH45 9JG
Mrs David Coltman

This seventeenth-century house (not open) has a charming walled garden with an ancient yew tree, herbaceous beds and vegetable garden. There is a wonderful burnside walk created since 1980, with azaleas and rhododendrons leading to a small ornamental loch (cleared in 1990) with stunning views up Glensax Valley.

Open: Saturday/Sunday, 22/23 May, 1:30pm - 5pm, admission £5.00, children free.

Directions: Cross the River Tweed in Peebles to the south bank and follow *Scotland's Gardens Scheme* sign for approximately one mile.

Opening for: *St. Columba's Hospice Limited*

Haystoun © Kathy Henry

Peeblesshire & Tweeddale

8 KIRKTON MANOR HOUSE

Peebles EH45 9JH
Mrs Rosemary Thorburn
T: 01721 740220 E: rpthorburn@icloud.com

Kirkton Manor House has a delightful, three-acre, informal country garden set in the beautiful Manor Valley. It enjoys spectacular open views and calling curlews from its riverside position. Bluebells flank the impressive entrance leading to a new shrub border. Stone steps continue through to terraced slopes filled with bulbs, roses and hellebores providing height, interest and fragrance. Grass paths meander along the burn where blue and white camassia, meconopsis, and ligularia thrive in this sunny meadow environment. Later, in June, sisyrinchiums, irises, orchids and many flowering shrubs and roses are abundant. The natural woodland includes many interesting trees.

Open: By arrangement 1 February - 30 September, admission £5.00, children free. Snowdrops and Winter Walks in February.

Directions: Turn off the A72 west of Neidpath Castle, signposted to *Kirkton Manor*. After crossing the River Tweed, enter a garden gate which is a mile downhill, opposite a *Beware Horses* sign.

Opening for: All proceeds to SGS Beneficiaries

Kirkton Manor House © Kathy Henry

Peeblesshire & Tweeddale

9 LAMANCHA COMMUNITY HUB PLANT SALE
Old Moffat Road, Lamancha EH46 7BD
Mike Madden
T: 07774 609547 E: hello@lamanchahub.org.uk

A small community garden with shrubs for year-round interest, and herbaceous and cottage garden borders. It is currently in the process of being developed as an organic demonstration garden, following the recent erection of a Keder house, rainwater collection and composting areas.

Open: Sunday 6 June, 10am - noon, admission by donation.

Directions: Three miles south of the Leadburn Junction on the A701.

Opening for: Lamancha Hub

10 PORTMORE
Eddleston EH45 8QU
Mr and Mrs David Reid
T: 07825 294388
W: www.portmoregardens.co.uk

Lovingly created by the current owners over the past 30 years; the gardens surrounding the David Bryce-designed mansion house contain mature trees and offer fine views of the surrounding countryside. Large walled garden with box-edged herbaceous borders is planted in stunning colour harmonies, potager, rose garden, pleached lime walk and ornamental fruit cages. The Victorian glasshouses contain fruit trees, roses, geraniums, pelargoniums and a wide variety of tender plants. There is also an Italianate grotto and water garden with shrubs and meconopsis. The woodland walks are lined with rhododendrons, azaleas and shrub roses. Starred in *Good Gardens Guide* and featured in Kenneth Cox's book *Scotland for Gardeners* and on *The Beechgrove Garden*.

Open: 1 July - 31 August (Wednesdays only), 1pm - 5pm. Also open by arrangement 1 June - 31 August. Admission £6.00, children free.

Directions: Off the A703 one mile north of Eddleston. Bus 62.

Opening for: Eddleston Parish Church of Scotland

11 PRIESTON HOUSE
Melrose TD6 9HQ
Jilly Bhamra
T: 07903 560818 E: jilly.bhamra@hotmail.co.uk
W: www.theghilliebnb.com

A delightful three-and-a-half-acre garden designed around a Georgian farmhouse dating from 1720. It has a woodland area with many interesting trees and a small pond. The terraced lawns are enhanced by several secluded seating areas surrounded by yew hedges and mature shrubs including many rhododendrons and azaleas. The walls of the house are covered by old roses, clematis and wisteria and a side gate leads to a paddock and views across open countryside to the Eildon Hills and Cheviots.

Open: Friday 11 June & Saturday 19 June, 2pm - 5pm, admission £5.00, children free.

Directions: Off the A699 Selkirk to St. Boswells road, signposted.

Opening for: Borders Childrens Charity

Peeblesshire & Tweeddale

12 QUERCUS GARDEN PLANTS
Whitmuir Farm, West Linton EH46 7BB
Rona Dodds
T: 01968 660708 E: quercusgardenplants@gmail.com
W: www.quercusgardenplants.co.uk

We are a small, independent nursery growing and selling a wide range of happy, healthy plants propagated from our nursery gardens. At just under two acres, these gardens were started in 2015 to show visitors and customers what can be grown in our conditions here on a north-west-facing hill at 850 feet above sea level. Explore our herb garden, scented garden, wildlife garden and all the other inspirational smaller borders. New areas are being developed to include prairie-style planting of grasses and perennials. Many of the plants seen in the gardens are available to buy in the nursery.

Open: Sunday 30 May & Sunday 11 July, 10am - 5pm, admission by donation. A percentage of plant sales on these dates will be donated to Scotland's Garden Scheme and Breast Cancer Care. The 16 inch narrow gauge garden railway will be running from 2pm.

Directions: On the A701, four miles south of the Leadburn junction or two miles north of West Linton.

Opening for: *Breast Cancer Care*

13 THE PINES
43, St Ronan's Terrace, Innerleithen EH44 6RB
Fiona and Bill Jack
T: 07969 081965 E: fgbwjack@gmail.com

Camellias, rhododendrons and hydrangeas thrive in this terraced one-and-a-half-acre garden, perched on the hillside overlooking the town of Innerleithen in the Tweed Valley. Set over four levels, the gardens were created in 1905 around the Arts and Crafts house. Formal lawns, rose garden and herbaceous borders fill the lower terraces. The owners have concentrated on bee friendly flowers to encourage insects as they have a fenced-in area for their apiary. On the upper level, a large walled garden with restored glasshouse, original espalier apple trees leading through to wildflower meadows and hillside woodland.

Open: Sunday 9 May, 2pm - 5pm, admission £5.00, children free.

Directions: Bus X62. From Peebles turn left off the A72 on Hall Street which bears right into St Ronan's Terrace. The garden has green gates and is uphill on the left. Free car park at bottom of hill.

Opening for: *Innerleithen Community Trust*

Peeblesshire & Tweeddale

14 THE POTTING SHED
Broughton Place, Broughton, Biggar ML12 6HJ
Jane and Graham Buchanan-Dunlop
T: 01899 830574 E: buchanandunlop@btinternet.com

A one-acre garden, begun from scratch in 2008, on an exposed hillside at 900 feet. It contains herbaceous plants, climbers, shrubs and trees, all selected for wind resistance and ability to cope with the poor, stony soil. There are (usually) fine views to the Southern Uplands.

Open: Tuesdays 1 June, 8 June, 29 June & 6 July, 11am - 5pm. Also open by arrangement 1 May - 31 October. Admission £5.00, children free.

Directions: Signposted from the main A701 Edinburgh – Moffat Road, immediately north of Broughton village.

Opening for: Macmillan Cancer Support: Borders General Hospital

15 THE SCHOOLHOUSE
Skirling by Biggar ML12 6HD
Mike and Annie Thompson
T: 01899 860396 E: info@schoolhouseflowers.co.uk
W: www.schoolhouseflowers.co.uk

A village garden extending to approximately half an acre which has been developed over the past 18 years by the owners. The gardens are home to a seasonal cut flower business with a secluded cutting garden of raised beds filled with a large variety of unusual annuals and a wildlife pond. There are lawns with deep herbaceous borders, a productive kitchen garden, orchard with heritage fruit trees and thriving beehives, mini parkland recently planted with native trees. Featured in *Scotland on Sunday*.

Open: Sunday 25 July, 11am - 5pm, admission £5.00, children free.

Directions: Take the A701 or A702 and follow road signs to *Skirling*. The garden is directly opposite the village green.

Opening for: Skirling Village Hall

16 WEST LINTON VILLAGE GARDENS
West Linton EH46 7EW
West Linton Village Gardeners
T: 01968 660669 E: j.bracken101@gmail.com

A varied and interesting selection of gardens including one new garden and two that were last opened in 2017. Included is a walled manse garden in a beautiful riverside setting. Main features amongst all the gardens are large herbaceous borders, greenhouses full of pelargoniums and show begonias, alpine planting and vegetable beds. In addition, a new garden features an extensive woodland walk, a wildlife pond and collection of hostas.

Open: Sunday 18 July, 2pm - 5pm, admission £5.00, children free. Teas, tickets and plant sale at the Graham Institute in the centre of the village, which will be signposted. Subject to Covid-19 restrictions.

Directions: About 15 miles south west of Edinburgh, take the A701 or the A702 and follow signs. Bus 101 or 102 to Gordon Arms Hotel.

Opening for: Ben Walton Trust & Borders General Hospital, Margaret Kerr Unit

Perth & Kinross

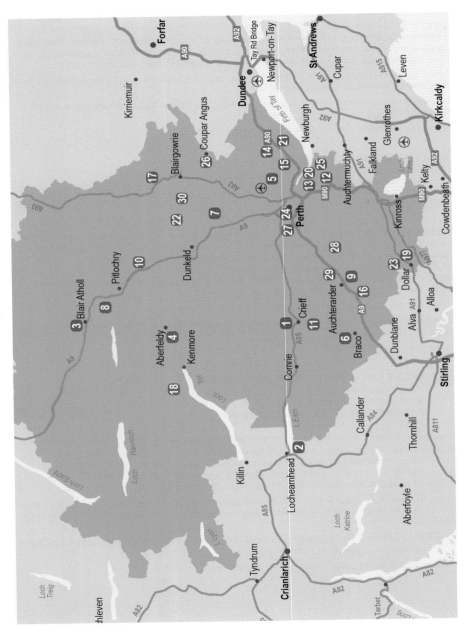

Perth & Kinross

OUR VOLUNTEER ORGANISERS

District Organiser:	Margaret Gimblett	Fehmarn, Bridge of Earn PH2 9AH E: perthkinross@scotlandsgardens.org
Area Organisers:	Gill Boardman	16, Acremoar Drive, Kinross KY13 8RE
	Henrietta Harland	Easter Carmichael Cottage, Forgandenny Road, Bridge of Earn PH2 9EZ
	Elizabeth Mitchell	Woodlee, 28 St Mary's Drive, Perth PH2 7BY
	Lizzie Montgomery	Burleigh House, Milnathort, Kinross KY13 9SR
	Judy Norwell	Dura Den, 20 Pitcullen Terrace, Perth PH2 7EQ
	Richenda Pearson	Spinneyburn, Rumbling Bridge PH2 0PY
	Kareen Robertson	2 The Orchard, Bridge of Earn PH2 9DX
	Clarinda Snowball	The Limes, Dallerie, Crieff PH7 4JH
	Fiona Stewart	7 Craigend Cottages, Craigend PH2 8PX
	Mary Thompson	Mosspark House, Rumbling Bridge KY13 0QE
	Heather Wood	Mill of Forneth, Forneth, Blairgowrie PH10 6SP
Media Officer:	Jo Houldsworth	Barrowmore House, Milnathort KY13 9SL
District Photographers:	Carolyn Bell	6 Strathearn Terrace, Perth PH2 0LS
	Mike Bell	
	David Hay	21A, Robertson Crescent, Pitlochry PH16 5HD
	Camelia Hudema	64a Scott Street, Perth PH2 8JW
	Mike Nicoll	
Treasurer:	Michael Tinson	Parkhead House, Burghmuir Road, Perth PH1 1JF

GARDENS OPEN ON A SPECIFIC DATE

Cloan, by Auchterarder	Sunday, 14 February
Megginch Castle, Errol	Sunday, 11 April
Fingask Castle, Rait	Saturday, 1 May
The Bield at Blackruthven, Blackruthven House, Tibbermore	Saturday, 15 May
Cloan, by Auchterarder	Sunday, 16 May
Eastbank Cottage, Perth Road, Abernethy	Saturday/Sunday, 22/23 May
Muckhart Open Gardens, Coronation Hall, Pool of Muckhart	Saturday/Sunday, 29/30 May
Cloan, by Auchterarder	Sunday, 6 June
Mill of Forneth, Forneth, Blairgowrie	Sunday, 6 June
Lower Earn Small Gardens Trail, Fehmarn, Bridge of Earn	Sunday, 13 June
Blair Castle Gardens, Blair Atholl	Saturday, 26 June
Allotment Association of Crieff, Turretbank Road Crieff	Saturday, 10 July
Drummond Castle Gardens, Muthill, Crieff	Sunday, 1 August
Cloan, by Auchterarder	Sunday, 15 August

Perth & Kinross

GARDENS OPEN REGULARLY

Glenericht House Arboretum, Blairgowrie	1 January - 19 December
Fingask Castle, Rait	25 January - 4 March (Mons & Thurs)
Princeland House, Blairgowrie Road, Coupar Angus, Blairgowrie	6 February - 14 March (Sats & Suns)
Braco Castle, Braco	13 February - 31 October
Glendoick, Glencarse, Perthshire	1 April - 31 May
Bolfracks, Aberfeldy	1 April - 31 October
Ardvorlich, Lochearnhead	29 April - 30 May
Gleneagles House, Auchterader	3 May - 24 May (Mondays only)
Bradystone House, Murthly	3 June - 5 August

GARDENS OPEN BY ARRANGEMENT – BOOK A VISIT WITH THE GARDEN OWNER

Hollytree Lodge, Muckhart, Dollar	1 April - 31 October
The Old Farmhouse, Dunning Road	1 April - 31 July
Bonhard House, Perth	1 April - 31 October
Eastbank Cottage, Perth Road, Abernethy	1 April - 30 June
Glenlyon House, Fortingall	1 April - 30 September
The Steading at Clunie, The Steading	1 April - 31 July
Craigowan, Ballinluig	10 April - 31 July
Pitcurran House, Abernethy	1 May - 1 September
Carig Dhubh, Bonskeid, Pitlochry	1 May - 30 September
Fehmarn, Bridge of Earn	1 May - 30 September
The Crofts, Perth Road, Dunning	1 May - 25 June
Parkhead House, Parkhead Gardens, Burghmuir Road, Perth	1 June - 31 August

Perth & Kinross

1 ALLOTMENT ASSOCIATION OF CRIEFF
Turretbank Road Crieff PH7 4AR
The Allotmenteers
E: crieffplots@gmail.com

The Allotment Association of Crieff (AAC) is set high up above the River Turret with stunning panoramic views of Glen Turret and towards St Fillans. The AAC is now nine years old and previously the ground was used for grazing horses and sheep. Without vehicular access the Allotmenteers had to manually create this little bit of paradise which was a huge task. It is without doubt one of the most scenic locations of any allotment association in Scotland. We invite guests to wander round and enjoy the 30+ allotments which produce a huge variety of vegetables, fruit and flowers. Without mains water or electricity and subject to high winds and cold winter temperatures the allotments face special challenges but nonetheless, the products range from asparagus to grapes and specialist raspberries, along with the more usual veg and fruit.

Open: Saturday 10 July, 1pm - 4:30pm, admission £5.00, children free.

Directions: Leaving Crieff on the A85 take right turn towards Glenturret Distillery, turn immediately left up a track. You will see a small parking area and the path to the allotments which will be signposted. It is uphill and is not wheelchair accessible. Parking is available on Turretbank Road and is signposted. To access the allotments cross the A85 to the beginning of the path and follow signs.

Opening for: Local charities

2 ARDVORLICH
Lochearnhead FK19 8QE
Mr and Mrs Sandy Stewart
T: 01567 830335

Beautiful hill garden featuring over 170 different species of rhododendrons and many hybrids, grown in a glorious setting of oaks and birches on either side of the Ardvorlich Burn. The paths are quite steep and rough in places and boots are advisable, especially when wet.

Open: 29 April - 30 May, 9am - dusk, admission £5.00, children free.

Directions: On South Loch Earn Road three miles from Lochearnhead, five miles from St Fillans.

Opening for: The Ghurka Welfare Trust

3 BLAIR CASTLE GARDENS
Blair Atholl PH18 5TL
Blair Charitable Trust
T: 01796 481207 E: office@blair-castle.co.uk
W: www.blair-castle.co.uk

Blair Castle stands as the focal point in a designed landscape of some 2,500 acres within a Highland estate. Hercules Garden is a walled enclosure of about nine acres recently restored to its original 18th-century design with landscaped ponds, a Chinese bridge, contemporary plantings, vegetables and an orchard of more than 100 fruit trees. The glory of this garden in summer is the herbaceous border, which runs along the 275 yard south-facing wall. A delightful sculpture trail incorporates contemporary and 18th-century sculpture as well as eight new works, letter-carving on stone from the *Memorial and Commemorative Arts* charity's 'Art and Memory Collection'. Diana's Grove is a magnificent stand of tall trees including grand fir, Douglas fir, larch and wellingtonia running along the Banvie Burn, with the 12th-century ruins of St Bride's Church on the far bank.

Open: Saturday 26 June, 9:30am - 4:30pm, admission details can be found on the garden's website.

Directions: Off A9, follow signs to *Blair Castle, Blair Atholl.*

Opening for: Donation to SGS Beneficiaries

Perth & Kinross

4 BOLFRACKS
Aberfeldy PH15 2EX
Under new ownership from 2021
T: 01887 820344 E: info@bolfracks.com

Special three-acre garden with wonderful views overlooking the Tay Valley. Burn garden with rhododendrons, azaleas, primulas and meconopsis in a woodland garden setting. Walled garden with shrubs, herbaceous borders and rose 'rooms' with old-fashioned roses. There is also a beautiful rose and clematis walk. Peony beds are underplanted with tulips and Japanese anemone. The garden has a great selection of bulbs in spring and good autumn colour.

Open: 1 April - 31 October, 10am - 6pm, admission £5.00, children free.

Directions: Two miles west of Aberfeldy on A827. White gates and lodge are on the left. Look out for the brown tourist signs.

Opening for: *Donation to SGS Beneficiaries*

5 BONHARD HOUSE
Perth PH2 7PQ
Stephen and Charlotte Hay
T: 07990 574570 E: stephenjohnhay@me.com

A 19th-century, five-acre garden approached via an avenue of magnificent oaks. Mature trees, six classified by the National Tree Register as 'remarkable', including a monkey puzzle, sequoias, Douglas fir and various hollies. Grassy paths wind around ponds, rockeries, shrubbery and smaller trees, providing some splendid views. Rhododendron and azalea beds. A Pinetum behind the house contains 25 species, beehives and a kitchen garden. Shifting of garden emphasis to habitat. First fruits of rewilding visible. Orchard in process of extension. Possible sighting of red squirrels and green and greater-spotted woodpeckers.

Open: By arrangement 1 April - 31 October, admission £4.00, children free. Sensible shoes should be worn. Tea and cake by arrangement.

Directions: On A94 just under a mile north of Perth take right turn, signed *Murrayshall Hotel.* After approximately one mile take entrance right marked *Bonhard House*, at a sharp left turn. From Balbeggie turn left, signposted for *Bonhard*, one mile north of Scone. Turn right in a half a mile, pass any sign for *Bonhard Nursery*, and enter drive at sharp right turn.

Opening for: *Freedom from Fistula Foundation*

6 BRACO CASTLE
Braco FK15 9LA
Mr and Mrs M van Ballegooijen
T: 01786 880437

A 19th-century landscaped garden with a plethora of wonderful and interesting trees, shrubs, bulbs and plants. An old garden for all seasons that has been extensively expanded over the last 33 years. The partly walled garden is approached on a rhododendron and tree-lined path featuring an ornamental pond. Spectacular spring bulbs, exuberant shrub and herbaceous borders and many ornamental trees are all enhanced by the spectacular views across the park to the Ochils. From snowdrops through to vibrant autumn colour this garden is a gem. Look out for the embothrium in June, hoheria in August, eucryphia in September and an interesting collection of rhododendrons and azaleas with long flowering season.

Open: 13 February - 31 October, 10am - 5pm. Snowdrops and Winter walks February/early March. Admission £4.00, children free. No dogs allowed.

Directions: Take a one-and-a-half-mile drive from the gates at the north end of Braco Village, just west of the bridge on the A822. Parking at the castle is welcome.

Opening for: *The Woodland Trust Scotland*

Perth & Kinross

7 BRADYSTONE HOUSE
Murthly PH1 4EW
Mrs James Lumsden
T: 01738 710308 E: pclumsden@me.com

This cottage garden was converted from a derelict farm steading to create a unique courtyard garden that bursts with colour throughout the season. It has been imaginatively planted by Patricia and her gardener Scott and has recently undergone some exciting changes. There is a woodland walk with interesting trees underplanted with shrubs, that leads to a duck pond where ducks and hens roam freely. There is also a small, productive kitchen garden. A real gem of a garden; visitors who are fortunate enough to meet the owner and Scott will be impressed by their enthusiasm and knowledge.

Open: 3 June - 5 August, 11am - 4pm, admission £5.00, children free. Thursdays only.

Directions: From south/north follow A9 to Bankfoot, then signs to *Murthly*. At crossroads in Murthly take private road to Bradystone.

Opening for: Scotland's Charity Air Ambulance

8 CARIG DHUBH
Bonskeid, Pitlochry PH16 5NP
Jane and Niall Graham-Campbell
T: 01796 473469 E: niallgc@btinternet.com

'I don't know how Niall and Jane manage to grow their splendid meconopsis on the sand and rock of their garden but they do, most successfully.' In this stunning situation, when not admiring the views, you will find wonderful primulas, cardiocrinum and meconopsis, all interspersed between beautiful shrubs and other herbaceous plants. Look up and in July you will see roses flowering 40 feet up in the tree. This is a gem of a garden and you will be welcomed by Niall and Jane Graham-Campbell with all their expert knowledge.

Open: By arrangement 1 May - 30 September, admission £5.00, children free.

Directions: Take the old A9 between Pitlochry and Killiecrankie, turn west on the Tummel Bridge Road B8019, Carig Dhubh is three-quarters of a mile on north side of the road.

Opening for: Earl Haig Fund Poppy Scotland

9 CLOAN
by Auchterarder PH3 1PP
Neil Mitchison
T: 07958 155831 E: niall@fastmail.co.uk

Two acres of wild garden, with a wide variety of rhododendrons and azaleas, and an impressive collection of trees, including metasequoia, cryptomeria, *Acer cappadocicum*, *Sequoia sempervirens*, *Quercus robur* 'Filicifolia', liriodendron, several Japanese maples, magnificent beech and Scots pine trees, and extensive yew topiary; also an acre of walled garden with embothriums, *Acer griseum*, liquidambar, several sorbus varieties, parrotia and a large herbaceous border. Fine views of Strathearn from the front of the house.

Open: Sunday 14 February, 10am - 3pm, for Snowdrops and Winter Walks. Sunday 16 May, Sunday 6 June & Sunday 15 August 11am - 5pm. Admission £4.00, children free.

Directions: From A823, just south of A9, follow small road heading north east, signposted *Duchally*. Continue for approximately two-and-a-half miles, turn right at sign *Coulshill*. Continue just under half a mile. Follow signs for car parking.

Opening for: Tiphereth Limited: Camphill Scotland

Perth & Kinross

10 CRAIGOWAN
Ballinluig PH9 0NE
Ian and Christine Jones
T: 01796 482244 E: i.q.jones@btinternet.com

This is a specialist garden with a major collection of rhododendrons put together over the last 40 years; initially, mainly species from Glendoick following the plant hunting and discoveries of Peter Cox and the late Sir Peter Hutchison and others. In the last 20 years there have been added noteworthy hybrids sourced from Glendoick and the major English nurseries. Each year further additions are made and earlier introductions which have outgrown their original or secondary planting spot are moved to new locations. With growth rates tending to increase, this is a major exercise but the result is a constantly changing garden and more plants are developing into a spectacular presentation. Other plant types include magnolias, ornamental acers and a collection of unusual trees. There are areas of more formal beds where there is a large collection of meconopsis, lilies including cardiocrinum with roughly a hundred flowering each year. The rhododendron flowering period lasts from January to August but the best months are April, May and June. There is adjoining woodland which is being replanted with trees free of disease risk and with the larger rhododendrons which have outgrown the more formal areas. In June and July two large herbaceous borders give summer colour and interest.

Open: By arrangement 10 April - 31 July, admission £5.00, children free.

Directions: From north or south A9 to Ballinluig junction. Follow sign for *Tulliemet* and *Dalcapon*. Pass the filling station and Ballinluig Hotel. Turn right following the *Tulliemet/Dalcapon* sign; this is a steep narrow road so take care. About a half mile up the road take a left turning with fields on either side and Craigowan is the first house on the left about a half mile along. Park on paviours adjoining house.

Opening for: LUPUS UK

11 DRUMMOND CASTLE GARDENS
Muthill, Crieff PH7 4HN
Grimsthorpe & Drummond Castle Trust Ltd
T: 01764 681433
W: www.drummondcastlegardens.co.uk

Activities and events for a great family day out. The gardens of Drummond Castle were originally laid out in 1630 by John Drummond, second Earl of Perth. In 1830 the parterre was changed to an Italian style. One of the most interesting features is the multi-faceted sundial designed by John Mylne, Master Mason to Charles I. The formal garden is said to be one of the finest in Europe and is the largest of its type in Scotland.

Open: Sunday 1 August, 1pm - 5pm, admission details can be found on the garden's website.

Directions: Entrance two miles south of Crieff on Muthill road (A822).

Opening for: BLESMA

12 EASTBANK COTTAGE
Perth Road, Abernethy PH2 9LR
Mike and Elsa Thompson
T: 01738 850539 E: mikestuartthompson@hotmail.com

Traditional Scottish cottage, a third-of-an-acre garden, walled and bounded by a small burn to the east. Erythroniums, varieties of wood anemones, trillium, a fine display of clematis, rhododendrons and azaleas. Altogether a little haven in the country.

Open: Saturday/Sunday, 22/23 May, 10am - 4pm. Open by arrangement 1 April - 30 June and open from 10am - 4pm on Sunday 13 June as part of the Lower Earn Small Gardens Trail.

Perth & Kinross

Directions: When coming from Perth, drive to the Abernethy *30 mph* sign. A layby is on the left. The gate has the property name on it. Bus 36 stops very close by.

Opening for: All proceeds to SGS Beneficiaries

| 13 | **FEHMARN** |

Bridge of Earn PH2 9AH
Mr and Mrs Gimblett
T: 01738 813653 E: gimblettsmill@aol.com

A big 'small garden' with woodland, water, rocks and a cottage garden to the front. Shady and very sunny borders with more trees and lawn to the back. Tucked away, a tiny but productive fruit and vegetable garden. All looked after and loved by two 'oldies', passionate chief gardener, Margaret, and her husband, Iain, head groundsman.

Open: By arrangement 1 May - 30 September, admission £5.00, children free. Also open Sunday, 13 June, 10 am - 4 pm, as part of the Lower Earn Small Gardens Trail.

Directions: From the north and south, take the exit on the M90 for Bridge of Earn and follow the road into the village. Go ahead at the mini-roundabout and take the first right into Old Edinburgh Road. At the T junction turn right and go straight on for about half a mile. Turn right by a group of bungalows. Fehmarn is first on the right.

Opening for: Perth Autism Support SCIO

Fehmarn © Camelia Hudema

Perth & Kinross

14 **FINGASK CASTLE**
Rait PH2 7SA
Mr and Mrs Andrew Murray Threipland
T: 01821 670777 ext 2 E: andrew@fingaskcastle.com
W: www.fingaskcastle.com

Scotland's surrealist garden: spectacular topiary staggers across the garden bumping into stone globes, marble balls, statues and a figure of Alice (in Wonderland). Other literary and historical characters are scattered among the 17th-century pleasure gardens. Bonnie Prince Charlie and his father are said to have approached the castle up the long yew avenue known as 'The King's Walk'. A 15-minute walk takes you down to the dell beneath the castle and St Peter's Well – a stopping place for medieval pilgrims on their way to the bones of the saintly Queen Margaret at Dunkeld Cathedral. Return via a Chinese bridge, Gabriel's bridge, an iron age fort, along a stream, past Sir Stuart's House, and back to the castle via the Old Orchard parking area. There are large drifts of snowdrops, daffodils and flowering shrubs depending on the season.

Champion Trees: *Pinus wallichiana* (Bhutan Pine) and the handsome remnants of what was the largest walnut in Scotland.

Open: 25 January - 4 March, Mondays and Thursdays, 10am - 4pm for Snowdrops and Winter Walks. Admission £3.00, children free. Also open Saturday 1 May, 1.30pm - 4.30pm, admission £4.00, children free. Homemade teas on 1 May only.

Directions: Half-way between Perth and Dundee. From the A90 follow signs to *Rait* until small crossroad, turn right and follow signs to *Fingask*.

Opening for: *All Saints Episcopal Church & Fingask Follies*

Fingask Castle © Mike Bell

Perth & Kinross

15 GLENDOICK
Glencarse, Perthshire PH2 7NS
Cox Family
T: 01738 860260 E: manager@glendoick.com
W: www.glendoick.com

Glendoick's gardens and garden centre with its award-winning café is the ideal spring day out in April and May. In 2019, Glendoick celebrated 100 years since Euan Cox returned from Burma with the first rhododendron seeds to be grown and planted in the gardens. Glendoick Gardens were included in the Independent on Sunday survey of Europe's top 50 Gardens and boasts a unique collection of plants from three generations of Cox plant-hunting expeditions in China and the Himalaya. Enjoy one of the finest collections of rhododendrons and azaleas, primulas, meconopsis and other acid-loving plants in the woodland garden and the gardens surrounding the house. Many of the rhododendron and azalea species and hybrids have been introduced from the wild or bred by the Cox family and the gardens boast a vast range of plants from as far afield as Chile, Tasmania and Tibet. There are fine waterfall views in the woodland gardens. The award-winning Glendoick Garden Centre has one of Scotland's best selections of plants including their world-famous rhododendrons and azaleas as well as a gift shop and café. National Plant Collection: *Rhododendron* sect. *Pogonanthum*, subsect. *Uniflora*, subsect. *Campylogyna* & subsect. *Glauca* and Cox hybrids.

Open: 1 April - 31 May, 10am - 4pm, admission £5.00, children free. No dogs allowed, please. Tickets must be purchased from the Garden Centre before you drive up to the garden. For Group bookings email: jane@glendoick.com. Groups should pay by single cheque made out to Glendoick Gardens Ltd. Any restaurant bill needs to be paid for separately. We can offer guided tours for keen gardening groups only. Visiting at other times by appointment, please email: gardencentre@glendoick.com.

Directions: Follow brown signs to Glendoick Garden Centre off A90 Perth – Dundee road. Gardens are a half mile behind the Garden Centre. After buying tickets at the Garden Centre, please drive up & park at gardens (free parking).

Opening for: *Donation to SGS Beneficiaries*

16 GLENEAGLES HOUSE
Auchterarder PH3 1PJ
Mr and Mrs Martin Haldane
T: 01764 682388 E: petronella@gleneagles.org

Gleneagles has been the home of the Haldanes since the 13th century. This is a wild garden which has been evolving for the last 25 years. There's a walk round the pond and along the burn past the 15th-century chapel to the ruins of a laird's tower.
Champion Trees: *Tallest Leylandii in Scotland.*

Open: 3 May - 24 May (Mondays only), 2pm - 5pm, admission £5.00, children free.

Directions: A823 Crieff/Dunfermline road just south of the A9.

Opening for: *St Kessog's Episcopal Church – Auchterarder*

Perth & Kinross

17 **GLENERICHT HOUSE ARBORETUM**
Blairgowrie PH10 7JD
Mrs Mary McCosh
T: 01250 872092 E: m.mccosh123@gmail.com

Spectacular collection of Victorian-planted trees and shrubs which are centred around a Grade 'A' listed suspension bridge (1846). Ninety-two tree varieties, mostly conifers including a top Douglas fir which is 171 feet and still growing, also a collection of younger trees. In late May and June you will be able to view the wonderful daffodils and the rhododendrons in flower.

Open: 1 January - 19 December, dawn - dusk, admission £4.00, children free. Honesty box.

Directions: Off the A93, the Lodge House is four miles north of Blairgowrie on the right-hand side A93 when coming from Blairgowrie. Follow the avenue towards the bridge and the parking area is beside the river.

Opening for: Sands

18 **GLENLYON HOUSE**
Fortingall PH15 2LN
Mr and Mrs Iain Wotherspoon
T: 07974 350533 E: thewotherspoons@ednet.co.uk

Interesting garden framed by hedges, with colourful herbaceous borders and fruit trees underplanted with perennials and annuals. There is a kitchen and cutting garden as well as a wildlife pond.

Open: By arrangement 1 April - 30 September, admission £5.00, children free.

Directions: Take the A827 to Aberfeldy, then B846 to Coshieville then turn off for Glen Lyon.

Opening for: Fortingall Parish Church

19 **HOLLYTREE LODGE**
Muckhart, Dollar FK14 7JW
Liz and Peter Wyatt
T: 07973 374687 E: elizwyatt@aol.com

A tranquil one-acre garden, divided by internal hedges into 'rooms' as featured in *Country Homes & Interiors* in January 2018. Highlights include a small Japanese garden, mini orchard, naturalised spring bulbs and wildflowers, rill and wildlife pond, mixed herbaceous borders, a good collection of rhododendrons and azaleas, a variety of unusual trees and shrubs, snow gum, *Metasequoia glyptostroboides*, Persian ironwood and acers, many producing spectacular autumn colours. Our aim is to garden with nature, complementing our beekeeping interests.

Open: By arrangement 1 April - 31 October, admission £5.00, children free. Open to anyone calling or emailing. Singles or groups welcome. Also open Saturday/Sunday 29/30 May, 12pm - 5pm, as part of Muckhart Open Gardens.

Directions: Approximately 100 yards from the A91 (between Dollar and Milnathort) down the small lane directly opposite the entrance to the Inn at Muckhart.

Opening for: Coronation Hall, Muckhart

Perth & Kinross

20 LOWER EARN SMALL GARDENS TRAIL
Fehmarn, Bridge of Earn, Perthshire PH2 9AH
The Gardeners of Lower Earn

Eastbank Cottage Perth Road, Abernethy PH2 9LR (Mike and Elsa Thompson): Traditional Scottish cottage, a third-of-an-acre garden, walled and bounded by a small burn. Erythroniums, varieties of wood anemones, trillium, a fine display of clematis, rhododendrons and azaleas. A little haven in the country.

Nurse Peattie's Garden Main Street, Abernethy (Abernethy in Bloom): This garden is dedicated to the memory of the District Nurse who served Abernethy. The garden aims to have year-round interest starting with a sea of spring bulbs. The aim of AIB is to make it a haven for people to enjoy the peacefulness and beauty of the garden.

Fehmarn (NEW), Bridge of Earn PH2 9AH (Mr and Mrs Gimblett): See separate entry in Perth & Kinross District.

Craigievairn Heughfield Road, Bridge of Earn PH2 9BG (George Watson): This small garden is well-stocked with fruit trees, shrubs, roses, perennials and annuals and an established vegetable plot. It is a haven for wildlife with a beaver run to the burn in the wild section of the garden.

Heughfield House Walled Garden Heughfield House, Heughfield Road, Bridge of Earn PH2 9BH (Ian Cuthbert Imrie): This garden is like a painting, contrast, colour, light, dark, composition, perspective, all come into play. Designed for birds and wildlife, this unusual garden has a formal garden with clipped box balls, and a pagoda style summer house surrounded with unusual shrubs and shade loving plants to the rear.

Inverine (NEW), Main Street, Bridge of Earn PH2 9PN (Margaret and Ron Cowie): The garden is divided into three areas. The first area features a rockery with varieties of alpines and heathers. The second area has raised beds used for growing vegetables. The third area features flower, shrub and gravel beds. This area also has a patio, summerhouse and pergola. Along the two walls are five trained espalier apple trees.

Oaklea (NEW), Forgandenny, Perthshire PH2 9EL (Liz & Ron Smith): This was the old smithy on what was the main street of a pretty Perthshire village. Every bit of space has been turned into a garden full of interest for all seasons. Dozens of pots of all sizes from old cattle troughs to decorative ones and a raised bed bring colour.

South Dumbuils Farm (NEW), Forgandenny, Perthshire PH2 9EX (Clare McQueen): A small farm cottage garden slowly being brought back to life by a new gardener. Raised borders and beds, pots of all sizes, an old pear tree, two hollies and box hedges are the framework for a cheerful jumble of flowers for bees and insects. Wonderful views and an interesting collection of 'treasures'.

Open: Sunday 13 June, 10am - 4pm, admission £7.50, children free. Tickets and teas (an additional £3 pp) available at 'Fehmarn'. Advance tickets also available online – please check SGS website closer to the date for information.

Directions: From north and south, take the exit on the M90 for Bridge of Earn and follow the road into the village. Go ahead at the mini roundabout and take the first right into Old Edinburgh Road. At the T junction turn right and go straight on for about half a mile. Turn right by a group of bungalows. Fehmarn is first on the right.

Opening for: Dunbarney and Forgandenny Parish Church

Perth & Kinross

21 MEGGINCH CASTLE
Errol PH2 7SW
Giles Herdman and Catherine Drummond-Herdman
T: 01821 642222 E: info@megginch.com
W: megginchcastle.com

Come and wander through our hosts of golden daffodils under the ancient trees and avenues of Megginch. Head through the charming, cobbled courtyard where you will find a vibrant outdoor market with Local Producers showcasing their products from milk and honey to meat and vegetables (NeighbourFood.co.uk/markets/megginch-castle/30). On into the walled garden where there is a collection of daffodils from the renowned collectors, Duncan and Kate Donald from Croft 16 Daffodils. In the orchard, have a chat with Gavin and his bees, walk back past some of the apple and pear trees that make up our two National Collections, and we will somehow ensure that there will be homemade cakes and tea under the tallest yew trees in Scotland! National Plant Collection: Scottish cider apples, Scottish Heritage apples and pears. Champion Trees: *Acer palmatum*.

Open: Sunday 11 April, 2pm - 5pm, admission £5.00, children free.

Directions: Ten miles from Perth and Dundee directly off the A90, Perth-bound carriageway, 600 yards after the Errol/Rait flyover, on the left hand side, 300 yards after *Beware Pedestrians Crossing* sign, or signed entrance just before the level crossing in Errol Station.

Opening for: *All proceeds to SGS Beneficiaries*

22 MILL OF FORNETH
Forneth, Blairgowrie PH10 6SP
Mr and Mrs Graham Wood
E: gaw@forneth-mill.co.uk

Built on the site of a former watermill on the Lunan Burn, originally laid out in the 1970s by James Aitken, the Scottish landscape designer and naturalist. The sheltered four-acre garden has a range of mature trees, including a Himalayan blue cedar, large rhododendrons, azaleas and a wide range of shrubs. The former mill lade feeds rocky waterfalls and a lily pond. Planting includes established perennials with seasonal colours, many bulbs, primulas and heathers, plus a vegetable garden on the site of an old tennis court and a new wildflower meadow.

Open: Sunday 6 June, 2pm - 5pm, admission £5.00, children free.

Directions: Take the A923 Dunkeld to Blairgowrie road. Six miles east of Dunkeld turn south onto a minor road signposted Snaigow and Clunie. Mill of Forneth is the first gate on the left-hand side. PLEASE NOTE: Due to wet weather conditions there may be limited safe meadow parking on site (exceptions will be made for people with mobility problems).

Opening for: *Community Connections: Wellmeadow House, Gas Brae, Blairgowrie PH10 6AY*

23 MUCKHART OPEN GARDENS
Coronation Hall, Pool of Muckhart, Dollar FK14 7JF
The Gardeners of Muckhart Village

A collection of 10 gardens in and around the Pool o'Muckhart and Yetts o'Muckhart. For a small village Muckhart boasts an enchanting variety of large and small, formal and informal gardens displaying some of the best and most thoughtfully considered aspects of amateur gardening in this part of Scotland. From wildlife friendly gardens, magnificent trees, statues and hugely colourful banks of rhododendrons and azaleas, to beautiful and constantly evolving gardens where paths meander through terraced beds and ponds, and pocket-sized cottage gardens where lettuces jostle for position amongst the bluebells. Visitors cannot fail to be inspired by the variety of gardens, and the commitment of our gardeners.

Perth & Kinross

Open: Saturday/Sunday, 29/30 May, noon - 5pm, admission £6.00, children free. (£8.00 for both days.) Tickets, garden details and map available at Muckhart Coronation Hall where teas are also available for a donation.

Directions: Parking at Muckhart Coronation Hall, Pool of Muckhart FK14 7JF. On A91, four miles east of Dollar. Occasional bus X53

Opening for: Coronation Hall, Muckhart & Muckhart Primary School

24 PARKHEAD HOUSE

Parkhead Gardens, Burghmuir Road, Perth PH1 1RB
Mr and Mrs M S Tinson
T: 01738 625983 M:07748 186 815 E: maddy.tinson@gmail.com
W: www.parkheadgardens.com

Parkhead is an old farmhouse sited within an acre of beautiful gardens. Mature trees include an outstanding 300-year-old Spanish chestnut. This hidden gem is a garden for all seasons. Gentle terracing and meandering paths lead you past a large variety of unusual and interesting plants and shrubs. If you seek colour and inspiration come and see this garden.
National Plant Collection: *Lilium* (Mylnefield lilies).

Open: By arrangement 1 June - 31 August, admission £5.00, children free.

Directions: Parkhead Gardens is on a small lane off the west end of Burghmuir Road in Perth. More detailed directions on request.

Opening for: Plant Heritage

Parkhead House

Perth & Kinross

25 **PITCURRAN HOUSE**
Abernethy PH2 9LH
The Hon Ranald and Mrs Noel-Paton
T: 01738 850933 E: patricianp@pitcurran.com

This end-of-village garden was created 16 years ago. It includes an interesting combination of trees, rare shrubs and herbaceous plants including azaleas, rhododendrons, tree peonies, trilliums and veratrum. Also a rose pergola, eucryphias and a large west-facing hydrangea border for the later summer. Above the pond there is a good collection of pink- and white-barked birches and an embryonic arboretum.

Open: By arrangement 1 May - 1 September, admission £6.00, children free.

Directions: South east of Perth. From M90 (exit nine) take A912 towards Glenfarg, go left at roundabout onto A913 to Abernethy. Pitcurran House is at the far eastern end of the village. Buses run through Abernethy from Perth and surrounding districts.

Opening for: Juvenile Diabetes Research Foundation Limited

26 **PRINCELAND HOUSE**
Blairgowrie Road, Coupar Angus, Blairgowrie PH13 9AU
Helen and Alistair Carmichael
T: 07864778170 E: carmichaelhf@hotmail.com

A previously overgrown garden on the edge of Coupar Angus, currently under active renovation and replanting by Mrs Carmichael. There is a wooded area around the drive and entrance with a beautiful selection of different snowdrops planted among mature trees.

Open: 6 February - 14 March (Saturdays & Sundays), 10am - 2pm for Snowdrops and Winter Walks, admission by donation. No refreshments. Dogs on a lead only.

Directions: From the outskirts of Coupar Angus, take the A94 Blairgowrie Road from the mini roundabout junction with the A923, to the junction with School Road. Entry to Princeland House is on the corner of School Road, past a lodge cottage on the left of the entrance.

Opening for: Shelter Scotland

27 **THE BIELD AT BLACKRUTHVEN**
Blackruthven House, Tibbermore PH1 1PY
The Bield Christian Co Ltd
T: 01738 583238 E: info@bieldatblackruthven.org.uk

The Bield is set in extensive grounds with well-maintained lawns, hedges, flower meadow and specimen trees. A labyrinth is cut into the grass of the old orchard and there is a wheelchair-friendly labyrinth. Traditional walled garden with colourful, richly stocked borders and lawns, plus cut-flower garden, Healing Garden, glasshouse, trained fruit trees and organic vegetable plot. Walk through extensive woodland and visit the old curling pond. Southton Smallholding is a social enterprise ten minutes walk away, featuring vegetable plots, polytunnels and a number of animals (not staffed on the day).

Open: Saturday 15 May, 2pm - 5pm, admission £5.00, children free.

Directions: From Dundee or Edinburgh, follow signs for *Glasgow, Stirling* and *Crianlarich* which lead onto the Perth bypass. Head west on the A85 signed to *Crieff/Crianlarich* to West Huntingtower. Turn left at the crossroads to *Madderty/Tibbermore*. Entrance is left after a half-mile passing the gate lodge on your right. Parking signed to right at the steading.

Opening for: Southton Smallholding

Perth & Kinross

28 THE CROFTS
Perth Road, Dunning PH2 0SF
Lorna and Alistair Radbourne
T: 01764 684452 E: lradbourne@btinternet.com

The garden of a watercolour and stained glass artist; small, welcoming, natural and full of year-round interest. Old roses and honeysuckle round the windows, a gravel garden, small lawn surrounded by trees, shrubs and flowers and a greenhouse tucked away near the studio. Small sculptures nestle among the plants or appear in the gravel. Under apple trees in the wild garden is a beautiful drystone curving seat, and on the cottage roof, a flock of fan and straight tail white doves bask in the sun. Sit quietly for five minutes in this garden and feel your cares slip away.

Open: By arrangement 1 May - 25 June, admission £5.00, children free.

Directions: From Dunning take the B934 towards Forteviot and Bridge of Earn. The Crofts is behind the last house on the right up a red gravel drive. Limited parking.

Opening for: Perth Autism Support SCIO

29 THE OLD FARMHOUSE
Dunning Road PH3 1DU
Jane and Nigel Gallier
T: 01764 662471 E: thegalliers@msn.com

A garden of approximately one acre with herbaceous borders, a gravel garden, vegetable garden, trained fruit trees in half-wine barrels, wild areas under-planted with bulbs, and woodland areas, with other areas still being developed. As you approach the house, look out for our kamikaze hens and the fantailed doves taunting the local sparrow hawk in their netted area. The garden is not always immaculate; a well-ordered winter garden and a floriferous summer garden.

Open: By arrangement 1 April - 31 July, 10.30am - 4.30pm. Admission £5.00, children free.

Directions: From the A9, halfway along the A824 between Auchterarder and Aberuthven take the B8062 at Grand Eagles and head towards Dunning. We are on the left just before the A9 bridge.

Opening for: ABF The Soldiers' Charity

30 THE STEADING AT CLUNIE
The Steading PH10 6SG
Jean and Dave Trudgill
T: 01250884263 E: davetrudgill@googlemail.com

The Steading at Newmill lies on the Lunan Burn midway between Lochs Clunie and Marlee. The policies include paths that extend for 800yds along the Lunan, a small, colourful cottage garden and 6 acres of woodland, ponds and a wildflower meadow. In spring, the ponds come alive with frogs (and spawn) and toads. Wooded areas have a profusion of primroses, wood anemones and then bluebells, snake's head fritillary flowers in the meadow, followed by cowslips and lady's smock. In early summer, eleven species of native orchids flower in the meadow, more than in any other meadow in Scotland, including rarities such as marsh hellebore and the two species of butterfly orchids.

Open: By arrangement 1 April - 31 July, admission £4.50, children free.

Directions: Three miles west of Blairgowrie on the A923. About 600 yards after the Kinloch Hotel in the direction of Dunkeld take the track on the left, just after a mobile phone mast and a breeze-block wall. There is parking for ten vehicles in paved area & ample parking in a neighbour's field, provided the ground is not soft.

Opening for: Save the Children UK

Renfrewshire

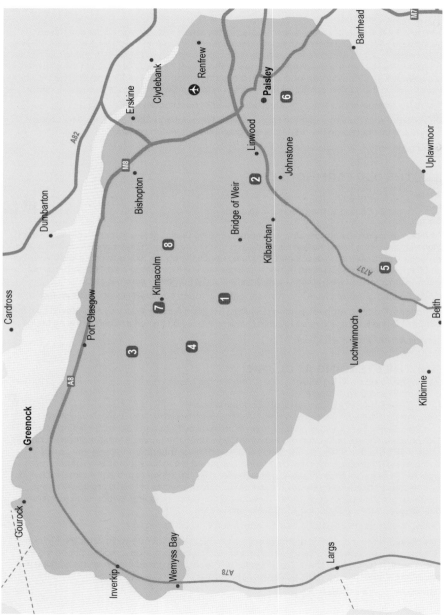

Renfrewshire

OUR VOLUNTEER ORGANISERS

District Organiser:	Alexandra MacMillan	Langside Farm, Kilmacolm, PA13 4SA renfrewshire@scotlandsgardens.org
Area Organisers:	Helen Hunter Barbara McLean	2 Bay Street, Fairlie, North Ayrshire KA29 0AL 49 Middlepenny Road, Langbank, PA14 6XE
Treasurer:	Jean Gillan	Bogriggs Cottage, Carlung KA23 9PS

GARDENS OPEN ON A SPECIFIC DATE

SGS Kilmacolm Plant Sale, Outside Kilmacolm Library, Kilmacolm	Saturday, 24 April
Highwood, off Lochwinnoch Road, Kilmacolm	Sunday, 9 May
Wraes, Corseliehill Road, nr Houston	Sunday, 16 May
Perch Corner, 25 Stanely Crescent, Paisley	Sunday, 23 May
Carruth, Bridge of Weir	Sunday, 30 May
Newmills Cottage, Burnthills, Nr Lochwinnoch	Sunday, 6 June
High Mathernock Farm, Auchentiber Road, Kilmacolm	Sunday, 13 June
Craig Hepburn Memorial Garden, Stirling Drive, Linwood	Tuesday/Wednesday, 22/23 June

GARDENS OPEN BY ARRANGEMENT – BOOK A VISIT WITH THE GARDEN OWNER

Wraes, Corseliehill Road, nr Houston	1 April - 1 September

Renfrewshire

1 CARRUTH
Bridge of Weir PA11 3SG
Mr and Mrs Charles Maclean

Over 20 acres of long-established rhododendrons, woodland with good bluebells, young arboretum and lawn gardens in a lovely landscaped setting. New landscaping carried out in 2020.

Open: Sunday 30 May, 2pm - 5pm, admission £5.00, children free.

Directions: Access from the B786 Kilmacolm/Lochwinnoch road. From Bridge of Weir take the Torr Road until you get to the B786. Turn right and after about 100 yards, the garden entrance is on the right. About three-and-a-half miles from Kilmacolm and five-and-a-half miles from Lochwinnoch on the B786.

Opening for: Marie Curie

Carruth

Renfrewshire

2 CRAIG HEPBURN MEMORIAL GARDEN

Stirling Drive, Linwood PA3 3NB
Linwood High School
T: 01505 336146 E: craighepburnmemorialgarden@yahoo.co.uk
W: facebook.com/welovegardening14/

The Craig Hepburn Memorial Garden and Outdoor Learning Centre is located in Linwood High School. Our original garden with an outdoor classroom has been expanded to include community raised beds, an orchard, greenhouse and presentation area. We work with all years in the school reconnecting them to the natural world whether it is through growing in our organic garden, encouraging biodiversity or learning about sustainability. Winners of the *Cultivation Street* competition 2020.

Open: Tuesday (4pm - 6pm)/Wednesday (3pm - 6pm), 22/23 June, admission £3.50, children free.

Directions: Exit the M8 at St James Interchange and take the A737. Take the exit for Linwood onto the A761, follow to Clippens Road and then Stirling Drive. Accessible by McGill buses.

Opening for: Teenage Cancer Trust

3 HIGH MATHERNOCK FARM

Auchentiber Road, Kilmacolm PA13 4SP
Rosemary Leslie

A south-facing half-acre garden planted by the present owner, comprising different areas for relaxation and contemplation. A productive vegetable patch with all-year-round produce, areas of colourful planting, shrubs and a modified Zen garden with pond and fish. New for 2021 is a herbalist's garden and areas planted for perfume and to attract bees.

Open: Sunday 13 June, 2pm - 5pm, admission £4.00, children free.

Directions: From Kilmacolm cross, head north on Port Glasgow Road towards Port Glasgow. Just out of the village take left onto Auchenbothie Road. Approximately a quarter-of-a-mile take a left under the bridge (Penny's Arch) onto Auchentiber Road and carry on for 1.2 miles. High Mathernock Farm is on the left. There will be *SGS* signs.

Opening for: Worldwide Veterinary Service

4 HIGHWOOD

off Lochwinnoch Road, Kilmacolm PA13 4TF
Dr Jill Morgan

A beautiful woodland walk around 50 acres of native bluebells, primroses and wild garlic in a delightful setting bordering the Green Water river with tumbling waterfalls. Great outdoor space for children to run and explore and splash in the burn (under supervision). A haven of tranquillity only three miles from the centre of Kilmacolm.

Open: Sunday 9 May, 2pm - 5pm, admission £4.00, children free. Stout footwear is recommended as the footpath is uneven and can be muddy in inclement weather. Dogs are welcome on a lead. Fantastic opportunity for lovers of wildflowers and photography.

Directions: Take the B786 Lochwinnoch road out of Kilmacolm and continue for approximately two miles. From Lochwinnoch take the B786 Kilmacolm road for approximately six miles. Then follow the yellow *SGS* signs.

Opening for: Orkidstudio

Renfrewshire

5 NEWMILLS COTTAGE
Burnthills, Nr Lochwinnoch PA12 4JR
Patricia Allan

Surviving mill in a series of five built in 1864. Well-established colourful garden on different levels sloping down to the burn. The garden is divided into different areas with pots and hanging baskets filling areas which cannot be planted. There is also a pond. Steps down to the garden are steep but it can be accessed from a gate on the road if needed and can still be seen from the lower level. The garden has been extended since first opening in 2014 and there have been a few small changes since the last opening in 2017.

Open: Sunday 6 June, 2pm - 5pm, admission £4.00, children free.

Directions: Approach from the Roadhead roundabout near Lochwinnoch (junction of A760/ A737). Take turning by *Powerdoors* onto Auchengrange Hill. At the T junction turn left onto Belltrees Road. Drive for 20 seconds then turn right. Single track road, garden is on the left after one mile. Follow *SGS* signs.

Opening for: *Kilbarchan Improvement Projects*

6 PERCH CORNER
25 Stanely Crescent, Paisley PA2 9LF
Bob and Elaine Moffett

Perch Corner is a large, south-facing garden extending to over half an acre with formal areas and woodland paths. The garden overlooks Stanely Reservoir and beyond to the Gleniffer Braes. Planting consists of a vibrant array of mature shrubs and rare trees, which are more often found in extensive west coast gardens, including a range of magnolias, camellias, rhododendrons, azaleas and acers. Specimens include *Davidia Involucrata*, tulipa, copper beeches and cornus. Children are welcome to explore in the woodland area and garden.

Open: Sunday 23 May, 2pm - 5pm, admission £4.00, children free.

Directions: From the M8 take exit 28a and follow signs for *RAH Hospital.* Continue on Corsebar Road past the hospital to Moredun Road. Right onto Stanely Road, first right to Stanely Avenue. Continue and bear left at the postbox. Look for the *SGS* signs. From the south, take the B775 down Gleniffer Braes. First left after the Jet petrol station onto Stanely Avenue then as above. From Barrhead take the B774 to Paisley, left at the Splash carwash onto Glenburn Road. Follow Glenburn Road to the end, turn right onto Gleniffer Road, then as above.

Opening for: *Parkinsons UK*

7 SGS KILMACOLM PLANT SALE
Outside Kilmacolm Library, Kilmacolm PA13 4LE
SGS Kilmacolm Plant Sale

Spring plant sale in the centre of Kilmacolm.

Open: Saturday 24 April, 10am - noon

Directions: The plant sale will be held at the Cross outside the Library and Cargill Centre. Accessible by McGill buses.

Opening for: *Pancreatic Cancer Scotland*

Renfrewshire

8 **WRAES**
Corseliehill Road, nr Houston PA6 7HU
Tim and Jo Mack
T: 07985156555 E: jomack22@gmail.com

Tranquil seven-acre garden developed since 2012, with far-reaching rural views. Only surviving historic 1860 wood planted by Lady Anne Spiers of Houston House for the Wraes, currently undergoing renovation with extensive new tree planting. Formal garden with raised herbaceous borders, woodland walk with 100 different rhododendron species and hybrids. Pond, burnside and cliffside walks, peaceful woodland walk with plentiful seating areas to relax and enjoy the views and tranquillity. A great space for children to run and explore (under supervision). New in 2020 – apple and pear orchard, wildflower meadow and grass maze.

Open: Sunday 16 May, 2pm - 5pm. Also open by arrangement 1 April - 1 September. Admission £5.00, children free.

Directions: From Houston follow Barochan Road towards Langbank B789 for about a mile, turn left down Corseliehill Road. From Kilmacolm leave the village on Houston Road, past the golf course, turn left down Corseliehill Road for about a mile. Follow the yellow *SGS* signs.

Opening for: Breast Cancer Care

Wraes

Roxburghshire

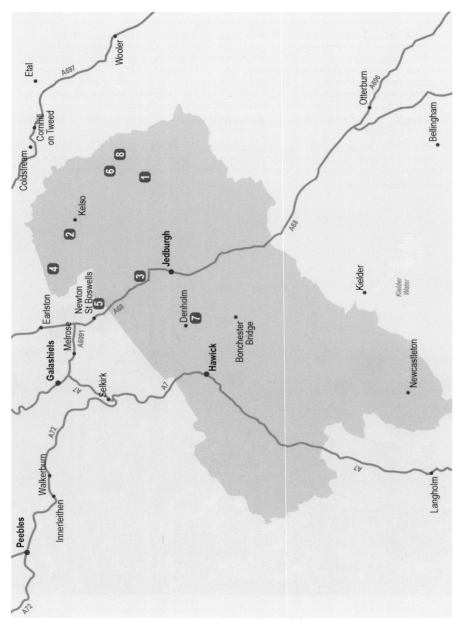

Roxburghshire

OUR VOLUNTEER ORGANISERS

District Organiser:	Sally Yonge	Newtonlees House, Kelso TD5 7SZ E: roxburghshire@scotlandsgardens.org
Area Organisers:	Julie Golding Penny Wright	5 Manorhill Farm Cottages Kelso TD5 7PA 6 Nisbet Mill Farm Cottages TD8 6TT
District Photographer:	Christopher Jones	South Lodge, Ravenswood House, Melrose TD6 9DF
Treasurers:	Veronica Ruiz De Edmond Peter Yellowlees	Flat 3, 31 West Granton Road, Edinburgh EH5 1HN 19 Frogston Road West, Edinburgh EH10 7AB

GARDENS OPEN ON A SPECIFIC DATE

Smailholm Village Gardens, Smailholm Village Hall, Smailholm	Sunday, 20 June
Corbet Tower, Morebattle, near Kelso	Saturday, 26 June
Yetholm Village Gardens, Town Yetholm	Sunday, 4 July

GARDENS OPEN REGULARLY

Floors Castle and Gardens, Kelso	3 January - 31 December
Monteviot, Jedburgh	1 April - 31 October
Stable House, Maxton, St Boswells, Melrose	1 May - 31 October (Mondays only)

GARDENS OPEN BY ARRANGEMENT – BOOK A VISIT WITH THE GARDEN OWNER

West Leas, Bonchester Bridge	1 January - 31 December
Thirlestane, Kelso	31 March - 31 October
Stable House, Maxton, St Boswells, Melrose	1 May - 31 October

Roxburghshire

1 CORBET TOWER
Morebattle, near Kelso TD5 8AQ
Simon and Bridget Fraser

Charming Scottish Victorian garden set in parklands in the foothills of the Cheviots. The established garden includes a formal box parterre rose garden with old fashioned roses, a well stocked, traditional walled vegetable and cutting garden, terraced lawns around the Victorian house and medieval peel tower. The gardens are approached via an attractive woodland walk with lime avenue.

Open: Saturday 26 June, 2pm - 5pm, admission £5.00, children free.

Directions: From A68 north of Jedburgh take A698 for Kelso. At Kalemouth (Teviot Smokery) follow B6401 to Morebattle, then road marked Hownam to Corbet Tower.

Opening for: *Cheviot Churches: Church of Scotland: Morebattle*

2 FLOORS CASTLE AND GARDENS
Kelso TD5 7SF
The Duke of Roxburghe
T: 01573 223333
W: www.floorscastle.com

The gardens are situated within the grounds of Floors Castle. Meander through to the formal Millennium Parterre and soak up the spectacular visions of colour, texture and the most delicious scents around the four herbaceous borders in one of the finest Victorian kitchen gardens in Scotland. Perennial gardens, fruit cage, Tapestry Garden and glasshouse access. Terrace Café, Castle Kitchen Deli shop and play area. Explore the grounds, which offer woodland and riverside walks from Easter to October.

Open: Castle, Courtyard Café & Grounds (Including special event closures) 1 May - 30 September. **Walled Garden, Gardens and Terrace Café**, April - September, 10.30am - 5.00pm. October - March, 10.30am - 4.00pm. **Christmas and New Year**, closed 25th & 26th December, 1st & 2nd January and 6th - 10th January. Admission details can be found on the garden's website.

Directions: Floors Castle can be reached by following the A6089 from Edinburgh; the B6397 from Earlston; or the A698 from Coldstream. Go through Kelso, up Roxburgh Street to the Golden Gates.

Opening for: *Donation to SGS Beneficiaries*

3 MONTEVIOT
Jedburgh TD8 6UQ
Marquis and Marchioness of Lothian
T: 01835 830380
W: www.monteviot.com

A series of differing gardens displaying rose and herbaceous plants surrounded by foliage plants. A water feature linked by bridges and falls passes through the Dene Garden and Water Garden. The Garden of Persistent Imagination is planted with rose and clematis beside paths which meander across a bridge and under the Moonstone Gate, past the Dali-style clock.

Open: 1 April - 31 October, noon - 5pm, admission £6.00, children U16 free, card payment preferred.

Directions: Turn off A68, three miles north of Jedburgh on to B6400. After one mile turn right.

Opening for: *Donation to SGS Beneficiaries*

Roxburghshire

Floors Castle and Gardens © Pete Seaward

Monteviot

Roxburghshire

4 SMAILHOLM VILLAGE GARDENS
Smailholm Village Hall, Smailholm TD5 7PH
The Gardeners of Smailholm
W: www.smailholm-village.org.uk

This small rural village, centred around an ancient church and a historic 'farm town', boasts a number of gardens of the cottage variety with varying degrees of formality and maturity. They range from the ancient to new 'works in progress', and offer a combination of traditional and contemporary approaches – often in a single garden! While not having a formal group, the villagers embrace gardening and are at present planting the verges and returning the green spaces around the church to wildflowers. The village hall is famed for its teas, especially fine cakes, and superb plant sales. All of the open gardens are within an easy walk of the hall, from which tickets can be obtained. Access to gardens is generally good, with most gardens being wheelchair friendly.

Open: Sunday 20 June, noon - 5pm, admission £5.00, children free. Tickets, route maps and refreshments available from the village hall.

Directions: Smailholm is a small village between Earlston and Kelso on the B6397. From the centre of the village take the Gattonside road and then after 100 yards turn right into the village hall car park.

Opening for: Smailholm Village Hall Committee

5 STABLE HOUSE
Maxton, St Boswells, Melrose TD6 0EX
Ian Dalziel
T: 01835 824262 E: imd4@mac.com

An enclosed private garden around converted stables with a sunny courtyard. The garden extends to over half an acre and includes mixed borders in sun and shade, a wildflower meadow, a plant house and a hot border. A crevice garden with alpine plants has been created over the winter. The garden was featured in the *Border Life* programme on ITV Border in January 2021.

Open: 1 May - 31 October (Mondays only), 2pm - 5pm. Also open by arrangement 1 May - 31 October. Admission £4.00, children free. Please call or email to arrange a visit.

Directions: Two minutes from A68 on A699 to Kelso.

Opening for: · Sight Scotland

6 THIRLESTANE
Kelso TD5 8PD
Catherine Ross and John Wylie
T: 01573 420487

Thirlestane is a large, informal garden, with some rough ground and long grass. It previously opened as one of the Yetholm gardens, but since then a nine-acre wood has been planted. This young woodland has a wide mix of trees, including some specimen trees, with fine autumn colour in October. There are two ponds and a burn. An orchard has about 50 varieties of apples and other fruit trees. Beech hedges enclose prairie planting in a formal setting. There is an enclosed flower garden, raised beds for vegetables and colour-themed planting.

Open: By arrangement 31 March - 31 October, admission £5.00, children free. Please feel free to bring a picnic to enjoy in the garden.

Directions: Thirlestane is near Yetholm, not to be confused with Thirlestane, Lauder. Do not follow SatNav, it will try to take you to Lochside. From Kelso, take the B6352 towards Yetholm

Roxburghshire

for about six miles. Continue past a cottage on the edge of the road. Thirlestane is next on the left, opposite the road to Lochside. From Yetholm, take the road to Kelso for about two miles. After a very sharp corner, Thirlestane is on the right.

Opening for: Macmillan Cancer Support

7 WEST LEAS

Bonchester Bridge TD9 8TD
Mr and Mrs Robert Laidlaw
T: 01450 860711 E: ann@johnlaidlawandson.co.uk

The visitor to West Leas can share in an exciting and dramatic project on a grand scale, still in the making. At its core is a passion for plants, allied to a love and understanding of the land in which they are set. Collections of perennials and shrubs, many in temporary holding quarters, lighten up the landscape to magical effect. New lily pond and woodland planting added in 2019 and a new courtyard garden is under construction.

Open: By arrangement 1 January - 31 December, admission £4.00, children free.

Directions: Signposted off the Jedburgh/Bonchester Bridge Road.

Opening for: Macmillan Cancer Support: Borders Appeal

8 YETHOLM VILLAGE GARDENS

Town Yetholm TD5 8RL
The Gardeners of Yetholm Village

The villages of Town Yetholm and Kirk Yetholm are situated at the north end of the Pennine Way, close to the Bowmont Water in the dramatic setting of the foothills of the Cheviots. A variety of gardens will be open, each with their own unique features and style, reflecting distinctive horticultural interests. The Yew Tree Allotments running along the High Street, Town Yetholm, will open again, providing an ever popular feature with their unique water collection and distribution system. The short walking distance between the majority of the gardens provides magnificent views of the surrounding landscape to include Staerough and The Curr which straddle both the Bowmont and Halterburn Valleys where evidence of ancient settlements remains.

Open: Sunday 4 July, 1pm - 5pm, admission £5.00, children free. Attractions include the ever popular music, local wood-turning products at Almond Cottage. Refreshments may be available on the day. An excellent plant stall supported by Newton Don Nursery is also planned for the afternoon. Tickets for entrance to all the gardens will be on sale in or near the Wauchope Hall, east end of the High Street, Town Yetholm.

Directions: Equidistant between Edinburgh and Newcastle and south of Kelso in the Scottish Borders. Take the B6352 to Town Yetholm. Ample parking is available along the High Street.

Opening for: To be confirmed

Stirlingshire

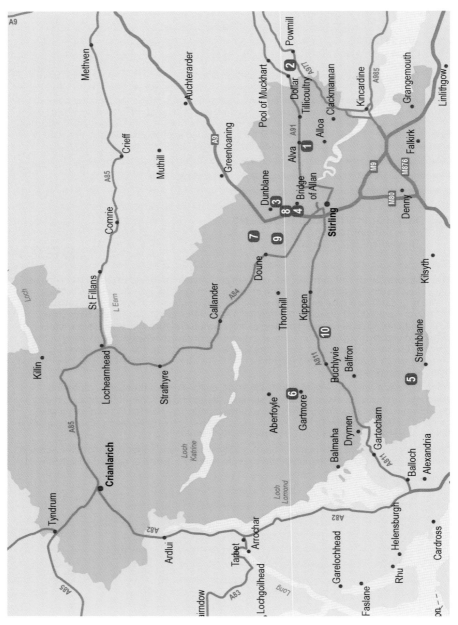

Stirlingshire

OUR VOLUNTEER ORGANISERS

District Organiser:	Mandy Readman	Hutcheson Farm, Dunblane FK15 9JS E: stirlingshire@scotlandsgardens.org
Area Organisers:	Jo Dormer	
	Clare Giles	Carselea Farm, Blair Drummond FK9 4UP
	Teresa Hill	11 Clifford Road, Stirling, FK8 2AQ
	Maurie Jessett	The Walled Garden, Lanrick FK16 6HJ
	Morna Knottenbelt	Ballochruin Road, Killearn G63 9QB
	Rosemary Leckie	16 Chalton Road, Bridge of Allan FK9 4DX
	Iain Morrison	Clifford House, Balkerach Street, Doune FK16 6DE
	Ann Shaw	Plaka, 5 Pendreich Road, Bridge of Allan FK9 4LY
	Graham Silcocks	Craigrennie, Queen Street, Doune FK16 6DP
District Photographer:	Des Coll	27 Meadow View, Cumbernauld G67 2BZ
Treasurer:	David Ashton	Westmore Shiel, Cauldhame, Kippen FK8 3JB

GARDENS OPEN ON A SPECIFIC DATE

Kilbryde Castle, Dunblane	Sunday, 23 May
Shrubhill, Dunblane	Sunday, 30 May
Bridge of Allan Gardens, Bridge of Allan	Sunday, 6 June
Gartmore Village, Main Street, Gartmore	Sunday, 13 June
Ault Wharrie, Ardnablane, Dunblane	Sunday, 25 July
60 Greenhead, Alva, Clackmannanshire	Sunday, 1 August

GARDENS OPEN BY ARRANGEMENT – BOOK A VISIT WITH THE GARDEN OWNER

Thorntree, Arnprior	1 February - 31 October
Duntreath Castle, Blanefield	15 March - 30 November
Kilbryde Castle, Dunblane	15 March - 30 September
Milseybank, Bridge of Allan	1 May - 30 May
Arndean, by Dollar	10 May - 6 June

Stirlingshire

1 60 GREENHEAD
Alva, Clackmannanshire FK12 5HH
Lynn Cameron

A delightful hidden garden in Alva behind the primary school. Divided into 'rooms' with themes, two being Mediterranean and Oriental, there is extensive planting and clever use of pots throughout. Recycled materials are much in evidence, especially in the 'cosy' corner with a fireplace. There is a wide variety of shrubs, perennials and annuals as well as vegetables and fruit. There is a pond and a small wildlife area. There is also a 'folly' created during the lockdown of 2020. An inspiration for those trying to garden in a small space.

Open: Sunday 1 August, 2pm - 5pm, admission £4.00, children free.

Directions: Signposted from the A91. Please park with consideration for other houses in the area.

***Opening for:** Stirling Baptist Church: Christians Against Poverty(CAP) Forth Valley Debt Centre*

2 ARNDEAN
by Dollar FK14 7NH
Johnny and Katie Stewart
T: 01259 743525 E: johnny@arndean.co.uk

Opening for more than 40 years, this is a beautiful mature garden extending to 15 acres including the woodland walk. There is a formal herbaceous part, a small vegetable garden and an orchard. In addition, there are flowering shrubs, abundant and striking rhododendrons and azaleas as well as many fine specimen trees. There is a tree house for children.

Open: By arrangement 10 May - 6 June, admission £5.00, children free.

Directions: Arndean is well signposted off the A977.

***Opening for:** Marie Curie*

3 AULT WHARRIE
Ardnablane, Dunblane FK15 0NU
Bill Carman and Celia Aitken
E: Bill.f.carman@gmail.com

Ault Wharrie was formerly the Masonic Home in Dunblane. The extensive grounds have been redesigned and replanted over the last five years. These have benefitted from the shelter provided by mature trees and there are many flowering shrubs including rhododendron, camellia and magnolia. A parterre, a rockery and a large pond are all complemented by colourful herbaceous borders with a good mixture of plants including dahlias interspersed with annuals.

Open: Sunday 25 July, noon - 5pm, admission £5.00, children free. The paths are fine gravel and therefore very difficult for wheelchairs which would need to be pulled backwards. Plants for sale by Dunblane in Bloom and Dunblane Development Trust (DDT) Environment Group.

Directions: From the Fourways roundabout in Dunblane take the Glen Road, then the second left into Leewood Road. Continue and follow the *yellow* signs into Ardnablane. Take the first right beside a lodge and follow the directions given about parking. Overflow parking is on Leewood Road. The garden is about a 20 minute walk from Dunblane station.

***Opening for:** Strathcarron Hospice*

Stirlingshire

4 BRIDGE OF ALLAN GARDENS
Bridge of Allan FK9 4LY
The Gardeners of Bridge of Allan
E: mgshaw16@gmail.com

A mixture of garden sizes with a wide variety of shrubs, specimen trees, herbaceous borders, late flowering bulbs and some vegetable gardens. There are also some interesting sculptures and water features. The following gardens will open and there may be more joining nearer the time. Further details can be found on Scotland's Gardens Scheme website.

1 Anne Drive FK9 4RE (John and Elizabeth Rankin)
22A Blairforkie Drive FK9 4PH (Alastair and Nancie McLean)
9 Mayne Avenue (NEW) FK9 4QU (Donald and Nancy McLean)
Bridge of Allan Allotments (NEW) Cornton Road FK9 4DA (The Gardeners of Bridge of Allan Allotments)
Plaka 5 Pendreich Road FK9 4LY (Malcolm and Ann Shaw)

Open: Sunday 6 June, 1pm - 5pm, admission £5.00, children free. Tickets and maps will be available from all the gardens.

Directions: Gardens will be signposted from the village.

Opening for: St Saviours Episcopal Church: Bridge Of Allan & Strathcarron Hospice

Bridge of Allan Gardens, Plaka

Bridge of Allan Gardens, Plaka

5 DUNTREATH CASTLE
Blanefield G63 9AJ
Sir Archibald and Lady Edmonstone
T: 01360 770215 E: juliet@edmonstone.com
W: www.duntreathcastle.co.uk

Extensive gardens with mature and new plantings. Ornamental landscaped lake and bog garden. Sweeping lawns below formal fountain and rose parterre with an herbaceous border leading up to an attractive waterfall garden. Swathes of yellow daffodils and other colourful spring bulbs together with rhododendrons and many other ornamental shrubs surround the formal lawns. There is a woodland walk, a 15th century keep and a banqueting hall up a turreted staircase which is not to be missed! Horticultural interest throughout the year and superb autumn colours.

Open: By arrangement 15 March - 30 November, admission £5.00, children free. Groups welcome

Directions: A81 north of Glasgow between Blanefield and Killearn.

Opening for: All proceeds to SGS Beneficiaries

Stirlingshire

6 GARTMORE VILLAGE
Main Street, Gartmore FK8 3RW
The Gardeners of Gartmore
E: ant@vinbay.co.uk

Several attractive and interesting medium and small gardens will be open in and around this beautiful peaceful village with splendid views. A wide variety of planting with shrubs, roses and herbaceous borders, water features, also some vegetable gardens and fruit trees. The following gardens will be opening and there will be several more joining on the day. Further details can be found on the Scotland's Gardens Scheme website.

Bridgend (NEW) Station Road, Gartmore FK8 3RR (Brian Patterson)
Bruach (NEW) Gartmore FK8 3RP (Cathy Haughton-Evans)
Glenartney (NEW) Station Road, Gartmore FK8 3RR (John and Romma Davidson Kelly):
Tadmor (NEW) Gartmore FK8 3RW (Janey Fleming)
The Old Manse (NEW) Gartmore FK8 3RP (Anthony and Jo Weld-Forester)

Open: Sunday 13 June, 2pm - 5pm, admission £5.00, children free. There will be a map outside the Black Bull Inn, which is community owned, showing the location of the gardens, and where tickets for entry to all the gardens can be purchased. It is hoped that teas can be served outside and there will also be a plant stall at the Black Bull. Please park with consideration for the houses in the village.

Directions: Gartmore Village is on a small loop road off the A81 Glasgow – Aberfoyle Road which is well signposted. It is about four miles from Aberfoyle.

Opening for: Green Routes Stirling: The Walled Garden, Gartmore

7 KILBRYDE CASTLE
Dunblane FK15 9NF
Sir James and Lady Campbell
T: 01786 824897 E: kilbryde1@aol.com
W: www.kilbrydecastle.com

The Kilbryde Castle gardens cover some 12 acres and are situated above the Ardoch Burn and below the castle. The gardens are split into three parts: formal, woodland and wild. Natural planting (azaleas, rhododendrons, camellias and magnolias) is found in the woodland garden. There are glorious snowdrops, spring bulbs, and autumn colour provided by clematis and acers. Some new plantings for additional late summer/autumn colour were added in 2017. Featured in *Scotland on Sunday* in September 2016.

Open: Sunday 23 May, 11am - 5pm. Also open by arrangement 15 March - 30 September. Admission £5.00, children free. There may be teas on 23 May only. Groups welcome.

Directions: Three miles from Dunblane and Doune, off the A820 between Dunblane and Doune. On Scotland's Gardens Scheme open days the garden is signposted from the A820.

Opening for: Leighton Library Trust

Stirlingshire

8 MILSEYBANK
Bridge of Allan FK9 4NB
Murray and Sheila Airth
T: 01786 833866 E: smairth@hotmail.com

Wonderful and interesting sloping garden with outstanding views, terraced for ease of access. Woodland with bluebells, rhododendrons, magnolias and camellias, and many other unusual plants, including a big variety of meconopsis, and water features. This is a true plantsman's garden with several quiet corners to sit, admire and reflect. A garden to inspire you and give you ideas to take home.
National Plant Collection: Meconopsis.

Open: By arrangement 1 May - 30 May, admission £5.00, children free.

Directions: Situated on the A9, one mile from junction 11, M9 and a quarter-of-a-mile from Bridge of Allan. Milseybank is at the top of the lane at Lecropt Nursery, 250 yards from the Bridge of Allan train station.

Opening for: Strathcarron Hospice

9 SHRUBHILL
Dunblane FK15 9PA
Tiff and Michaela Wright
T: 07821 693997 E: wrightrascals@btinternet.com

Two acres of mixed, informal planting of some unusual rhododendrons, azaleas, specimen trees and other shrubs. Beautiful all round views particularly over the Carse of Stirling and towards Ben Ledi and Ben Lomond. Herbaceous borders, meconopsis, late spring bulbs, water feature with a wide variety of primulas. Small walled garden predominantly for fruit and a greenhouse with a well-established vine.

Open: Sunday 30 May, 11:30am - 5pm, admission £5.00, children free. Parking is in a field and you are welcome to picnic beside your car, please take home any rubbish as the field is used for grazing.

Directions: Two miles from Keir roundabout on the B824 on the left, just after the *David Stirling Memorial*, follow the signs and parking advice. One mile from the A820 and on the right.

Opening for: Teapot Trust

10 THORNTREE
Arnprior FK8 3EY
Mark and Carol Seymour
T: 01786 870710 E: carolseymour666@gmail.com
W: www.thorntreebarn.co.uk

After the difficulties of 2020, this year Thorntree is opening by arrangement only, but they are looking forward to welcoming visitors. Carol will happily walk round the garden with you or you can wander on your own. The garden continues to evolve and cotoneasters by the saltire beds have been cut back which means the four flower beds are no longer hidden behind a hedge! Also, the view past the summerhouse can be seen and the Annabelle hydrangea has popped up now that there are less branches above it. An inspiring garden to visit at any time of the year.

Open: By arrangement 1 February - 31 October, admission £5.00, children free. Small groups are welcome. No dogs please.

Directions: On the A811, to Arnprior, then take the Fintry Road; Thorntree is second on the right.

Opening for: Forth Driving Group RDA SCIO

Wigtownshire

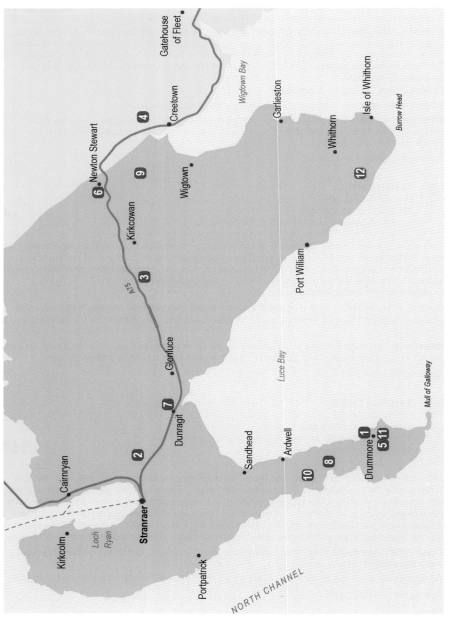

Wigtownshire

OUR VOLUNTEER ORGANISERS

District Organiser:	Ann Watson	Doonholm, Cairnryan Road, Stranraer DG9 8AT E: wigtownshire@scotlandsgardens.org
Area Organisers:	Eileen Davie Mary Gladstone Shona Greenhorn Enid Innes Annmaree Mitchell	Whitehills House, Minnigaff DG8 6SL Craichlaw, Kirkcowan DG8 0DQ Burbainie, Westwood Avenue DG9 8BT Crinan, Creetown DG8 7EP Cottage 2, Little Float, Sandhead DG9 9LD
District Photographer:	Stuart Littlewood	stu@f8.eclipse.co.uk
Treasurer:	George Fleming	Stablesend, Culreoch, Stranraer DG9 8LZ

GARDENS OPEN ON A SPECIFIC DATE

Logan Botanic Garden, Port Logan, by Stranraer	Sunday, 23 May
Castle Kennedy and Gardens, Stranraer	Saturday, 5 June
Rawson Garden, 1, High Drummore Cottages, Drummore	Sunday, 13 June
Woodfall Gardens, Glasserton	Saturday/Sunday, 19/20 June
Woodfall Gardens, Glasserton	Sunday, 11 July
Damnaglaur House, Drummore, Stranraer	Saturday/Sunday, 17/18 July
Amulree, 8 Mill Street, Drummore, Stranraer	Saturday/Sunday, 17/18 July

GARDENS OPEN REGULARLY

Glenwhan Gardens, Dunragit, by Stranraer	1 January - 31 December
Logan Botanic Garden, Port Logan, by Stranraer	7 - 28 Feb (Sundays) and 1 Mar - 15 Nov

GARDENS OPEN BY ARRANGEMENT – BOOK A VISIT WITH THE GARDEN OWNER

Amulree, 8 Mill Street, Drummore, Stranraer	1 January - 31 December
Craichlaw, Kirkcowan, Newton Stewart	1 January - 31 December
Liggat Cheek Cottage, Baltersan, Newton Stewart	1 April - 30 September
Hill Cottage, Portlogan, Stranraer	1 April - 31 October
Damnaglaur House, Drummore, Stranraer	1 April - 31 October
Fernlea Garden, Corvisel Road, Newton Stewart	1 April - 30 September
Crinan, Creetown	1 May - 4 July
Rawson Garden, 1, High Drummore Cottages, Drummore	1 June - 31 July

Wigtownshire

1 AMULREE
8 Mill Street, Drummore, Stranraer DG9 9PS
Mr Colin Belton and Mrs Gabrielle Reynolds
T: 0789 909 2070 E: gabygardeners@btinternet.com

Amulree is home to two complete plantaholics who probably should start taking their own advice and stop collecting quite so many plants! Starting from a blank canvas in 2017 the garden now consists of a sunny terrace with displays of half-hardy and tender plants, exuberantly planted borders separated by serpentine grass patches, a small vegetable patch, a glasshouse and a 'wild' bit. Amulree contains many unusual plants including a National Plant Collection.
National Plant Collection: *Nicotiana* species.

Open: Saturday/Sunday, 17/18 July, 10am - 4pm. Also open by arrangement 1 January - 31 December. Admission £4.00, children free. Garden contains steps and uneven surfaces.

Directions: Follow A716 signposted *Drummore and Mull of Galloway.* At the T junction in Drummore turn right. Amulree is on the left, a few doors up from the shop. Bus route 407 from Stranraer.

Opening for: *Kirkmaiden Old Kirk*

Amulree

Wigtownshire

2 CASTLE KENNEDY AND GARDENS
Stranraer DG9 8SL
The Earl and Countess of Stair
T: 01581 400225
W: www.castlekennedygardens.com

Romantically situated, these famous 75 acres of landscaped gardens are located on an isthmus surrounded by two large natural lochs. At one end the ruined Castle Kennedy overlooks a beautiful herbaceous walled garden with Lochinch Castle at the other end. With over 300 years of planting there is an impressive collection of rare trees, rhododendrons, exotic shrubs and many spectacular Champion Trees. The stunning snowdrop walks, daffodils, spring flowers, rhododendron and magnolia displays and herbaceous borders, make this a 'must visit' garden throughout the year.
Champion Trees: 95 in total; including 12 British, 30 Scottish, 44 for Dumfries and Galloway and 9 trees described as 'otherwise remarkable'.

Open: Saturday 5 June, 10am - 5pm as part of Scotland's Gardens Scheme. Castle Kennedy is also open from 1st April - 31st October and admission details for all openings can be found on their website.

Directions: On the A75, five miles east of Stranraer. The nearest train station is in Stranraer. On a local bus route.

Opening for: Home-Start Wigtownshire

3 CRAICHLAW
Kirkcowan, Newton Stewart DG8 0DQ
Mr and Mrs Andrew Gladstone
T: 01671 830208 E: craichlaw@aol.com

Formal garden with herbaceous borders around the house. Set in extensive grounds with lawns, lochs and woodland. A path around the main loch leads to a water garden returning past a recently planted arboretum in the old walled garden. The best times to visit the garden are early February for snowdrops, May to mid-June for the water garden and rhododendrons, and mid-June to August for herbaceous borders.

Open: By arrangement 1 January - 31 December, admission £5.00, children free. We have Snowdrops and Winter Walks from February to mid-March.

Directions: Take the B733 for Kirkcowan off the A75 at the Halfway House eight miles west of Newton Stewart. Craichlaw House is the first turning on the right.

Opening for: All proceeds to SGS Beneficiaries

Wigtownshire

4 CRINAN
Creetown DG8 7EP
Mrs Enid Innes
T: 01671 820323

`NEW`

A wonderful ten-acre garden, at its best in May and June with ten lochs. There are many unusual conifers including Wollemi Pine. There are also many different species of oak, birch, chestnut, acer, eucalyptus and many other varieties of hardwoods. The soil is peaty so the rhododendrons, azaleas, camellias and magnolias are star turns. There are substantial collections of viburnums, hydrangeas, pieris and cornus. Around the lochans there are irises, hostas, skunk cabbage and gunnera. The owner has a passion for trees and shrubs.

Open: By arrangement 1 May - 4 July, admission £5.00, children free.

Directions: From Creetown take the old station road and keep going up for about a mile until you reach a cattle grid and a timber-clad house, ignore any other turn off.

Opening for: All proceeds to SGS Beneficiaries

5 DAMNAGLAUR HOUSE
Drummore, Stranraer DG9 9QN
Frances Collins
T: 01776 840636 M: 07884 435353

Since moving into Damnaglaur House, in 1991, its owners have totally transformed the garden, putting in a series of 'semi-terraces' and, following the planting of wind-defeating shrubs, they were able to introduce many special herbaceous plants and trees. Just short of half an acre, it slowly evolved into one which feels substantially larger because of its design – the gravel paths weave their way through it towards many hidden corners to come upon countless gems. The views from the garden are stunning, down to Drummore, across Luce Bay and, in the far distance, to the Galloway Hills. An archway, arbour and pergola give extra height for the planting. Seating around the garden gives visitors a chance to sit and enjoy their surroundings, especially close to the pond, with its numerous fish and trickling waterfall.

Open: Saturday/Sunday, 17/18 July, 10am - 4pm. Also open by arrangement 1 April - 31 October. Admission £4.00, children free.

Directions: From Drummore, follow signs to the *Mull of Galloway* for a mile on B7041 to junction with B7065; Damnaglaur is on the right.

Opening for: British Red Cross: Yemen Appeal

6 FERNLEA GARDEN
Corvisel Road, Newton Stewart DG8 6LW
Mrs Jenny Gustafson
T: 07909 951 885 M:01671 638273 E: jennygustafson2@hotmail.com

A secluded town garden of a third of an acre. It was created in 2006 to complement a new house. There are many rare and unusual trees and shrubs. Two herbaceous borders, one with hot colours and the other pastels. A Chinese-inspired corner, small pond, fruit trees including a Galloway pippin apple and soft fruit. The upper part of the garden is hidden behind a tall beech hedge, where there is a summer house and adjacent woodland planting.

Open: By arrangement 1 April - 30 September, admission £4.50, children free.

Directions: Turn right at the roundabout on the A75 if coming from Dumfries direction. Go left at the cattle market (opposite Crown Hotel), first through road on the right.

Opening for: Host UK

Wigtownshire

7 **GLENWHAN GARDENS**
Dunragit, by Stranraer DG9 8PH
Tess Knott
T: 07787 990702
W: www.glenwhangardens.co.uk

Described as one of the most beautiful gardens in Scotland, Glenwhan Gardens is situated at 300 feet and overlooks Luce Bay and the Mull of Galloway, with clear views to the Isle of Man. Thirty-seven years ago there was wild moorland, but now, following considerable dedication and vision, you can see glorious collections of plants from around the world. There is colour in all seasons and the winding paths, well-placed seats and varied sculptures, set around small lakes, add to the tranquil atmosphere. There is a 17-acre moorland wildflower walk, the chance to see red squirrels and a well-marked Tree Trail.

Open: 1 January - 31 December, 10am - 5pm, admission details can be found on the garden's website. There is a new garden map and a designated garden walk for 2021.

Directions: Seven miles east of Stranraer, one mile off the A75 at Dunragit (follow brown *VisitScotland* and yellow SGS arrows).

Opening for: Donation to SGS Beneficiaries

8 **HILL COTTAGE**
Portlogan, Stranraer DG9 9NT
Mrs Mary Shaw
T: 01776 860314 M: 07810 541738

Hill Cottage is a half-acre cottage garden sitting amongst glorious scenery with marvellous views over hills and down to the coast. Mainly a cottage garden with a large natural rockery, small pond and vegetable plot.

Open: By arrangement 1 April - 31 October, admission £4.00, children free. Teas available on request.

Directions: Turn left from Port Logan, left again onto Killumpha Road about quarter of a mile and it is the second cottage on the right.

Opening for: Blood Bikes Scotland

9 **LIGGAT CHEEK COTTAGE**
Baltersan, Newton Stewart DG8 6AX
Philip and Jennifer Bradley
T: 01671 402639 E: bradley@liggat.plus.com

The garden is approximately half an acre and includes a small woodland and shade area with ferns, hostas, trilliums, erythroniums and many other shade-loving plants. The rest of the garden is divided into informal 'rooms' with large borders containing herbaceous perennials, shrubs, conifers, grasses, etc. There is one south-facing bed devoted to less hardy plants including agaves, yuccas, cordylines, aeoniums and tetrapanax. The garden was featured in an episode of *The Beechgrove Garden* on 5 September 2019.

Open: By arrangement 1 April - 30 September, admission £4.00, children free. Teas and plants may be available by prior request.

Directions: From Newton Stewart roundabout (A75) towards Wigtown (A714) *Scotland's National Book Town*. Approximately two miles from the roundabout on the right, above Baltersan Farm on the left.

Opening for: Euan Macdonald Centre for Motor Neurone Disease Research

Wigtownshire

10 LOGAN BOTANIC GARDEN
Port Logan, by Stranraer DG9 9ND
A Regional Garden of the Royal Botanic Garden Edinburgh
T: 01776 860231 E: logan@rbge.org.uk
W: www.rbge.org.uk/logan

Logan is a regional garden of the Royal Botanic Garden Edinburgh which celebrated its 350th anniversary in 2020. At the south western tip of Scotland lies Logan, which is unrivalled as the country's most exotic garden. With a mild climate washed by the Gulf Stream, a remarkable collection of bizarre and beautiful plants, especially from the southern hemisphere, flourish out of doors. Enjoy the colourful walled garden with its magnificent tree ferns, palms and borders along with the contrasting woodland garden with its unworldly gunnera bog. Visit the Logan Conservatory, which houses a special collection of tender South African species.
National Plant Collection: *Gunnera, Leptospermum, Griselinia, Clianthus* and *Sutherlandia*.
Champion Trees: *Polylepis* and *Eucalyptus*.

Open: Sunday 23 May, also open 7 - 28 February (Sundays) and 1 March - 15 November 10am - 5pm, admission details and other information can be found on the garden's website.

Directions: Ten miles south of Stranraer on the A716 then two-and-a-half miles from Ardwell village.

Opening for: *Board Of Trustees Of The Royal Botanic Garden Edinburgh*

11 RAWSON GARDEN
1, High Drummore Cottages, Drummore, Stranraer DG9 9QL
Beverley Darville
E: darvy@sky.com

Rawson Garden is a large cottage garden with a stunning sea view. The garden is divided into different parts, including a self-contained Bothy. It has a plethora of shrubs, flowers, pine trees, bamboo, palm trees and a small waterfall with a burn that runs through the garden. There are three tiers to the garden separated by paths and steps, with patios and a large decking area. Seating is interspersed throughout the garden and this year the owners have added some garden sculptures and bird houses. A wonderful garden to explore and somewhere to sit and admire the gorgeous view.

Open: Sunday 13 June, 2pm - 5pm. Also open by arrangement 1 June - 31 July. Admission £5.00, children free. Home baking on 13 June, tea and biscuits when visiting by arrangement. Public toilets in Drummore village.

Directions: From Stranraer, head out to Drummore and Mull of Galloway on the A716. 16 miles from Stranraer, follow signs through Drummore for Mull of Galloway, come up the hill past the farm building on the right, follow the road round and Rawson Garden is the first cottage on the right after farm and a pair of big green gates.

Opening for: *RNLI*

Wigtownshire

12	**WOODFALL GARDENS**

WOODFALL GARDENS
Glasserton DG8 8LY
Ross and Liz Muir
E: woodfallgardens@btinternet.com
W: www.woodfall-gardens.co.uk

This lovely three-acre 18th-century triple walled garden has been thoughtfully restored to provide year-round interest. It contains many mature trees and shrubs, including some less common species, herbaceous borders and shrub roses which surround the foundations of original greenhouses, grass borders, a parterre, extensive beds of fruit and vegetables, a herb garden and a small woodland walk. This unusual garden is well worth a visit.

Open: Saturday/Sunday, 19/20 June and Sunday 11 July, 10.30am - 4.30pm. Admission £5.00, children free. Please check the garden's website for further openings.

Directions: Two miles south west of Whithorn at junction of A746 and A747 (directly behind Glasserton Church).

Opening for: Whithorn Primary School

Rawson Garden

Hidden gardens 'by arrangement'

© D Blatchford

Did you know that we have many 'hidden' gardens that open 'by arrangement'?

This may be for a number of reasons; limited car parking, convenience or keeping visitor numbers at a more manageable level. This year there is another reason – Covid-19. In a normal year, it can be hard to commit to opening on a particular day, remember that the decision has to be made by October at the latest – and 2020 was anything but normal!

If garden owners are willing to be included in the Book and on the website, they are really looking forward to welcoming visitors. Smaller numbers, no car parking issues and probably no teas, it is also easier to cancel or rearrange appointments if we return to restrictions from the virus. It can be a great visit for a horticultural society or local group (restrictions permitting) or for a small group or couple – just ask the owner and go and have a look, you will love it! You might even get a personal tour and all those questions answered or you will be welcome to explore on your own, if you prefer.

Let's make 2021 the year of the 'by arrangement' garden; there are so many hidden gems to choose from and you can always visit again and have a whole new experience in a different season.

Mandy Readman
District Organiser

Scotland's
GARDENS
Scheme

Lanarkshire The Walled Garden Shieldhill © Alistair McNeill

Garden Photography
to document
to publish
to hang
to keep

www.andreajones.co.uk

Bluebell Wood
Photograph © Andrea Jones
Courtesy of The Teasses Estate, Fife.

WHY JOIN THE CALEY?

There are many benefits of joining The Caley

To Do:
~~Rake leaves~~
~~Tidy greenhouse~~
~~Divide perennials~~
Join the Caley

At Saughton Dig Day

Carrots from the allotment

thecaley.org.uk/join
(Only £26 a year!)

@TheCaley
Charity Number: SC 006522

Scotland's National Horticultural & Gardening Society

The Caley
Royal Caledonian Horticultural Society

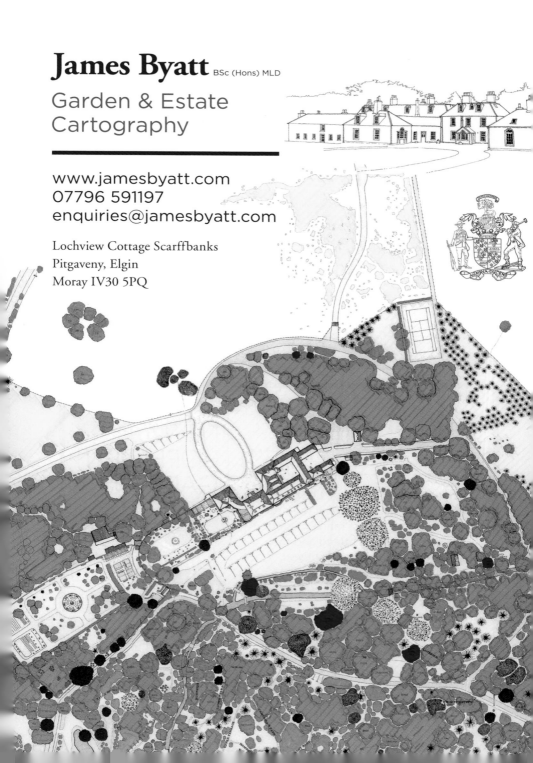

James Byatt BSc (Hons) MLD

Garden & Estate Cartography

www.jamesbyatt.com
07796 591197
enquiries@jamesbyatt.com

Lochview Cottage Scarffbanks
Pitgaveny, Elgin
Moray IV30 5PQ

Index of Gardens

PRE-ORDER YOUR SCOTLAND'S GARDENS SCHEME GUIDEBOOK FOR 2022!

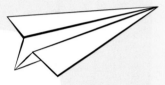

PLEASE SEND ME _____ COPY / COPIES OF THE SGS GUIDEBOOK FOR 2022, PRE-ORDER PRICE £7.50 PLUS £2.50 UK P&P AS SOON AS IT IS AVAILABLE.

I ENCLOSE A CHEQUE / POSTAL ORDER MADE PAYABLE TO SCOTLAND'S GARDENS SCHEME.

NAME

....

ADDRESS

....

....

POSTCODE

....

Scotland's
GARDENS
Scheme
OPEN FOR CHARITY

SCOTLAND'S GARDENS SCHEME,
23 CASTLE STREET, EDINBURGH
EH2 3DN

COPIES OF OUR GUIDEBOOK MAY ALSO BE PURCHASED ON OUR WEBSITE: SCOTLANDSGARDENS.ORG

Thank you
for visiting.

Kirkcudbrightshire: 3 Millhall © Sheila Sim

Always check our website before setting out in case of cancellations or changes to published listings